Dig Uni Ene 200

Production team: **Mike Janes (Managing editor)**
Sally Mercer (Production editor)
Cyd Namazie
Vandana Sood
Clive Sarjantson
and chapter authors

A National Statistics publication   **London: TSO**

ISO

1 3 0988502 8

First published 2005

ISBN 0 11 515513 9

Digest of United Kingdom Energy Statistics

Enquiries about statistics in this publication should be made to the contact named at the end of the relevant chapter. Brief extracts from this publication may be reproduced provided that the source is fully acknowledged. General enquiries about the publication, and proposals for reproduction of larger extracts, should be addressed to the Production Editor, Sally Mercer, at the address given in paragraph XXVIII of the Introduction.

Department of Trade and Industry reserves the right to revise or discontinue the text or any table contained in this Digest without prior notice.

About TSO's Standing Order Service

The Standing Order Service, open to all TSO account holders, allows customers to automatically receive the publications they require in a specified subject area, thereby saving them the time, trouble and expense of placing individual orders, also without handling charges normally incurred when placing ad-hoc orders.

Customers may choose from over 4,000 classifications arranged in 250 sub groups under 30 major subject areas. These classifications enable customers to choose from a wide variety of subjects, those publications that are of special interest to them. This is a particularly valuable service for the specialist library or research body. All publications will be dispatched immediately after publication date. A Standing Orders Handbook describing the service in detail and a complete list of classifications may be obtained on request. Write to TSO, Standing Order Department, PO Box 29, St Crispins, Duke Street, Norwich, NR3 1GN, quoting reference 12.01.013. Alternatively telephone 0870 600 5522 and select the Standing Order Department (option 2); fax us on 0870 600 5533; or finally e-mail us at book.standing.orders@tso.co.uk.

National Statistics

National Statistics are produced to high professional standards set out in the National Statistics Code of Practice. They undergo regular quality assurance reviews to ensure that they meet customer needs. They are produced free from any political interference.

You can find a range of National Statistics on the Internet – www.statistics.gov.uk

---

Contents

Monthly and quarterly data are also available for Energy, Solid fuels and derived gases, Petroleum, Gas and Electricity at:

www.dti.gov.uk/energy/inform/energy_stats/

Information on Energy Prices is available at:

www.dti.gov.uk/ energy/inform/energy_prices/index.shtml

A list of tables

Chapter 7   Renewable sources of energy

Annex A   Energy, commodity balances, calorific values and conversion factors

Introduction

I   This issue of the Digest of United Kingdom Energy Statistics continues a series which commenced with the Ministry of Fuel and Power Statistical Digest for the years 1948 and 1949, published in 1950. The Ministry of Fuel and Power Statistical Digest was previously published as a Command Paper, the first being that for the years 1938 to 1943, published in July 1944 (Cmd. 6538).

II   The current issue updates the figures given in the Department of Trade and Industry's (DTI) *Digest of United Kingdom Energy Statistics 2004*, published in July 2004.

III   This printed and bound issue consists of seven chapters and four annexes. The first chapter deals with overall energy. The other chapters cover the specific fuels, combined heat and power and renewable sources of energy. The annexes cover calorific values and conversion factors, a glossary of terms, further sources of information and major events in the energy industries,

IV   This Digest is also available on the Internet. Some additional information appears on the Internet only. The tables provided on the Internet are provided in Microsoft Excel format. Most Internet versions of the tables include data for earlier years which are not provided in the printed copy publication. For example commodity and energy balances (see VII and VIII, below) for 1998, 1999, 2000 and 2001 are included on the Internet, and tables that show five years in this printed version show 9 years in their Internet form because page sizes are not a limiting factor. In addition, the following appear on the Internet version only:

Long term trends text and tables
Major events from 1990 to 2002 - Annex D
(only Major events for 2003 to 2005 appear in the printed and bound version)
Energy and the environment – Annex E
UK oil and gas resources - Annex F
Foreign Trade – Annex G

V   Annual information on prices is included in the publication *Quarterly Energy Prices*. This is available together with *Energy Trends* on subscription from the DTI. Further information on these publications can be found in Annex C.

VI   Where necessary, data have been converted or adjusted to provide consistent series, however, in some cases changes in methods of data collection have affected the continuity of the series. The presence of remaining discontinuities is indicated in the chapter text or in footnotes to the tables.

VII   Chapters 2, 3, 4, 5 and 7 contain production and consumption of individual fuels and are presented using *commodity balances*. A commodity balance illustrates the flows of an individual fuel through from production to final consumption, showing its use in transformation (including heat generation) and energy industry own use. Further details of commodity balances and their use are given in Annex A, paragraphs A.7 to A.42.

VIII   The individual commodity balances are combined in an *energy balance,* presented in Chapter 1, *Energy*. The energy balance differs from a commodity balance in that it shows the interactions between different fuels in addition to illustrating their consumption. The energy balance thus gives a fuller picture of the production, transformation and use of energy showing all the flows. Expenditure on energy is also presented in energy balance format in Chapter 1. Further details of the energy balance and its use, including the methodology introduced two years ago for heat, are given in Annex A, paragraphs A.43 to A.58.

IX   Chapter 1 also covers general energy statistics and includes tables showing energy consumption by final users and an analysis of energy consumption by main industrial groups. Fuel production and consumption statistics are derived mainly from the records of fuel producers and suppliers.

X   Chapters 6 and 7 summarise the results of surveys conducted by Future Energy Solutions (part of AEA Technology) on behalf of the Department of Trade and Industry. These chapters estimate the contribution made by combined heat and power (CHP) and renewable energy sources to energy production and consumption in the United Kingdom.

XI   Some of the data shown in this Digest may contain unpublished revisions and estimates of trade from additional sources.

Definitions

XII   The text at the beginning of each chapter explains the main features of the tables. Technical notes and definitions, given at the end of this text, provide detailed explanations of the figures in the tables and how they are derived. Explanations of the logic behind an energy balance and for commodity balances are given in Annex A.

XIII   Most chapters contain some information on 'oil' or 'petroleum'; these terms are used in a general sense and vary according to usage in the field examined. In their widest sense they are used to include all mineral oil and related hydrocarbons (except methane) and any derived products.

XIV   An explanation of the terms used to describe electricity generating companies is given in Chapter 5, paragraphs 5.47 to 5.49.

XV   Data in this issue have been prepared on the basis of the Standard Industrial Classification (SIC 2003) as far as is practicable. For further details of classification of consumers see Chapter 1, paragraphs 1.52 to 1.56.

XVI   Where appropriate, further explanations and qualifications are given in footnotes to the tables.

Proposed methodological changes

XVII   DTI is proposing to make changes to the way in which energy data are calculated. This will affect the way data are reported in Chapters 1 (Energy), 4, (Natural gas) and parts of Chapters 5 (Electricity) and 7 (Renewables) beginning with the 2006 edition of this Digest. This proposal is to use net calorific values in place of the current gross calorific values when calculating the energy content of fuels. Further information on the proposed changes is shown in Chapter 1 on page 11 and also available at http://www.dti.gov.uk/energy/consultations/net_gross_cv.pdf

Geographical coverage

XVIII   The geographical coverage of the statistics is the United Kingdom. Shipments to the Channel Islands and the Isle of Man from the United Kingdom are not classed as exports, and supplies of solid fuel and petroleum to these islands are therefore included as part of United Kingdom inland consumption or deliveries.

Periods

XIX   Data in this Digest are for calendar years or periods of 52 weeks, depending on the reporting procedures within the fuel industry concerned. Actual periods covered are given in the notes to the individual fuel chapters

Revisions

XX   The tables contain revisions to some of the previously published figures, and where practicable the revised data have been indicated by an 'r'. The 'r' marker is used whenever the figure has been revised from that published in the printed copy of the 2004 Digest, even though some figures may have been amended on the Internet version of the tables. Statistics on energy in this Digest are classified as National Statistics. This means that they are produced to the professional standards set out in the National Statistics Code of Practice and relevant protocols. The National Statistics protocol on revisions requires that "Each organisation responsible for producing National

Statistics will publish and maintain a general statement describing its practice on revisions". The following statement outlines the policy on revisions for energy statistics.

Revisions to data published in the *Digest of UK Energy Statistics*.
It is intended that any revisions should be made to previous years' data only at the time of the publication of the Digest (ie in July 2005 when this Digest is published, revisions can be made to 2003 and earlier years). In exceptional circumstances previous years' data can be amended between Digest publication dates, but this will only take place when quarterly *Energy Trends* is published. The reasons for substantial revisions will be explained in the 'Highlights' sheet of the Internet version of the table concerned. Valid reasons for revisions of Digest data include:
- revised and validated data received from a data supplier;
- the figure in the Digest was wrong because of a typographical or similar error.

In addition, when provisional annual data for a new calendar year (eg 2005) are published in *Energy Trends* in March of the following year (eg March 2006), percentage growth rates are liable to be distorted if the prior year (ie 2004) data are constrained to to the Digest total, when revisions are known to have been made. In these circumstances the prior year (ie 2004) data will be amended for all affected tables in *Energy Trends* and Internet versions of all affected Digest tables will be clearly annotated to show that the data has been up-dated in *Energy Trends*.

Revisions to current years data published in *Energy Trends* but not in the *Digest of UK Energy Statistics*.
- All validated amendments from data suppliers will be updated when received and published in the next statistical release.
- All errors will be amended as soon as identified and published in the next statistical release.
- Data in energy and commodity balances format will be revised on a quarterly basis, to coincide with the publication of *Energy Trends*.

Further details on National Statistics Code of Practice and related protocols can be found at: www.statistics.gov.uk/about_ns/cop/default.asp

Energy data on the Internet
XXI   Energy data are held on the energy area of the DTI web site, under "information and statistics". The Digest is available at www.dti.gov.uk/energy/inform/dukes/ . Information on further DTI energy publications as in both printed copy and on the Internet is given in Annex C. The DTI web site is currently being redeveloped and the new site is expected to be available in the autumn. As a result the DTI web addresses used for the site in this publication may fail but mechanisms will be put in place to help customers locate the information they require.

XXII   Short term statistics are published:

- monthly, by the DTI on the Internet at www.dti.gov.uk/energy/inform/energy_stats/ .
- quarterly, by the DTI in paper and on the Internet in *Energy Trends,* and *Quarterly Energy Prices*: www.dti.gov.uk/energy/inform/energy_stats/ .

- quarterly, by the DTI in Statistical Press Release which provides a summary of information published in *Energy Trends* and *Quarterly Energy Prices* publications: www.gnn.gov.uk/

- monthly, by the Office for National Statistics in the *Monthly Digest of Statistics (The Stationery Office)*.

To subscribe to *Energy Trends* and *Quarterly Energy Prices,* please contact Clive Sarjantson at the address given at paragraph XXVIII. Single copies available from the DTI Publications Orderline, as given in Annex C, priced £5 for Energy Trends and £7 for Quarterly Energy Prices.

Table numbering
XXIII   Page 10 contains a list showing the tables in the order in which they appear in this issue, and their corresponding numbers in previous issues.

Symbols used

XXIV   The following symbols are used in this Digest:

..	not available
-	nil or negligible (less than half the final digit shown)
r	Revised since the previous edition

Rounding convention

XXV   Individual entries in the tables are rounded independently and this can result in totals which are different from the sum of their constituent items.

Acknowledgements

XXVI   Acknowledgement is made to the main coal producing companies, the electricity companies, the oil companies, the gas pipeline operators, the gas suppliers, National Grid Transco, the Institute of Petroleum, the Coal Authority, the United Kingdom Iron and Steel Statistics Bureau, the National Environmental Technology Centre, Future Energy Solutions, the Department for Environment, Food and Rural Affairs, the Department for Transport, OFGEM, Building Research Establishment, HM Revenue and Customs, the Office for National Statistics, and other contributors to the enquiries used in producing this publication.

Cover photograph

XXVII   The cover illustration used for this Digest and other 2004-2005 DTI energy statistics publications is from a photograph by Peter Askew. It was a winning entry in the DTI News Photographic Competition in 2002.

Contacts

XXVIII   For general enquiries on energy statistics contact:

Clive Sarjantson on 020 7215 2698,   Sally Mercer on 020 7215 2717
(E-mail:clive.sarjantson@dti.gsi.gov.uk)   **or**   (E-mail:sally.mercer@dti.gsi.gov.uk)

Department of Trade and Industry
Bay 209
1 Victoria Street
London SW1H 0ET
Fax: 020 7215 2723

Enquirers with hearing difficulties can contact the Department on the DTI Textphone: 020 7215 6740.

XXIX   For enquiries concerning particular data series or chapters contact those named on page 9 or at the end of the relevant chapter.

Sally Mercer, Production Editor
July 2005

Contact List

The following people in the Department of Trade and Industry may be contacted for further information about the topics listed:

Chapter	Contact	Telephone 020 7215	E-mail
Total energy statistics	Julian Prime	6178	Julian.Prime@dti.gsi.gov.uk
Solid fuels and derived gases	Tracy Halsey Sally Mercer	2684 2717	Tracy.Halsey@dti.gsi.gov.uk Sally.Mercer@dti.gsi.gov.uk
Oil and upstream gas resources	Clive Evans Martin Young	5189 5184	Clive.Evans@dti.gsi.gov.uk Martin.Young@dti.gsi.gov.uk
North Sea profits, operating costs and investments	Suhail Siddiqui	5262	Suhail.Siddiqui@dti.gsi.gov.uk
Petroleum (downstream)	Gregory Haigh Martin Young	2712 5184	Greg.Haigh@dti.gsi.gov.uk Martin.Young@dti.gsi.gov.uk
Gas supply (downstream)	Sally Mercer Tracy Halsey	2717 2684	Sally.Mercer@dti.gsi.gov.uk Tracy.Halsey@dti.gsi.gov.uk
Electricity	Mike Janes Joe Ewins	5186 5190	Mike.Janes@dti.gsi.gov.uk Joe.Ewins@dti.gsi.gov.uk
Combined heat and power	Mike Janes	5186	Mike.Janes@dti.gsi.gov.uk
Prices and values Industrial, international and oil prices	Peter Matejic Sara Atkins	2720 6532	Peter.Matejic@dti.gsi.gov.uk Sara.Atkins@dti.gsi.gov.uk
Renewable sources of energy	Mike Janes	5186	Mike.Janes@dti.gsi.gov.uk
Calorific values and conversion factors	Julian Prime Martin Young	6178 5184	Julian.Prime@dti.gsi.gov.uk Martin.Young@dti.gsi.gov.uk
General enquiries (energy helpdesk)	Clive Sarjantson	2698	Clive.Sarjantson@dti.gsi.gov.uk

All the above can be contacted by fax on 020 7215 2723

Tables as they appear in this issue and their corresponding numbers in the previous three issues

Chapter	2002	2003	2004	2005
ENERGY	-	-	-	1.1
	-	-	1.1	1.2
	-	1.1	1.2	1.3
	1.1	1.2	1.3	-
	1.2	1.3	-	-
	1.3	-	-	-
	-	-	-	1.4
	-	-	1.4	1.5
	-	1.4	1.5	1.6
	1.4	1.5	1.6	-
	1.5	1.6	-	-
	1.6	-	-	-
	1.7	1.7	1.7	1.7
	1.8	1.8	1.8	1.8
	1.9	1.9	1.9	1.9
SOLID FUELS & DERIVED GASES	-	-	-	2.1
	-	-	2.1	2.2
	-	2.1	2.2	2.3
	2.1	2.2	2.3	-
	2.2	2.3	-	-
	2.3	-	-	-
	-	-	-	2.4
	-	-	2.4	2.5
	-	2.4	2.5	2.6
	2.4	2.5	2.6	-
	2.5	2.6	-	-
	2.6	-	-	-
	2.7	2.7	2.7	2.7
	2.8	2.8	2.8	2.8
	2.9	2.9	2.9	2.9
	2.10	2.10	2.10	2.10
	2.11	2.11	2.11	2.11
PETROLEUM	-	-	-	3.1
	-	-	3.1	3.2
	-	3.1	3.2	3.3
	3.1	3.2	3.3	-
	3.2	3.3	-	-
	3.3	-	-	-
	-	-	-	3.4
	-	-	3.4	3.5
	-	3.4	3.5	3.6
	3.4	3.5	3.6	-
	3.5	3.6	-	-
	3.6	-	-	-
	3.7	3.7	3.7	3.7
	3.8	3.8	3.8	3.8
	3.9	3.9	3.9	3.9
	3.10	3.10	3.10	3.10

Chapter	2002	2003	2004	2005
NATURAL GAS	4.1	4.1	4.1	4.1
	4.2	4.2	4.2	4.2
	4.3	4.3	4.3	4.3
ELECTRICITY	5.1	5.1	5.1	5.1
	5.2	5.2	5.2	5.2
	5.3	5.3	5.3	5.3
	5.4	5.4	5.4	5.4
	5.5	5.5	5.5	5.5
	5.6	5.6	5.6	5.6
	5.7	5.7	5.7	5.7
	-	-	5.8	5.8
	5.8	5.8	5.9	5.9
	5.9	5.9	5.10	5.10
	5.10	5.10	5.11	5.11
	-	-	-	5.12
COMBINED HEAT AND POWER	6.1	6.1	6.1	6.1
	6.2	6.2	6.2	6.2
	6.3	6.3	6.3	6.3
	6.4	6.4	6.4	6.4
	6.5	6.5	6.5	6.5
	6.6	6.6	6.6	6.6
	6.7	6.7	6.7	6.7
	6.8	6.8	6.8	6.8
	6.9	6.9	6.9	6.9
RENEWABLE SOURCES	-	-	-	7.1
	-	-	7.1	7.2
	-	7.1	7.2	7.3
	7.1	7.2	7.3	-
	7.2	7.3	-	-
	7.3	-	-	-
	7.4	7.4	7.4	7.4
	-	-	-	7.5
	7.5	7.5	7.5	7.6
	7.6	7.6	7.6	7.7
ANNEX A CALORIFIC VALUES	A.1	A.1	A.1	A.1
	A.2	A.2	A.2	A.2
	-	-	-	A.3

Chapter 1
Energy

Introduction

1.1   This chapter presents figures on overall energy production and consumption. Figures showing the flow of energy from production, transformation and energy industry use through to final consumption are presented in the format of an energy balance based on the individual commodity balances presented in Chapters 2 to 5 and 7.

1.2   The chapter begins with aggregate energy balances covering the last three years (Tables 1.1 to 1.3) starting with the latest year, 2004. Energy value balances then follow this for the same years (Tables 1.4 to 1.6) and Table 1.7 shows sales of electricity and gas by sector. Table 1.8 covers final energy consumption by the main industrial sectors over the last five years followed by Table 1.9, which shows the fuels used for electricity generation by these industrial sectors. The explanation of the principles behind the energy balance and commodity balance presentations is set out in Annex A. Long term trends commentary and Tables (1.1.1 to 1.1.8) for energy production, consumption and expenditure on energy, temperatures as well as analyses such as the relationship between energy consumption and the economy of the UK appear on DTI's energy statistics web site only at:

www.dti.gov.uk/energy/inform/dukes/dukes2005/01longterm.pdf

Proposed changes to the calculation of energy statistics

1.3   DTI are proposing to make changes to the way in which energy data are calculated, which will affect the data shown in this chapter from the 2006 edition of DUKES; we are keen to hear the views of uses on the proposals, and have set in place a formal consultation on the issue. We are proposing to use net calorific values (NCVs) as opposed to gross calorific values (GCVs) when calculating the energy content of fuels.   As well as impacting on tables within this chapter, data contained in some tables within chapters 4, 5 and 7 will also alter. The difference between GCVs and NCVs depends on the fuel composition – a larger proportion of hydrogen (or water) in a fuel indicates a greater difference between GCV and NCV. Most international countries already use NCVs, and the IEA, the UN, and Eurostat have also adopted the NCV approach when aggregating data from individual countries. The full consultation document - which contains more details on the proposed changes - is available at http://www.dti.gov.uk/energy/consultations/net_gross_cv.pdf

The energy industries

1.4   The energy industries in the UK play a central role in the economy by producing, transforming and supplying energy in its various forms to all sectors. They are also major contributors to the UK's Balance of Payments through the exports of crude oil and oil products. The box below summarises the energy industries' contribution to the economy:

- 3.2 per cent of GDP;

- 5.8 per cent of total investment;

- 38.1 per cent of industrial investment;

- 148,900 people directly employed (4 per cent of industrial employment);

- Many others indirectly employed (eg an estimated 335,000 in support of UK Continental Shelf activities);

- Trade surplus in fuels of £1.3 billion.

Aggregate energy balance (Tables 1.1, 1.2 and 1.3)

1.5   These tables show the flows of energy in the United Kingdom from production to final consumption through conversion into secondary fuels such as coke, petroleum products, secondary electricity and heat sold. The principles behind the presentation used in the Digest and how this links with the figures presented in other chapters are explained in Annex A. The figures are presented on an energy supplied basis, in tonnes of oil equivalent.

1.6   In 2004, the primary supply of fuels was 247.5 million tonnes of oil equivalent, a 1 per cent increase compared to 2003. Indigenous production in 2004 was 8½ per cent lower than in 2003. Chart 1.1 illustrates the figures for the production and consumption of individual primary fuels in 2004. In 2004, overall primary fuel consumption was not met by indigenous production, and the UK became a net importer of fuel. The UK imported more coal, manufactured fuels, electricity and gas than it exported; however we were still a net exporter of petroleum and its products.

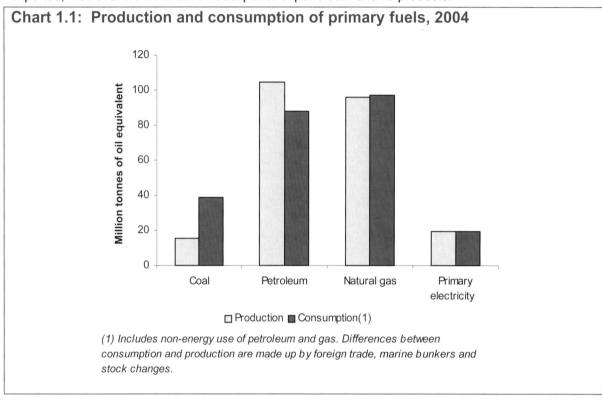

Chart 1.1: Production and consumption of primary fuels, 2004

(1) Includes non-energy use of petroleum and gas. Differences between consumption and production are made up by foreign trade, marine bunkers and stock changes.

1.7   Total primary energy demand was 1 per cent higher in 2004 than in 2003 at 247.3 million tonnes of oil equivalent. Chart 1.2 shows the composition of primary demand in 2004.

1.8   The transfers row in Tables 1.1 to 1.3 should ideally sum to zero with transfers from primary oils to petroleum products amounting to a net figure of zero. Similarly the manufactured gases and natural gas transfers should sum to zero.

1.9   The transformation section of the energy balance shows, for each fuel, the net inputs for transformation uses. For example, on Table 1.1, 3,997 thousand tonnes of oil equivalent of coal feeds into the production of 3,979 thousand tonnes of oil equivalent of coke, representing a loss of 18 thousand tonnes of oil equivalent in the manufacture of coke in 2004. In 2004, energy losses during the production of electricity and other secondary fuels amounted to 53,544 thousand tonnes of oil equivalent, shown in the transformation row in Table 1.1.

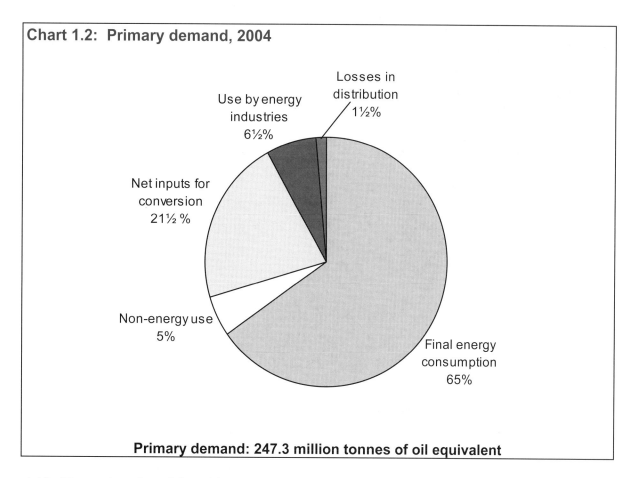

Chart 1.2: Primary demand, 2004

Losses in distribution 1½%

Use by energy industries 6½%

Net inputs for conversion 21½ %

Non-energy use 5%

Final energy consumption 65%

Primary demand: 247.3 million tonnes of oil equivalent

1.10   The next section of the table represents use of fuels by the energy industries themselves. This section also includes consumption by those parts of the iron and steel industry which behave like an energy industry ie they are involved in the transformation processes (see paragraph A.29 of Annex A). In 2004, energy industry use amounted to 16,683 thousand tonnes of oil equivalent of energy, a fall of 1½ per cent on 2003.

1.11   Losses presented in the energy balance include distribution and transmission losses in the supply of manufactured gases, natural gas, and electricity. Recorded losses increased by 8½ per cent between 2003 and 2004, and represents the first increase in loses since 2000. Losses in North Sea gas production are no longer separately identified in a simplified Petroleum Product Reporting System, which was introduced in January 2001. This has improved the quality of production data and reduced reported losses. Further details can be found in paragraph 4.30 in Chapter 4.

1.12   Total final consumption, which includes non-energy use of fuels, in 2004 was 173,456 thousand tonnes of oil equivalent, a 1½ per cent increase on 2003. Final energy consumption in 2004 was mainly accounted for by the transport sector (33 per cent), the domestic sector (28 per cent), the industrial sector (19½ per cent), the commercial sector (6 per cent) and non-energy use (7 per cent). These figures are illustrated in Chart 1.3. Recent trends in industrial consumption are shown in Table 1.8 and discussed in paragraphs 1.20 to 1.22.

1.13   The main fuels used by final consumers in 2004 were petroleum products (47 per cent), natural gas (33 per cent) and electricity (17 per cent). Of the petroleum products consumed by final users 14 per cent was for non-energy purposes; for natural gas 1½ per cent was consumed for non-energy purposes. The amount of heat that was bought for final consumption accounted for 1½ per cent of the total.

1.14 Non-energy use of fuels includes use as chemical feedstocks and other uses such as lubricants. Non-energy use of fuels for 2004 are shown in Table 1A. Further details of non-energy use are given in Chapter 3, paragraphs 3.57 to 3.63 and Chapter 4, paragraphs 4.17.

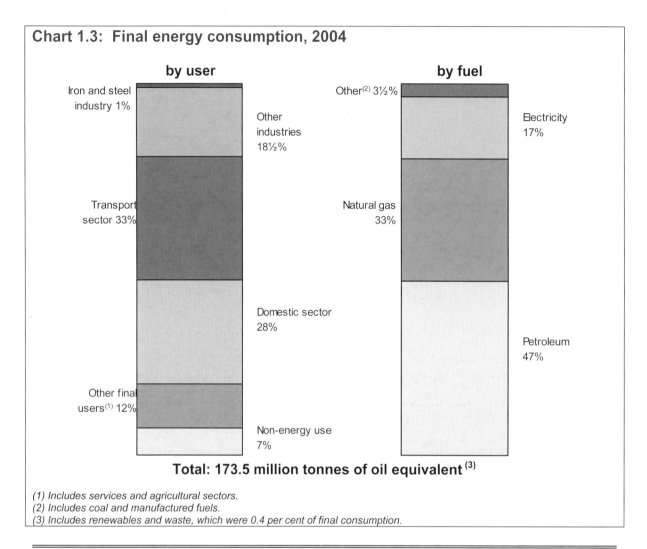

Chart 1.3: Final energy consumption, 2004

by user

- Iron and steel industry 1%
- Other industries 18½%
- Transport sector 33%
- Domestic sector 28%
- Other final users[1] 12%
- Non-energy use 7%

by fuel

- Other[2] 3½%
- Electricity 17%
- Natural gas 33%
- Petroleum 47%

Total: 173.5 million tonnes of oil equivalent [3]

(1) Includes services and agricultural sectors.
(2) Includes coal and manufactured fuels.
(3) Includes renewables and waste, which were 0.4 per cent of final consumption.

Table 1A: Non-energy use of fuels 2004

	Thousand tonnes of oil equivalent	
	Petroleum	Natural gas
Petrochemical feedstocks	8,177	862
Other	3,391	-
Total	**11,568**	**862**

Value balance of traded energy (Tables 1.4, 1.5 and 1.6)

1.15   Tables 1.4 to 1.6 present the value of traded energy in a similar format to the energy balances. The balance shows how the value of inland energy supply is made up from the value of indigenous production, trade, tax and margins (profit and distribution costs). The lower half of the table then shows how this value is generated from the final expenditure on energy through transformation processes and other energy sector users as well as from the industrial and domestic sectors. The balances only contain values of energy which is traded ie where a transparent market price is applicable. Further technical notes are given in paragraphs 1.24 to 1.57. In keeping with the energy balances, the value balances for 2000 onwards include data on heat generation and heat sold. Additionally, an estimate of the amount of Climate Change Levy paid is included in Tables 1.4, 1.5 and 1.6. This levy was introduced in April 2001 and is payable by non-domestic final consumers of gas, electricity, coal, coke and LPG.

1.16   Total expenditure by final consumers in 2004 is estimated at £75,450 million, (£75,165 million shown as actual final consumption and £285 million of coal consumed by the iron and steel sector in producing coke for their own consumption).

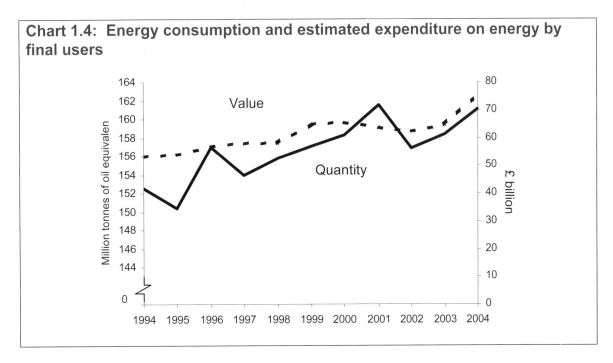

Chart 1.4: Energy consumption and estimated expenditure on energy by final users

1.17   This balance provides a guide on how the value chain works in the production and consumption of energy. For example in 2004, £15,345 million of crude oil were indigenously produced, of which £9,905 million were exported, and £8,615 million of crude oil were imported. Allowing for stock changes this provides a total value of inland crude oil supply of £14,035 million. This fuel was then completely consumed within the petroleum industry in the process of producing £19,795 million of petroleum products. Again some external trade and stock changes took place before arriving at a basic value of petroleum products of £17,700 million. In supplying the fuel to final consumers distribution costs were incurred and some profit was made amounting to £2,465 million, whilst duty and tax meant a further £31,010 million was added to the basic price to arrive at the final market value of £51,180 million. This was the value of petroleum products purchased of which industry purchased £1,775 million, domestic consumers for heating purposes purchased £765 million, with the vast majority purchased within the transportation sectors, £46,005 million.

1.18   Of the total final expenditure on energy in 2004 (£75,450 million) the biggest share, 61 per cent fell to the transport sector. Of the remaining 39 per cent, industry purchased around a quarter or £7,075 million, with the domestic sector purchasing over a half or £16,160 million.

Sales of electricity and gas by sector (Table 1.7)
1.19   Table 1.7 shows broad estimates for the total value of electricity and gas to final consumption. Net selling values provide some indication of typical prices paid in broad sectors and can be of use to supplement more detailed and accurate information contained in the rest of this chapter.

Energy consumption by main industrial groups (Table 1.8)
1.20   This table presents final energy consumption for the main industrial sub-sectors over the last 5 years.

1.21   So far as is practicable, the user categories have been grouped on the basis of the 2003 Standard Industrial Classification (see paragraphs 1.52 to 1.56). However, some data suppliers have difficulty in classifying consumers to this level of detail and the breakdown presented in these tables must therefore be treated with caution. The groupings used are consistent with those used in Table 1.9 which show industrial sectors' use of fuels for generation of electricity (autogeneration).

1.22   In 2004, 34.1 million tonnes of oil equivalent were consumed by the main industrial groups. The largest consuming groups were chemicals (18½ per cent), iron and steel and non-ferrous metals (8½ per cent), metal products, machinery and equipment (11½ per cent), food, beverages and tobacco (11½ per cent), and paper, printing and publishing (7½ per cent). The figures are illustrated in Chart 1.5.

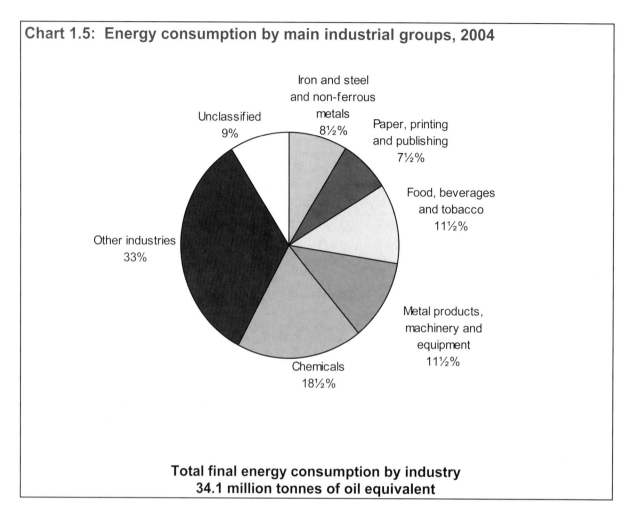

Chart 1.5: Energy consumption by main industrial groups, 2004

Iron and steel and non-ferrous metals 8½%

Paper, printing and publishing 7½%

Unclassified 9%

Food, beverages and tobacco 11½%

Other industries 33%

Metal products, machinery and equipment 11½%

Chemicals 18½%

**Total final energy consumption by industry
34.1 million tonnes of oil equivalent**

Fuels consumed for electricity generation by main industrial groups (autogeneration) (Table 1.9)

1.23   This table gives details of the amount of each fuel consumed by industries in order to generate electricity for their own use.   Fuel consumption is consistent with the figures given for "other generators" in Table 5.4 of Chapter 5. The term autogeneration is explained further in paragraphs 1.29 and 1.30. Electricity produced via autogeneration is included within the figures for electricity consumed by industrial sectors in Table 1.8. Table 1.9 has been produced using the information currently available and shows the same sector detail as Table 1.8, data cannot be given in as much detail as in the individual commodity balances and the energy balance because it could disclose information about individual companies.   Table 1.9 allows users to allocate the fuel used for autogeneration to individual industry groups in place of the electricity consumed. Further information on the way Table 1.9 links with the other tables is given in paragraph 1.30.

Technical notes and definitions

I Units and measurement of energy

Units of measurement

1.24 The original units of measurement appropriate to each fuel are used in the individual fuel chapters. A common unit of measurement, the tonne of oil equivalent (toe), which enables different fuels to be compared and aggregated, is used in Chapter 1. For consistency with the International Energy Agency and with the Statistical Office of the European Communities, the tonne of oil equivalent is defined as follows:

1 tonne of oil equivalent   = 10^7 kilocalories
     = 396.83 therms
     = 41.868 Gigajoules (GJ)
     = 11,630 kWh

1.25 This unit should be regarded as a measure of energy content rather than a physical quantity. There is no intention to represent an actual physical tonne of oil, and indeed actual tonnes of oil will normally have measurements in tonnes of oil equivalent which differ from units.

Thermal content - energy supplied basis of measurement

1.26 Tables 1.1 to 1.3, 1.8 and 1.1.1 to 1.1.5 (available on DTI's energy statistics site at www.dti.gov.uk/energy/inform/energy_stats/total_energy/) are compiled on an energy-supplied basis. Detailed data for individual fuels are converted from original units to tonnes of oil equivalent using gross calorific values and conversion factors appropriate to each category of fuel. The results are then aggregated according to the categories used in the tables. Gross calorific values represent the total energy content of the fuel, including the energy needed to evaporate the water present in the fuel (see also paragraph 1.50).

1.27 Estimated gross and net calorific values for 2004 are given on page 204. Calorific values are reviewed each year in collaboration with the fuel industries, and figures for earlier years can be found in Table A.2 and A.3 on pages 205 and 206. To construct energy balances on an energy supplied basis calorific values are required for production, trade, and stocks, as follows:

Coal The weighted average gross calorific value of all indigenous coal consumed is used to derive the thermal content of coal production and undistributed stocks. Thermal contents of imports and exports allow for the quality of coal. Thermal contents of changes in coal stocks at secondary fuel producers are the average calorific values of indigenous coal consumed.

Petroleum Work was carried out in 1997 to revise calorific values for petroleum products. It has not been possible to find any recent work on the subject. In the absence of such work, the gross calorific values, included in Annex A, and used in the construction of these energy balances from 1990 onwards have been calculated using a formula derived by the US Bureau of Standards. This formula estimates the gross calorific value of products according to their density as follows:

$Gj = 51.83 - 8.78 \times d^2$, where d is the density of the product in terms of kilograms per litre.

For crude petroleum and refinery losses, the weighted average calorific value for all petroleum products from UK refineries is used. A notional figure of 43.4 GJ per tonne is used for non-energy petroleum products (industrial and white spirits, lubricants, bitumen, petroleum coke, waxes and miscellaneous products).

Gases Although the original unit for gases is the cubic metre, figures for gases are generally presented in the fuel sections of this Digest in gigawatt hours (GWh), having been converted from cubic metres using gross calorific values provided by the industries concerned. Conversion factors between units of energy are given on the flap inside the back cover.

Electricity and heat Unlike other fuels, the original unit used to measure electricity and heat is a measure of energy. The figures for electricity and heat can therefore be converted directly to toe using the conversion factors on the flap inside the back cover.

Primary electricity Hydro electricity and net imports of electricity are presented in terms of the energy content of the electricity produced (the energy supplied basis). This is consistent with international practice. Primary inputs for nuclear electricity assume the thermal efficiencies at nuclear stations given in Chapter 5, Table 5.10 (37.9 per cent in 2004). (See Chapter 5, paragraphs 5.26 and 5.57.)

Non-energy uses of fuel

1.28 Energy use of fuel mainly comprises use for lighting, heating, motive power and power for appliances. Non-energy use includes use as chemical feedstocks, solvents, lubricants and road making material. It should be noted that the estimated amounts of non-energy use of natural gas included in the Digest are very approximate. Non-energy uses of petroleum and gas are included in the figures for final energy consumption following the move over to the presentation of energy data in the format of commodity and energy balances. Further discussion of non-energy uses of lubricating oils and petroleum coke appears in Chapter 3, paragraphs 3.57 to 3.63.

Autogeneration of electricity

1.29 Autogeneration is defined as the generation of electricity by companies whose main business is not electricity generation, the electricity being produced mainly for that company's own use. Estimated amounts of fuel used for thermal generation of electricity by such companies, the output of electricity and the thermal losses incurred in generation are included within the Transformation sector in the energy balances shown in Tables 1.1 to 1.3. Electricity used in the power generation process by autogenerators is shown within the Energy Industry Use section. Electricity consumed by industry and commerce from its own generation is included as part of Final consumption. This treatment is in line with the practice in international energy statistics.

1.30 Figures on total amount of fuel used and electricity generated by autogenerators, and the amount of electricity for own consumption is shown in Tables 1.9, 5.1, 5.3 to 5.6. Table 1.9 summarises the figures by broad industrial groups. Much of the power generated is from combined heat and power (CHP) plants and data from Chapter 6 are included within Table 1.9. Differences will occur where CHP plants are classified to major power producers, and this mainly affects the chemicals sector. The method of allocating fuel used in CHP plants between electricity production and heat production is described in Chapter 6 paragraphs 6.33 to 6.35. This method can give rise to high implied conversion efficiencies in some sectors, most notably in the iron and steel sector.

Final consumption, deliveries, stock changes

1.31 Figures for final consumption relate to deliveries, if fuels can be stored by users and data on actual consumption are not available. Final consumption of petroleum and solid fuels is on deliveries basis throughout, except for the use of solid fuels by the iron and steel industry. Figures for domestic use of coal are based on deliveries to merchants. Figures for stock changes in Tables 1.1 to 1.3 cover stocks held by primary and secondary fuel producers, major distributors of petroleum products, and stocks of coke and breeze held by the iron and steel industry. Figures for stock changes in natural gas represent the net amount put into storage by gas companies operating pipelines.

1.32 Figures for final consumption of electricity include sales by the public distribution system and consumption of electricity produced by generators other than the major electricity producing companies. Thus electricity consumption includes that produced by industry and figures for deliveries of other fuels to industry exclude amounts used to generate electricity (except for years prior to 1987).

Heat sold

1.33 Heat sold is defined as heat that is produced and sold under the provision of a contract. The heat sold figures have been derived from two sources covering CHP plants and community heating schemes without CHP plants. Data for heat sold were supplied by CHP plants to the Combined Heat and Power Quality Assurance Programme and were processed by Future Energy Solutions (part of AEA Technology Environment). Data for heat consumption from community heating schemes were derived from the Building Research Establishment's (BRE) 'Nationwide Survey of Community Heating' that was carried out in 1997, a database of community heating schemes in social housing in 2000, and an annual Community Heating Sales Survey undertaken since 2003. The estimates from these sources have been used to derive heat sold figures since 1999. When information about where the heat was generated was not available from the BRE sources, it was assumed that domestic sector heat consumption was provided by the commercial sector, public sector heat consumption was provided by the public administration and industrial sectors (using proportions derived from CHP statistics) and that industrial sector heat consumption was provided by the industrial sector. The introduction of heat sold into the energy balances has not affected the individual fuel totals, since the energy used to generate the heat has been deducted from the final consumption section of the energy balance and transferred to the transformation section. The figures that are included in the balances should be treated as indicative of the amount of heat sold.

Valuation of energy purchases (Tables 1.4, 1.5, 1.6, 1.1.6)

1.34 In common with the rest of the chapter, these tables covering energy expenditure follow a balance format. While a user may derive data on a similar basis as that previously published, the balance table allows for more varied use and interpretation of traded energy value data. That said the table continues to only show values for energy that has to be purchased and therefore does not include estimated values of a sector's internal consumption, such as coal used in the process of coal extraction.

The balance

1.35 The table balances around **market value of inland consumption** with the lower half of the table showing the total value of consumption by end users, sub divided into energy sector users and final users both for energy and non-energy use. The top half of the table shows the supply components that go to make up the final market value of inland consumption, namely upstream cost of production, imports, taxes and the margins and costs of delivering and packaging the fuel for the final consumer. The total final consumers value of energy consumption is represented by the lines 'total non energy sector use' and iron and steel sectors purchases of coal for use in solid fuel manufacture.

Fuel definitions in value balances

1.36 **Crude oil** includes NGLs and refinery feedstocks. **Natural gas** does not include colliery methane. **Electricity** only includes electricity delivered via the public distribution system and therefore does not value electricity produced and consumed by autogenerators, but the input fuels are included in transformation. **Manufactured solid fuels** includes coke, breeze and other solid manufactured fuels, mainly products from patent fuel and carbonisation plants. **Other fuels** includes all other fuels not listed, where they can be clearly considered as traded and some reasonable valuation can be made. Fuels mainly contributing to this year's values are wood, coke oven and colliery methane gases sold on to other industrial users and some use of waste products such as poultry litter.

Valuation

1.37 All figures are estimates and have been rounded to the nearest £5 million.

Energy end use

1.38 Values represent the cost to the final user including transportation of the fuel. They are derived, except where actual values are available, from the traded element of the volumes presented in aggregate energy balance and end user prices collected from information supplied by users or energy suppliers. The **energy sector** consists of those industries engaged in the production and sale of energy products, but values are not given for consumption of self-generated fuels eg coke oven gas used by coke producers. Many of the processes in the **iron and steel** industry are considered to be part of the energy sector in the energy balances, but for the purposes of this economic balance their genuine purchases are treated as those of final consumers, except for purchases of coal directly used in coke manufacture, which is shown separately as part of manufacture of solid fuel. Coal used directly in or to heat blast furnaces is shown as iron and steel final use. **Transformation** are those fuels used directly in producing other fuels eg crude oil in petroleum products. **Electricity generators** keep and use significant stocks of coal and the stocks used in consumption each year are shown separately. The value and margins for these being assumed to be the same as other coal purchased in the year. **Road transport** includes all motor spirit and DERV use. **Commercial and other users** includes public administration and miscellaneous uses not classified to the industrial sector.

Supply

1.39 The supply side money chain is derived using various methods. **Indigenous production** represents the estimated basic value of in year sales by the upstream producers. This value is gross of any taxes or cost they must meet. The valuation problems in attributing network losses in gas and electricity between upstream and downstream within this value chain, means any costs borne are included in the production value. **Imports and exports** are valued in accordance with Annex G (which can be found on the internet). However crude oil is treated differently where the value is formed from price data taken from a census survey of refiners and volume data taken from Tables 3.1 to 3.3. These values are considered to reflect the complete money chain more accurately than Tables G.1 to G.4. **Stock changes** are those for undistributed stocks except for coal where coke oven and generators stocks are included. A stock increase takes money out of the money chain and is therefore represented as a negative. **Distribution costs** are arrived at by removing an estimate of producers value along with any taxes from the end user values shown. For most fuel the estimate of producer value is derived from the consumption used for end use and the producer price taken from survey of producers. For electricity the Pool Purchase Price is used to value public distribution supply. No sector breakdown is given for gas and electricity margins because it is not possible to accurately measure delivery costs for each sector. **Taxes** include VAT where not refundable and duties paid on downstream sales. Excluded are the gas and fossil fuel levies, petroleum revenue tax and production royalties and licence fees. The proceeds from the fossil fuel levy are redistributed across the electricity industry, whilst the rest are treated as part of the production costs.

Sales of electricity and gas by sector (Table 1.7)

1.40 This table provides data on the total value of gas and electricity sold to final consumers. The data are collected from the energy supply companies. The data are useful in indicating relative total expenditure between sectors, but the quality of data provided in terms of industrial classification has been worsening in recent years. Net selling values provide some indication of typical prices paid in broad sectors.

II Energy balances (Tables 1.1, 1.2 and 1.3)

1.41 Tables 1.1, 1.2 and 1.3 show the energy flows as the primary fuels are processed (or used) and as the consequent secondary fuels are used. The net inputs to transformation are shown in the transformation rows and hence outputs from transformation processes into which primary fuels are input (such as electricity generation, heat generation or petroleum refining) appear as positive figures under the secondary product's heading in the tables. Similarly the net inputs are shown as negative figures under the primary fuel headings.

III Measurement of energy consumption

Primary fuel input basis

1.42 Energy consumption is usually measured in one of three different ways. The first, known as the primary fuel input basis, assesses the total input of primary fuels and their equivalents. This measure includes energy used or lost in the conversion of primary fuels to secondary fuels (for example in power stations and oil refineries), energy lost in the distribution of fuels (for example in transmission lines) and energy conversion losses by final users. Primary demands as in Table 1.1, 1.2 and 1.3 are on this basis.

Final consumption - energy supplied basis

1.43 The second method, known as the energy supplied basis, measures the energy content of the fuels, both primary and secondary, supplied to final users. Thus it is net of fuel industry own use and conversion, transmission and distribution losses, but it includes conversion losses by final users. Table 1B presents shares of final consumption on this basis. The final consumption figures are presented on this basis throughout Chapter 1.

1.44 Although this is the usual and most direct way to measure final energy consumption, it is also possible to present final consumption on a primary fuel input basis. This can be done by allocating the conversion losses, distribution losses and energy industry use to final users. This approach can be used to compare the total primary fuel use which each sector of the economy accounts for. Table 1C presents shares of final consumption on this basis.

Final consumption - useful energy basis

1.45   Thirdly, final consumption may be expressed in the form of useful energy available after deduction of the losses incurred when final users convert energy supplied into space or process heat, motive power or light. Such losses depend on the type and quality of fuel and the equipment used and on the purpose, conditions, duration and intensity of use.   Statistics on useful energy are not sufficiently reliable to be given in this Digest; there is a lack of data on utilisation efficiencies and on the purposes for which fuels are used.

Shares of each fuel in energy supply and demand

1.46   The relative importance of the energy consumption of each sector of the economy depends on the method used to measure consumption. Shares of final consumption on an energy supplied basis (that is in terms of the primary and secondary fuels directly consumed) in 2004 are presented in Table 1B. For comparison, Table 1C presents shares of final consumption on a primary fuel input basis.

Table 1B: Primary and secondary fuels consumed by final users in 2004 – energy supplied basis

| | Percentage of each fuel | | | | | | Percentage of each sector | | | | |
	Industry	Transport	Domestic	Others	Total		Solid fuels	Petrol-eum	Gas	Secondary electricity	Total
Solid fuels	55	-	42	4	100	Industry	5	26	38	31	100
Petroleum	12	81	4	2	100	Transport	-	99	-	1	100
Gas	22	-	61	17	100	Domestic	3	6	70	21	100
Secondary electricity	34	2	34	29	100	Others	1	8	48	43	100
All fuels	**21**	**36**	**31**	**12**	**100**	**All users**	**2**	**44**	**35**	**18**	**100**

Table 1C: Total primary fuel consumption by final users in 2004 - primary input basis

| | Percentage of each fuel | | | | | | Percentage of each sector | | | | |
	Industry	Transport	Domestic	Others	Total		Coal	Petrol-eum	Gas	Primary electricity	Total
Coal	36	2	35	27	100	Industry	25	17	45	13	100
Petroleum	12	81	5	3	100	Transport	1	97	1	1	100
Gas	26	1	52	21	100	Domestic	18	5	67	9	100
Primary electricity	34	2	34	29	100	Others	27	5	52	16	100
All fuels	**24**	**28**	**31**	**17**	**100**	**All users**	**17**	**34**	**41**	**9**	**100**

1.47   In 2004, every 1 toe of secondary electricity consumed by final users required, on average, 1.0 toe of coal, 0.9 toe of natural gas, 0.6 toe of primary electricity (nuclear, natural flow hydro and imports) and 0.1 toe of oil and renewables combined. The extent of this primary consumption is hidden in Table 1B, which presents final consumption only in terms of the fuels directly consumed. When all such primary consumption is allocated to final users, as in Table 1C, the relative importance of fuels and sectors changes; the transport sector, which uses very little electricity, declines in importance, whilst the true cost of final consumption in terms of coal use can now be seen.

1.48   Another view comes from shares of users' expenditure on each fuel (Table 1D based on Table 1.4). In this case the importance of fuels which require most handling by the user (solids and liquid fuels) is slightly understated, and the importance of uses taxed at higher rates (transport) is overstated in the "All users" line.

Table 1D: Value of fuels purchased by final users in 2004

	Solid fuels	Petroleum	Gas	Secondary electricity	Heat	Percentage of each sector
						Total
Industry	3	26	21	48	2	100
Transport	-	99	-	1	-	100
Domestic	2	5	43	50	-	100
Others	-	6	22	69	3	100
All users	**1**	**65**	**13**	**21**	**0**	**100**

Systems of measurement - international statistics
1.49   The systems of energy measurement used in various international statistics differ from the methods of the Digest as follows:

Net calorific values
1.50   Calorific values (thermal contents) used internationally are net rather than gross.   The difference between the net and gross thermal content is the amount of energy necessary to evaporate the water present in the fuel or formed during the combustion process.   The differences between gross and net values are taken to be 5 per cent for liquid and solid fuels (except for coke and coke breeze where there is no difference), 10 per cent for gases (except for blast furnace gas, 1 per cent), 15 per cent for straw, and 16 per cent for poultry litter. The calorific value of wood is highly dependent on its moisture content. In Annex A, the gross calorific value is given as 10 GJ per tonne at 50 per cent moisture content and this rises to 14.5 GJ at 25 per cent moisture content and 19 GJ for dry wood (equivalent to a net calorific value). Both gross and net calorific values are shown in Annex A.

IV Definitions of fuels

1.51   The following paragraphs explain what is covered under the terms "primary" and "secondary" fuels.

Primary fuels
Coal - Production comprises all grades of coal, including slurry.

Primary oils - This includes crude oil, natural gas liquids (NGLs) and feedstock.

Natural gas liquids - Natural gas liquids (NGLs) consist of condensates (C_5 or heavier) and petroleum gases other than methane C_1, that is ethane C_2, propane C_3 and butane C_4, obtained from the onshore processing of associated and non-associated gas. These are treated as primary fuels when looking at primary supply but in the consumption data presented in this chapter these fuels are treated as secondary fuels, being transferred from the primary oils column in Tables 1.1, 1.2 and 1.3.

Natural gas - Production relates to associated or non-associated methane C_1 from land and the United Kingdom sector of the Continental Shelf. It includes that used for drilling production and pumping operations, but excludes gas flared or re-injected. It also includes colliery methane piped to the surface and consumed by collieries or others.

Nuclear electricity - Electricity generated by nuclear power stations belonging to the major power producers. See Chapter 5, paragraphs 5.49 and 5.51.

Natural flow hydro-electricity - Electricity generated by public supply and industrial natural flow hydroelectric power stations. Pumped storage stations are not included (see under secondary electricity below).

Renewable energy sources - In this chapter figures are presented for renewables and waste in total. Further details, including a detailed breakdown of the commodities covered are in Chapter 7.

Secondary fuels
Manufactured fuel - This heading includes manufactured solid fuels such as coke and breeze, other manufactured solid fuels, liquids such as benzole and tars and gases such as coke oven gas and blast furnace gas. Further details are given in Chapter 2, Tables 2.4, 2.5 and 2.6.

Coke and breeze - Coke oven coke and hard coke breeze (Chapter 2, Tables 2.4, 2.5 and 2.6).

Other manufactured solid fuels – Manufactured solid fuels produced at low temperature carbonisation plants and other manufactured fuel and briquetting plants (Chapter 2, Tables 2.4, 2.5 and 2.6).

Coke oven gas - Gas produced at coke ovens, excluding low temperature carbonisation plants. Gas bled or burnt to waste is included in production and losses (Chapter 2, Tables 2.4, 2.5 and 2.6).

Blast furnace gas - Blast furnace gas is mainly produced and consumed within the iron and steel industry (Chapter 2, Tables 2.4, 2.5 and 2.6).

Petroleum products - Petroleum products produced mainly at refineries, together with inland deliveries of natural gas liquids.

Secondary electricity - Secondary electricity is that generated by the combustion of another fuel, usually coal, natural gas or oil. The figure for outputs from transformation in the electricity column of Tables 1.1, 1.2 and 1.3 is the total of primary and secondary electricity, and the subsequent analysis of consumption is based on this total.

Heat sold – Heat sold is heat that is produced and sold under the provision of a contract.

V Classification of consumers

1.52   The Digest has been prepared, as far as is practicable, on the basis of the *Standard Industrial Classification (SIC) 2003* (www.statistics.gov.uk/methods_quality/classifications.asp).   SIC(2003) replaced SIC(1992) on 1 January 2003. SIC(1992) had been the basis of the industrial classification of energy statistics since 1995. Between 1986 and 1994 data in the Digest were prepared on the basis of the previous classification, SIC(1980). The changes in classification between SIC(1992) and SIC(2003) are mainly in the very detailed classifications at the four or five digit level. As such the classifications used for energy statistics are unaffected by these changes.   However, not all consumption/disposals data are on this new basis, and where they are, there are sometimes constraints on the detail available. In particular the sectoral breakdown in the petroleum chapter is based on data that continue to be classified according to SIC (1968) by the oil industry. The main differences between the 1968 SIC (which was used as the basis for most data published for years prior to 1984) and the 1980 SIC were described in the 1986 and 1987 issues of the Digest. The differences between SIC 1980 and SIC 1992 are relatively minor. At the time of the change from the 1980 SIC to the 1992 SIC the main difference was that under the former showrooms belonging to the fuel supply industries were classified to the energy sector, whilst in the latter they are in the commercial sector.   Since privatisation few gas, coal and electricity companies have retained showrooms and the difference is therefore minimal.

1.53   Table 1E shows the categories of consumers together with their codes in SIC 2003.   The coverage varies between tables (eg in some instances the 'other' category is split into major constituents, whereas elsewhere it may include transport). This is because the coverage is dictated by what data suppliers can provide. The table also shows the disaggregation available within industry. This disaggregation forms the basis of virtually all the tables that show a disaggregated industrial breakdown.

Table 1E: SIC 2003 classifications

Fuel producers	10-12, 23, 40

Final consumers:

Industrial

Unclassified	See paragraph 1.54 below
Iron and steel	27, *excluding 27.4, 27.53, 27.54*
Non-ferrous metals	27.4, 27.53, 27.54
Mineral products	14, 26
Chemicals	24
Mechanical engineering and metal products	28, 29
Electrical and instrument engineering	30-33
Vehicles	34, 35
Food, beverages & tobacco	15, 16
Textiles, clothing, leather, & footwear	17-19
Paper, printing & publishing	21, 22
Other industries	13, 20, 25, 36, 37, 41
Construction	45

Transport   60-63

Other final users

Domestic	Not covered by SIC 2003.
Public administration	75, 80, 85
Commercial	50-52, 55, 64-67, 70-74
Agriculture	01, 02, 05
Miscellaneous	90-93, 99

1.54   There is also an 'unclassified' category in the industry sector (see Table 1E). Wherever the data supplier is unable to allocate an amount between categories, but the Department of Trade and Industry has additional information, not readily available to readers, with which to allocate between categories, then this has been done. Where such additional information is not available the data are included in the 'unclassified' category, enabling the reader to decide whether to accept a residual, pro-rate, or otherwise adjust the figures. The 'miscellaneous' category also contains some unallocated figures for the services sector.

1.55   In Tables 6.8 and 6.9 of Chapter 6 the following abbreviated grouping of industries, based on SIC 2003, is used in order to prevent disclosure of information about individual companies:

Table 1F: Abbreviated grouping of Industry

Iron and steel and non-ferrous metal	27
Chemicals	24
Oil refineries	23.2
Paper, printing and publishing	21, 22
Food, beverages and tobacco	15, 16
Metal products, machinery and equipment	28, 29, 30, 31, 32, 34, 35
Mineral products, extraction, mining and agglomeration of solid fuels	10, 11, 14, 26
Sewage Treatment	(parts of 41 and 90)
Electricity supply	40.1
Other industrial branches	12, 13, 17, 18, 19, 20, 23.1, 23.3, 25, 33, 36, 37, 40.2, 41 (remainder) 45
Transport, commerce, and administration	1, 2, 5, 50 to 99 (except 90 and 92)
Other	40.3, 90 (remainder), 92

1.56 In Tables 1.8 and 1.9 the list above is further condensed and includes only manufacturing industry and construction as follows:

Table 1G: Abbreviated grouping of Industry for Tables 1.8 and 1.9

Iron and steel and non-ferrous metals	27
Chemicals	24
Paper, printing and publishing	21, 22
Food, beverages and tobacco	15, 16
Metal products, machinery and equipment	28, 29, 30, 31, 32, 34, 35
Other (including construction)	12, 13, 14, 17, 18, 19, 20, 23.1, 23.3, 25, 26, 33, 36, 37, 45

VI Monthly and quarterly data

1.57 Monthly and quarterly data on energy production and consumption (including on a seasonally adjusted and temperature corrected basis) split by fuel type are provided on the DTI website at www.dti.gov.uk/energy/inform/energy_stats/. Quarterly figures are also published in the DTI's quarterly statistical bulletin *Energy Trends and Quarterly Energy Prices*. See Annex C for more information about these bulletins.

Contact: *Julian Prime (Statistician)*
julian.prime@dti.gsi.gov.uk
020-7215 6178

Chris Michaels
chris.michaels@dti.gsi.gov.uk
020-7215 2710

Sara Atkins
Energy Prices
sara.atkins@dti.gsi.gov.uk
020-7215 6532

1.1 Aggregate energy balance 2004

Thousand tonnes of oil equivalent

	Coal	Manu-factured fuels (1)	Primary oils	Petroleum products	Natural gas (2)	Renewable & waste (3)	Primary electricity	Elect-ricity	Heat sold	Total
Supply										
Indigenous production	15,685	-	104,547	-	96,006	3,341	18,917	-	-	238,496
Imports	23,621	725	68,214	21,158	11,439	212	-	841	-	126,211
Exports	-447	-124	-70,513	-32,860	-9,812	-	-	-197	-	-113,953
Marine bunkers	-	-	-	-2,220	-	-	-	-	-	-2,220
Stock change (4)	+96	-84	-149	-327	-536	-	-	-	-	-1,000
Primary supply	**38,955**	**518**	**102,099**	**-14,249**	**97,097**	**3,553**	**18,917**	**644**	**-**	**247,534**
Statistical difference (5)	+86	+62	-140	-46	+103	-	-	+136	-	+201
Primary demand	**38,869**	**456**	**102,239**	**-14,203**	**96,994**	**3,553**	**18,917**	**508**	**-**	**247,333**
Transfers	-	-118	-4,159	+4,176	-3	-	-614	+614	-	-104
Transformation	**-36,790**	**1,685**	**-98,080**	**97,226**	**-31,866**	**-2,818**	**-18,303**	**33,199**	**2,203**	**-53,544**
Electricity generation	-31,568	-922	-	-679	-29,127	-2,818	-18,303	33,199	-	-50,218
Major power producers	-30,635	-	-	-153	-26,182	-539	-18,303	30,246	-	-45,566
Autogenerators	-933	-922	-	-526	-2,945	-2,279	-	2,954	-	-4,651
Heat generation	-340	-73	-	-83	-2,739	-	-	-	2,203	-1,031
Petroleum refineries	-	-	-98,080	98,297	-	-	-	-	-	217
Coke manufacture	-3,997	3,979	-	-	-	-	-	-	-	-18
Blast furnaces	-652	-1,541	-	-309	-	-	-	-	-	-2,502
Patent fuel manufacture	-233	241	-	-	-	-	-	-	-	8
Other	-	-	-	-	-	-	-	-	-	-
Energy industry use	**6**	**850**	**-**	**5,853**	**7,520**	**-**	**-**	**2,441**	**13**	**16,683**
Electricity generation	-	-	-	-	-	-	-	1,478	2	1,480
Oil and gas extraction	-	-	-	-	6,612	-	-	48	-	6,660
Petroleum refineries	-	-	-	5,851	190	-	-	531	11	6,583
Coal extraction	6	-	-	-	13	-	-	88	-	107
Coke manufacture	-	398	-	1	-	-	-	8	-	407
Blast furnaces	-	449	-	-	63	-	-	40	-	552
Patent fuel manufacture	-	3	-	-	-	-	-	-	-	3
Pumped storage	-	-	-	-	-	-	-	73	-	73
Other	-	-	-	-	643	-	-	175	-	818
Losses	**-**	**201**	**-**	**-**	**703**	**-**	**-**	**2,642**	**-**	**3,546**
Final consumption	**2,073**	**972**	**-**	**81,346**	**56,902**	**735**	**-**	**29,238**	**2,189**	**173,456**
Industry	**979**	**706**	**-**	**8,317**	**12,488**	**286**	**-**	**10,073**	**1,237**	**34,086**
Unclassified	-	138	-	2,632	6	286	-	-	-	3,062
Iron and steel	-	568	-	35	760	-	-	465	-	1,828
Non-ferrous metals	138	-	-	42	269	-	-	626	-	1,075
Mineral products	255	-	-	201	1,064	-	-	675	-	2,195
Chemicals	175	-	-	130	3,427	-	-	1,992	618	6,344
Mechanical engineering etc.	6	-	-	117	694	-	-	732	3	1,552
Electrical engineering etc.	4	-	-	28	328	-	-	586	-	945
Vehicles	69	-	-	99	845	-	-	489	-	1,501
Food, beverages, etc.	128	-	-	345	2,317	-	-	1,060	2	3,851
Textiles, leather, etc.	53	-	-	74	571	-	-	292	-	989
Paper, printing etc.	111	-	-	59	1,277	-	-	1,140	14	2,600
Other industries	41	-	-	4,400	698	-	-	1,862	600	7,600
Construction	-	-	-	156	234	-	-	155	-	545
Transport	**-**	**-**	**-**	**56,758**	**-**	**-**	**-**	**691**	**-**	**57,449**
Air	-	-	-	13,157	-	-	-	-	-	13,157
Rail	-	-	-	185	-	-	-	-	-	185
Road	-	-	-	42,221	-	-	-	-	-	42,221
National navigation	-	-	-	1,195	-	-	-	-	-	1,195
Pipelines	-	-	-	-	-	-	-	-	-	-
Other	**1,094**	**266**	**-**	**4,703**	**43,553**	**449**	**-**	**18,475**	**952**	**69,492**
Domestic	1,041	266	-	3,102	34,085	251	-	9,933	52	48,731
Public administration	39	-	-	473	3,940	104	-	1,799	900	7,256
Commercial	2	-	-	417	3,533	-	-	6,381	-	10,334
Agriculture	6	-	-	277	202	74	-	361	-	920
Miscellaneous	6	-	-	434	1,791	19	-	-	-	2,251
Non energy use	**-**	**-**	**-**	**11,568**	**862**	**-**	**-**	**-**	**-**	**12,429**

(1) Includes all manufactured solid fuels, benzole, tars, coke oven gas and blast furnace gas.
(2) Includes colliery methane.
(3) Includes geothermal and solar heat.
(4) Stock fall (+), stock rise (-).
(5) Primary supply minus primary demand.

1.2 Aggregate energy balance 2003

Thousand tonnes of oil equivalent

	Coal	Manu-factured fuels (1)	Primary oils	Petroleum products	Natural gas (2)	Renewable & waste (3)	Primary electricity	Elect-ricity	Heat sold	Total
Supply										
Indigenous production	17,648r	-	116,242	-	102,926r	3,066	20,428r	-	-	260,310
Imports	20,704r	695r	59,114	18,795	7,420	110	-	440	-	107,278r
Exports	-396	-133r	-81,927	-25,274	-15,223	-	-	-254	-	-123,207r
Marine bunkers	-	-	-	-1,879	-	-	-	-	-	-1,879
Stock change (4)	+1,596r	-92	+511	-294	+304r	-	-	-	-	+2,025r
Primary supply	**39,552r**	**470r**	**93,940**	**-8,653**	**95,427r**	**3,176r**	**20,428r**	**186**	**-**	**244,527r**
Statistical difference (5)	-94r	+66r	+210	-659r	+100r	-	-	+92r	-	-283r
Primary demand	**39,645r**	**404r**	**93,730**	**-7,994r**	**95,327r**	**3,176r**	**20,428r**	**94r**	**-**	**244,811r**
Transfers	-	-124r	-1,367	+1,294	-7	-	-388r	+388r	-	-204r
Transformation	**-38,024r**	**1,852r**	**-92,363**	**91,553r**	**-29,614r**	**-2,449r**	**-20,040**	**33,638r**	**1,789r**	**-53,658r**
Electricity generation	-32,549r	-933r	-	-583r	-27,909r	-2,449	-20,040	33,638r	-	-50,825r
Major power producers	-31,592r	-	-	-105r	-24,477	-381r	-20,040	30,722	-	-45,872r
Autogenerators	-957r	-933r	-	-478r	-3,432r	-2,068r	-	2,916r	-	-4,953r
Heat generation	-383r	-116r	-	-158r	-1,705r	-r	-	-	1,789r	-573r
Petroleum refineries	-	-	-92,363	92,533	-	-	-	-	-	170
Coke manufacture	-4,169r	4,212r	-	-2	-	-	-	-	-	41r
Blast furnaces	-642r	-1,601r	-	-238	-	-	-	-	-	-2,481r
Patent fuel manufacture	-282	291	-	-	-	-	-	-	-	10
Other	-	-	-	-	-	-	-	-	-	-
Energy industry use	**4**	**897r**	**-**	**5,889r**	**7,645r**	**-**	**-**	**2,540r**	**2**	**16,978r**
Electricity generation	-	-	-	-	-	-	-	1,564r	2	1,566r
Oil and gas extraction	-	-	-	-	6,607	-	-	47	-	6,654
Petroleum refineries	-	-	-	5,889r	238r	-	-	510r	-	6,638r
Coal extraction	4	-	-	-	16	-	-	94r	-	114r
Coke manufacture	-	421r	-	-	-	-	-	9r	-	430r
Blast furnaces	-	473r	-	-	46r	-	-	42r	-	562r
Patent fuel manufacture	-	3	-	-	-	-	-	-	-	3
Pumped storage	-	-	-	-	-	-	-	70	-	70
Other	-	-	-	-	737r	-	-	204	-	942r
Losses	**-**	**160r**	**-**	**-**	**534r**	**-**	**-**	**2,568**	**-**	**3,262r**
Final consumption	**1,617r**	**1,075r**	**-**	**78,963r**	**57,527r**	**728r**	**-**	**29,013r**	**1,787r**	**170,709r**
Industry	**640r**	**729r**	**-**	**7,345r**	**14,292r**	**285r**	**-**	**9,828r**	**1,128r**	**34,248r**
Unclassified	-	140r	-	2,014r	6	285r	-	-	-	2,445r
Iron and steel	-	572r	-	19	888r	-	-	467r	-	1,947r
Non-ferrous metals	22r	17	-	63	413r	-	-	571r	-	1,086r
Mineral products	197r	-	-	263	1,209r	-	-	658r	-	2,327r
Chemicals	160r	-	-	395r	3,882r	-	-	1,948r	1,097r	7,480r
Mechanical engineering etc.	3r	-	-	270	785r	-	-	760r	12	1,831r
Electrical engineering etc.	1	-	-	55	378r	-	-	518	-	951r
Vehicles	31r	-	-	122	996r	-	-	487	14r	1,650r
Food, beverages, etc.	82	-	-	326	2,478r	-	-	1,027	5	3,918r
Textiles, leather, etc.	25	-	-	225	675r	-	-	296	-	1,221r
Paper, printing etc.	61r	-	-	124	1,368r	-	-	1,096r	-	2,649r
Other industries	58r	-	-	3,148	954r	-	-	1,854r	-	6,014r
Construction	-	-	-	322	260	-	-	146r	-	728r
Transport	**-**	**-**	**-**	**55,334**	**-**	**-**	**-**	**712r**	**-**	**56,046r**
Air	-	-	-	11,936	-	-	-	-	-	11,936
Rail	-	-	-	342	-	-	-	-	-	342
Road	-	-	-	41,823	-	-	-	-	-	41,823
National navigation	-	-	-	1,233	-	-	-	-	-	1,233
Pipelines	-	-	-	-	-	-	-	-	-	-
Other	**977r**	**346r**	**-**	**4,859r**	**42,373r**	**442r**	**-**	**18,473r**	**659r**	**68,130r**
Domestic	934r	346r	-	3,559r	33,232r	247	-	9,954	11	48,282r
Public administration	30r	-	-	513	3,814r	104	-	1,790r	627	6,879r
Commercial	4r	-	-	367	3,400r	-	-	6,383	-	10,155r
Agriculture	5r	-	-	328	200r	72	-	346	-	951r
Miscellaneous	4	-	-	91	1,728r	20	-	-	21r	1,863r
Non energy use	**-**	**-**	**-**	**11,424r**	**862r**	**-**	**-**	**-**	**-**	**12,286r**

(1) Includes all manufactured solid fuels, benzole, tars, coke oven gas and blast furnace gas.
(2) Includes colliery methane.
(3) Includes geothermal and solar heat.
(4) Stock fall (+), stock rise (-).
(5) Primary supply minus primary demand.

1.3 Aggregate energy balance 2002

Thousand tonnes of oil equivalent

	Coal	Manu-factured fuels (1)	Primary oils	Petroleum products	Natural gas (2)	Renewable & waste (3)	Primary electricity	Elect-ricity	Heat sold	Total
Supply										
Indigenous production	18,807	-	127,037	-	103,646	2,791r	20,619	-	-	272,901r
Imports	18,815	181	62,152	16,578	5,201	-	-	790	-	103,717
Exports	-395	-272	-95,288	-25,470r	-12,961	-	-	-66	-	-134,451r
Marine bunkers	-	-	-	-2,043	-	-	-	-	-	-2,043
Stock change (4)	+279	+188r	+158	+1,356	-633	-	-	-	-	+1,349r
Primary supply	**37,507**	**96r**	**94,060**	**-9,580r**	**95,255**	**2,791r**	**20,619**	**723**	**-**	**241,472r**
Statistical difference (5)	-44r	-34r	-556	+67r	+153r	-	-	+84r	-	-330r
Primary demand	**37,551r**	**131r**	**94,616**	**-9,647r**	**95,102r**	**2,791r**	**20,619**	**639r**	**-**	**241,802r**
Transfers	-	-102	-2,017	+1,971r	-9	-	-	-520	+520	-157
Transformation	**-35,374r**	**2,390r**	**-92,599**	**90,817r**	**-30,254r**	**-2,074r**	**-20,099**	**32,549r**	**2,107**	**-52,537r**
Electricity generation	-29,683	-594r	-	-730	-28,362r	-2,074r	-20,099	32,549r	-	-48,993r
Major power producers	-28,706	-	-	-124	-25,044	-275r	-20,099	29,872	-	-44,375r
Autogenerators	-977	-594r	-	-606	-3,318r	-1,799r	-	2,677r	-	-4,618r
Heat generation	-621r	-164r	-	-260	-1,892r	-r	-	-	2,107	-831r
Petroleum refineries	-	-	-92,599	92,002r	-	-	-	-	-	-597r
Coke manufacture	-4,226r	4,193r	-	-1	-	-	-	-	-	-35r
Blast furnaces	-528r	-1,362	-	-193	-	-	-	-	-	-2,083r
Patent fuel manufacture	-316	317	-	-	-	-	-	-	-	2r
Other	-	-	-	-	-	-	-	-	-	-
Energy industry use	**6**	**829**	**-**	**6,044r**	**7,847r**	**-**	**-**	**2,463r**	**6**	**17,196r**
Electricity generation	-	-	-	-	-	-	-	1,473r	6	1,478r
Oil and gas extraction	-	-	-	-	6,824r	-	-	46	-	6,871r
Petroleum refineries	-	-	-	6,044r	288r	-	-	563r	-	6,895r
Coal extraction	6	-	-	-	17	-	-	91r	-	115r
Coke manufacture	-	411	-	-	-	-	-	8	-	419
Blast furnaces	-	399	-	-	19	-	-	43r	-	461r
Patent fuel manufacture	-	20	-	-	-	-	-	-	-	20
Pumped storage	-	-	-	-	-	-	-	70	-	70
Other	-	-	-	-	699	-	-	168r	-	867r
Losses	**-**	**89**	**-**	**-**	**831**	**-**	**-**	**2,578**	**-**	**3,498**
Final consumption	**2,170r**	**1,501r**	**-**	**77,097r**	**56,161r**	**717r**	**-**	**28,667r**	**2,101**	**168,415r**
Industry	**737r**	**1,085r**	**-**	**6,355r**	**14,202r**	**285r**	**-**	**9,686r**	**1,338**	**33,687r**
Unclassified	-	307r	-	1,654r	8	285r	-	-	-	2,254r
Iron and steel	-	736r	-	82	756r	-	-	438r	-	2,011r
Non-ferrous metals	90r	42	-	85	452r	-	-	547r	-	1,216r
Mineral products	259r	-	-	264	1,215r	-	-	612r	4	2,354r
Chemicals	78r	-	-	333	3,807r	-	-	1,966r	1,327	7,511r
Mechanical engineering etc.	-r	-	-	281	797r	-	-	756r	-	1,834r
Electrical engineering etc.	3	-	-	54	397r	-	-	506r	-	960r
Vehicles	34	-	-	203	991r	-	-	484r	-	1,711r
Food, beverages, etc.	85	-	-	329	2,484r	-	-	1,046r	7	3,950r
Textiles, leather, etc.	44	-	-	192	674r	-	-	298r	-	1,208r
Paper, printing etc.	112r	-	-	115	1,329r	-	-	1,031r	-	2,586r
Other industries	32r	-	-	2,288r	1,009r	-	-	1,857r	-	5,185r
Construction	-	-	-	476	284r	-	-	146r	-	906r
Transport	**-**	**-**	**-**	**54,670r**	**-**	**-**	**-**	**727r**	**-**	**55,397r**
Air	-	-	-	11,658	-	-	-	-	-	11,658
Rail	-	-	-	374	-	-	-	-	-	374
Road	-	-	-	41,936r	-	-	-	-	-	41,936r
National navigation	-	-	-	702	-	-	-	-	-	702
Pipelines	-	-	-	-	-	-	-	-	-	-
Other	**1,434r**	**416**	**-**	**5,454r**	**41,032r**	**432**	**-**	**18,254r**	**763**	**67,786r**
Domestic	1,392r	416	-	3,618r	32,362r	243	-	9,848	33	47,913r
Public administration	27r	-	-	769	3,697r	97	-	1,776r	730	7,095r
Commercial	4r	-	-	401	3,115r	-	-	6,274	-	9,793r
Agriculture	5r	-	-	563	202r	72	-	356	-	1,199r
Miscellaneous	6	-	-	104	1,657r	20	-	-	-	1,786r
Non energy use	**-**	**-**	**-**	**10,618r**	**927r**	**-**	**-**	**-**	**-**	**11,545r**

(1) Includes all manufactured solid fuels, benzole, tars, coke oven gas and blast furnace gas.
(2) Includes colliery methane.
(3) Includes geothermal and solar heat.
(4) Stock fall (+), stock rise (-).
(5) Primary supply minus primary demand.

1.4 Value balance of traded energy in 2004[1]

£million

	Coal	Manufactured solid fuels	Crude oil	Petroleum products	Natural gas	Electricity	Heat sold	Other fuels	Total
Supply									
Indigenous production	600	90	15,345	19,795	7,065	5,645	425	65	49,035
Imports	1,330	75	8,615	4,805	670	345	-	-	15,840
Exports	-35	-15	-9,905	-6,485	-650	-	-	-	-17,090
Marine bunkers	-	-	-	-340	-	-	-	-	-340
Stock change	-	-5	-20	-75	-5	-	-	-	-100
Basic value of inland consumption	**1,895**	**150**	**14,035**	**17,700**	**7,080**	**5,995**	**425**	**65**	**47,340**
Tax and margins									
Distribution costs and margins	**480**	**50**	**-**	**2,465**	**4,750**	**8,935**	**-**	**-**	**16,685**
Electricity generation	210	-	-	10	-	-	-	-	220
Solid fuel manufacture	70	-	-	-	-	-	-	-	70
of which iron & steel sector	65	-		-	-	-	-	-	65
Iron & steel final use	10	35		15	-	-	-	-	60
Other industry	5	10	-	375	-	-	-	-	390
Air transport	-	-	-	80	-	-	-	-	80
Rail and national navigation	-	-	-	15	-	-	-	-	15
Road transport	-	-	-	1,380	-	-	-	-	1,380
Domestic	180	5	-	110	-	-	-	-	295
Agriculture	-	-	-	10	-	-	-	-	10
Commercial and other services	-	-	-	35	-	-	-	-	35
Non energy use	-	-	-	440	95	-	-	-	535
VAT and duties	**15**	**5**	**-**	**31,010**	**330**	**385**	**-**	**-**	**31,745**
Electricity generation	-	-	-	20	-	-	-	-	20
Iron & steel final use	-	-	-	-	-	-	-	-	-
Other industry	-	-	-	245	-	-	-	-	245
Air transport	-	-	-	20	-	-	-	-	20
Rail and national navigation	-	-	-	60	-	-	-	-	60
Road transport	-	-	-	30,565	-	-	-	-	30,565
Domestic	15	5	-	35	330	385	-	-	770
Agriculture	-	-	-	5	-	-	-	-	5
Commercial and other services	-	-	-	60	-	-	-	-	60
Climate Change Levy	**5**	**-**			**195**	**575**			**775**
Total tax and margins	**495**	**55**	**-**	**33,480**	**5,280**	**9,895**	**-**	**-**	**49,205**
Market value of inland consumption	**2,390**	**205**	**14,035**	**51,180**	**12,360**	**15,885**	**300**	**65**	**96,425**
Energy end use									
Total energy sector	**2,005**	**-**	**14,035**	**125**	**2,670**	**170**	**-**	**25**	**19,035**
Transformation	**2,005**	**-**	**14,035**	**125**	**2,600**	**-**	**-**	**25**	**18,790**
Electricity generation	1,670	-	-	115	2,575	-	-	25	4,380
of which from stocks	45	-	-	-	-	-	-	-	45
Heat Generation	20	-	-	10	25	-	-	-	55
Petroleum refineries	-	-	14,035	-	-	-	-	-	14,035
Solid fuel manufacture	320	-	-	-	-	-	-	-	320
of which iron & steel sector	285	-	-	-	-	-	-	-	285
Other energy sector use	**-**	**-**	**-**	**-**	**75**	**145**	**-**	**-**	**245**
Oil & gas extraction	-	-	-	-	-	20	-	-	20
Petroleum refineries	-	-	-	-	15	110	-	-	130
Coal extraction	-	-	-	-	-	40	-	-	40
Other energy sector	-	-	-	-	55	-	-	-	55
Total non energy sector use	**385**	**205**	**-**	**48,930**	**9,590**	**15,715**	**300**	**40**	**75,165**
Industry	**105**	**120**	**-**	**1,775**	**1,400**	**3,255**	**120**	**15**	**6,790**
Iron & steel final use	50	100	-	50	85	110	-	-	395
Other industry	55	20	-	1,725	1,315	3,150	120	15	6,395
Transport	**-**	**-**	**-**	**46,005**	**-**	**260**	**-**	**-**	**46,265**
Air	-	-	-	2,785	-	-	-	-	2,785
Rail and national navigation	-	-	-	295	-	260	-	-	555
Road	-	-	-	42,920	-	-	-	-	42,920
Other final users	**280**	**80**	**-**	**1,155**	**8,190**	**12,200**	**185**	**30**	**22,115**
Domestic	275	80	-	765	6,895	8,105	10	30	16,160
Agriculture	-	-	-	65	30	230	-	-	325
Commercial and other services	5	-	-	320	1,265	3,865	175	-	5,630
Total value of energy end use	**2,390**	**205**	**14,035**	**49,055**	**12,265**	**15,885**	**300**	**65**	**94,200**
Value of non energy end use	**-**	**-**	**-**	**2,125**	**95**	**-**	**-**	**-**	**2,225**
Market value of inland consumption	**2,390**	**205**	**14,035**	**51,180**	**12,360**	**15,885**	**300**	**65**	**96,425**

(1) For further information see paragraphs 1.34 to 1.39.

1.5 Value balance of traded energy in 2003[1]

£million

	Coal	Manufactured solid fuels	Crude oil	Petroleum products	Natural gas	Electricity	Heat sold	Other fuels	Total
Supply									
Indigenous production	715r	120r	14,310r	15,340r	7,215r	7,240r	345	55	45,385r
Imports	925	70	6,495	3,600r	135	170	-	-	11,390r
Exports	-35	-15	-9,815r	-4,950r	-1,000r	-	-	-	-15,815r
Marine bunkers	-	-	-	-255	-	-	-	-	-255
Stock change	65r	-5	65	-45r	-	-	-	-	80r
Basic value of inland consumption	**1,670r**	**170r**	**11,055**	**13,680r**	**6,350r**	**7,410r**	**345**	**55**	**40,735r**
Tax and margins									
Distribution costs and margins	**305r**	**20**	**-**	**2,625r**	**4,260r**	**6,160r**	**-**	**-**	**13,370r**
Electricity generation	80r	-	-	5	-	-	-	-	85r
Solid fuel manufacture	50r	-	-	-	-	-	-	-	50r
of which iron & steel sector	45	-	-	-	-	-	-	-	45
Iron & steel final use	10	5	-	5	-	-	-	-	20r
Other industry	5	5	-	315r	-	-	-	-	325r
Air transport	-	-	-	110	-	-	-	-	110
Rail and national navigation	-	-	-	15	-	-	-	-	15
Road transport	-	-	-	1,660r	-	-	-	-	1,660r
Domestic	160r	5	-	90	-	-	-	-	260r
Agriculture	-	-	-	10r	-	-	-	-	10r
Commercial and other services	-	-	-	20	-	-	-	-	25r
Non energy use	-	-	-	390r	80r	-	-	-	470r
VAT and duties	**10**	**5**	**-**	**25,970r**	**300**	**365**	**-**	**-**	**26,650r**
Electricity generation	-	-	-	15	-	-	-	-	15
Iron & steel final use	-	-	-	-	-	-	-	-	-
Other industry	-	-	-	230r	-	-	-	-	230r
Air transport	-	-	-	20	-	-	-	-	20
Rail and national navigation	-	-	-	70	-	-	-	-	70
Road transport	-	-	-	25,545r	-	-	-	-	25,545r
Domestic	10	5	-	45r	300	365	-	-	725r
Agriculture	-	-	-	10	-	-	-	-	10
Commercial and other services	-	-	-	40	-	-	-	-	40
Climate Change Levy	**5**	**-**	**-**	**-**	**195**	**620**	**-**	**-**	**820**
Total tax and margins	**320r**	**25r**	**-**	**28,595r**	**4,750r**	**7,145r**	**-**	**-**	**40,840r**
Market value of inland consumption	**1,990r**	**190r**	**11,055**	**42,275r**	**11,100r**	**14,560r**	**335r**	**55**	**81,565r**
Energy end use									
Total energy sector	**1,685r**	**-**	**11,055**	**120r**	**2,300**	**145**	**-**	**20**	**15,320**
Transformation	**1,685r**	**-**	**11,055**	**120r**	**2,225**	**-**	**-**	**20**	**15,100**
Electricity generation	1,445r	-	-	100r	2,210	-	-	20	3,770
of which from stocks	35	-	-	-	-	-	-	-	35
Heat Generation	15	-	-	25	15	-	-	-	55
Petroleum refineries	-	-	11,055	-	-	-	-	-	11,055
Solid fuel manufacture	220	-	-	-	-	-	-	-	220
of which iron & steel sector	195	-	-	-	-	-	-	-	195
Other energy sector use	**-**	**-**	**-**	**-**	**75**	**145**	**-**	**-**	**220**
Oil & gas extraction	-	-	-	-	-	15	-	-	15
Petroleum refineries	-	-	-	-	20r	90	-	-	115r
Coal extraction	-	-	-	-	-	30r	-	-	30r
Other energy sector	-	-	-	-	60	-	-	-	60
Total non energy sector use	**305r**	**190r**	**-**	**40,250r**	**8,720**	**14,415r**	**335r**	**40**	**64,260r**
Industry	**65r**	**90r**	**-**	**1,430r**	**1,345r**	**2,925r**	**210r**	**10**	**6,075r**
Iron & steel final use	30	70	-	35	85r	100r	-	-	320r
Other industry	30r	20	-	1,395r	1,265r	2,830r	210r	10	5,760r
Transport	**-**	**-**	**-**	**37,820r**	**-**	**215r**	**-**	**-**	**38,035r**
Air	-	-	-	2,445r	-	-	-	-	2,445r
Rail and national navigation	-	-	-	320	-	215r	-	-	535r
Road	-	-	-	35,055r	-	-	-	-	35,055r
Other final users	**245r**	**105r**	**-**	**1,000r**	**7,375r**	**11,270**	**125**	**30**	**20,150r**
Domestic	240r	105r	-	730r	6,260r	7,660	-	30	15,025r
Agriculture	-	-	-	70	30r	195	-	-	290r
Commercial and other services	5r	-	-	200r	1,085r	3,420	125	-	4,830r
Total value of energy end use	**1,990r**	**190r**	**11,055**	**40,370r**	**11,020r**	**14,560r**	**335r**	**55**	**79,580r**
Value of non energy end use	**-**	**-**	**-**	**1,905r**	**80r**	**-**	**-**	**-**	**1,985r**
Market value of inland consumption	**1,990r**	**190r**	**11,055**	**42,275r**	**11,100r**	**14,560r**	**335r**	**55**	**81,565r**

(1) For further information see paragraphs 1.34 to 1.39.

1.6 Value balance of traded energy in 2002[1]

£million

	Coal	Manufactured solid fuels	Crude oil	Petroleum products	Natural gas	Electricity	Heat sold	Other fuels	Total
Supply									
Indigenous production	900	180	14,580	12,800r	6,390r	7,535	405	50	42,840r
Imports	850	20	6,425	3,165r	260	190	-	-	10,905r
Exports	-30	-25	-10,510	-4,220r	-850	-	-	-	-15,640r
Marine bunkers	-	-	-	-245	-	-	-	-	-245
Stock change	-10	-	5	190	-5	-	-	-	180
Basic value of inland consumption	**1,710**	**175**	**10,495**	**11,680r**	**5,795r**	**7,725**	**405**	**50**	**38,040r**
Tax and margins									
Distribution costs and margins	**325r**	**25**	-	**1,930r**	**4,275r**	**5,995**			**12,550r**
Electricity generation	50	-	-	5	-	-	-	-	55
Solid fuel manufacture	5	-	-	-	-	-	-	-	5
of which iron & steel sector	5	-	-	-	-	-	-	-	5
Iron & steel final use	-	5	-	5r	-	-	-	-	10r
Other industry	10	10	-	235	-	-	-	-	260r
Air transport	-	-	-	50	-	-	-	-	50
Rail and national navigation	-	-	-	5	-	-	-	-	5
Road transport	-	-	-	1,190	-	-	-	-	1,190
Domestic	250	10	-	85r	-	-	-	-	345
Agriculture	-	-	-	15	-	-	-	-	15
Commercial and other services	-	-	-	30	-	-	-	-	35
Non energy use	-	-	-	305r	85r	-	-	-	390r
VAT and duties	**15**	**5**	-	**26,115r**	**290**	**360**	-	-	**26,785r**
Electricity generation	-	-	-	15	-	-	-	-	15
Iron & steel final use	-	-	-	-	-	-	-	-	-
Other industry	-	-	-	185	-	-	-	-	185
Air transport	-	-	-	20	-	-	-	-	20
Rail and national navigation	-	-	-	45	-	-	-	-	45
Road transport	-	-	-	25,735r	-	-	-	-	25,735r
Domestic	15	5	-	40	290	360	-	-	710
Agriculture	-	-	-	20	-	-	-	-	20
Commercial and other services	-	-	-	50	-	-	-	-	50
Climate Change Levy	**5**	**-**	**-**	**-**	**205**	**625**	**-**	**-**	**835**
Total tax and margins	**345r**	**30**	-	**28,045r**	**4,770r**	**6,980**	-	-	**40,170r**
Market value of inland consumption	**2,055r**	**205**	**10,495**	**39,725r**	**10,570r**	**14,705**	**405**	**50**	**78,210r**
Energy end use									
Total energy sector	**1,640**	-	**10,495**	**130**	**2,090r**	**150**	-	**15**	**14,520r**
Transformation	**1,640**	-	**10,495**	**130**	**2,020r**	**-**	**-**	**15**	**14,300r**
Electricity generation	1,365	-	-	100	2,005r	-	-	15	3,485r
of which from stocks	35	-	-	-	-	-	-	-	35
Heat Generation	30	-	-	35	15	-	-	-	75
Petroleum refineries	-	-	10,495	-	-	-	-	-	10,495
Solid fuel manufacture	245	-	-	-	-	-	-	-	245
of which iron & steel sector	210	-	-	-	-	-	-	-	210
Other energy sector use	**-**	-	-	-	**70**	**150**	-	-	**220**
Oil & gas extraction	-	-	-	-	-	15	-	-	15
Petroleum refineries	-	-	-	-	20	100r	-	-	120r
Coal extraction	-	-	-	-	-	35r	-	-	35r
Other energy sector	-	-	-	-	50	-	-	-	50
Total non energy sector use	**410**	**205**	-	**38,065r**	**8,395r**	**14,550**	**400**	**40**	**62,075r**
Industry	**70r**	**85**	-	**1,065**	**1,280r**	**2,995**	**255**	**10**	**5,760r**
Iron & steel final use	30	55	-	35	65r	85r	-	-	270r
Other industry	40	30	-	1,030	1,215r	2,905r	255	10	5,495r
Transport	**-**	**-**	-	**36,005r**	**-**	**220**	**-**	**-**	**36,005r**
Air	-	-	-	1,795r	-	-	-	-	1,795r
Rail and national navigation	-	-	-	190r	-	220	-	-	410r
Road	-	-	-	34,020r	-	-	-	-	34,020r
Other final users	**345**	**120**	-	**995r**	**7,110r**	**11,340**	**145**	**30**	**20,090r**
Domestic	345	120	-	645r	6,090r	7,510	5	30	14,740r
Agriculture	-	-	-	105	30r	215	-	-	350r
Commercial and other services	-	-	-	245	995r	3,615	140	-	5,000r
Total value of energy end use	**2,055r**	**205**	**10,495**	**38,200r**	**10,485r**	**14,705**	**405**	**50**	**76,600r**
Value of non energy end use	-	-	-	**1,525r**	**85r**	-	-	-	**1,610r**
Market value of inland consumption	**2,055r**	**205**	**10,495**	**39,725r**	**10,570r**	**14,705**	**405**	**50**	**78,210r**

(1) For further information see paragraphs 1.34 to 1.39.

1.7 Sales of electricity and gas by sector

United Kingdom

	2000	2001	2002	2003	2004
Total selling value (£ million)[1]					
Electricity generation - Gas	2,005	2,065	2,006r	2,209r	2,573
Industrial - Gas	1,243	1,749	1,519r	1,567r	1,654
- Electricity	3,601	3,319	3,146	3,071r	3,428
of which:					
Fuel industries	166	175	152	144	171
Industrial sector	3,435	3,144	2,994	2,927r	3,257
Domestic sector - Gas	5,222	5,460	5,798r	5,964r	6,565
- Electricity	7,120	7,182	7,154	7,295	7,719
Other - Gas	1,004	1,413	1,283r	1,325r	1,533
- Electricity	4,951	4,327	4,046	3,827r	4,354
of which:					
Agricultural sector	228	227	213	193	228
Commercial sector	3,433	3,072	2,895	2,748	3,115
Transport sector	287	242	218	216r	260
Public lighting	99	86	75	75	82
Public admin. and other services	901	706	645	595	669
Total, all consumers	**25,146**	**25,515**	**24,952r**	**25,258r**	**27,826**
of which gas	**9,474**	**10,687**	**10,606r**	**11,065r**	**12,325**
of which electricity	**15,672**	**14,828**	**14,346**	**14,193r**	**15,501**
Average net selling value per kWh sold (pence)[1]					
Electricity generation - Gas	0.618	0.667	0.609	0.682r	0.761
Industrial - Gas	0.583	0.838	0.840r	0.872r	0.969
- Electricity	3.530	3.247	3.096	2.971	3.320
of which:					
Fuel industries	3.524	3.362	3.194	2.974	3.672
Industrial sector	3.530	3.241	3.092	2.971	3.304
Domestic sector - Gas	1.412	1.440	1.540	1.543	1.656
- Electricity	6.366	6.227	6.246	6.302	6.682
Other - Gas	0.805	1.114	1.147r	1.133r	1.277
- Electricity	4.912	4.180	3.903	3.637r	4.149
of which:					
Agricultural sector	6.033	5.537	5.149	4.804	5.447
Commercial sector	4.935	4.266	3.967	3.701	4.197
Transport sector	4.018	3.247	3.085	2.872	3.546
Public lighting	4.985	4.207	3.913	3.651	4.140
Public admin. and other services	4.918	3.945	3.669	3.423	3.881
Average, all consumers	**1.867**	**1.896**	**1.893r**	**1.897r**	**2.063**
of which gas	**0.918**	**1.043**	**1.062r**	**1.099r**	**1.202**
of which electricity	**4.981**	**4.618**	**4.486**	**4.376r**	**4.789**

(1) Excludes VAT where payable - see paragraph 1.40 for a definition of average net selling value.

1.8 Final energy consumption by main industrial groups[1]

Thousand tonnes of oil equivalent

	2000	2001	2002	2003	2004
Iron and steel and non-ferrous metals					
Coal	36	118	90	22	138
Manufactured solid fuels [2]	597	717	477	504	482
Blast furnace gas	96	272	226	36	25
Coke oven gas	199	123	75	49	60
Natural gas	1,277	1,218	1,208	1,301	1,028
Petroleum	191	386	167	82	77
Electricity	1,075	1,086	985	1,038	1,091
Total iron and steel and non-ferrous metals	**3,471**	**3,920**	**3,228**	**3,033**	**2,902**
Chemicals					
Coal	58	85	78	160	175
Natural gas	4,260	4,305	3,807	3,882	3,427
Petroleum	216	386	333	395	130
Electricity	2,041	1,812	1,966	1,948	1,992
Heat sold	1,087	988	1,327	1,097	618
Total chemicals	**7,663**	**7,576**	**7,511**	**7,480**	**6,344**
Metal products, machinery and equipment					
Coal	38	64	37	35	78
Natural gas	2,424	2,297	2,185	2,159	1,866
Petroleum	372	521	538	447	244
Electricity	1,886	1,727	1,745	1,764	1,807
Heat sold	..	..	..	26	3
Total metal products, machinery and equipment	**4,720**	**4,609**	**4,505**	**4,432**	**3,998**
Food, beverages and tobacco					
Coal	82	146	85	82	128
Natural gas	2,565	2,553	2,484	2,478	2,317
Petroleum	224	370	329	326	345
Electricity	1,008	995	1,046	1,027	1,060
Heat sold	..	..	7	5	2
Total food, beverages and tobacco	**3,880**	**4,064**	**3,950**	**3,918**	**3,851**

(1) Industrial categories used are described in Table 1G. Data excludes energy used to generate heat for all fuels except manufactured solid fuels and electricity.

(2) Includes tars, benzole, coke and breeze and other manufactured solid fuels.

1.8 Final energy consumption by main industrial groups[1] (continued)

Thousand tonnes of oil equivalent

	2000	2001	2002	2003	2004
Paper, printing and publishing					
Coal	36	85	112	61	111
Natural gas	1,485	1,425	1,329	1,368	1,277
Petroleum	44	111	115	124	59
Electricity	982	990	1,031	1,096	1,140
Heat sold	..	..	..	..	14
Total paper, printing and publishing	**2,422**	**2,531**	**2,419**	**2,652**	**2,600**
Other industries					
Coal	222	607	335	280	348
Natural gas	3,752	3,657	3,182	3,099	2,567
Petroleum	2,631	3,282	3,220	3,957	4,831
Electricity	2,821	2,963	2,913	2,954	2,983
Heat sold	12	13	4	-	600
Total other industries	**9,437**	**10,522**	**9,653**	**10,290**	**11,329**
Unclassified					
Manufactured solid fuels (2)	227	212	303	135	138
Coke oven gas	17	32	3	5	-
Natural gas	10	9	8	6	6
Petroleum	2,399	2,122	1,654	2,014	2,632
Renewables & waste	213	213	285	285	286
Total unclassified	**2,866**	**2,587**	**2,254**	**2,445**	**3,062**
Total					
Coal	473	1,103	737	640	979
Manufactured solid fuels (2)	824	929	780	640	621
Blast furnace gas	96	272	226	36	25
Coke oven gas	216	154	78	53	60
Natural gas	15,773	15,464	14,202	14,292	12,488
Petroleum	6,078	7,179	6,355	7,345	8,317
Renewables & waste	213	213	285	285	286
Electricity	9,812	9,573	9,686	9,828	10,073
Heat sold	1,099	1,001	1,338	1,128	1,237
Total	**34,583**	**35,888**	**33,687**	**34,248**	**34,086**

1.9 Fuels consumed for electricity generation (autogeneration) by main industrial groups[1]

Thousand tonnes of oil equivalent
(except where shown otherwise)

	2000	2001	2002	2003	2004
Iron and steel and non-ferrous metals					
Coal	703	769	750	766r	764
Blast furnace gas	728	481	466	774	791
Coke oven gas	166	124	123	153r	107
Natural gas	75	63	58	57r	61
Petroleum	34	20	18	14	31
Other (including renewables) *(2)*	58	55	57	47	57
Total fuel input *(3)*	**1,764**	**1,512**	**1,471**	**1,812r**	**1,811**
Electricity generated by iron & steel and non-ferrous	**459**	**504**	**402r**	**474r**	**474**
metals *(4)* (in GWh)	5,338	5,863	4,669r	5,511r	5,518
Electricity consumed by iron and steel and non-ferrous	**378**	**412**	**316r**	**326r**	**397**
metals from own generation *(5)* (in GWh)	4,395	4,795	3,671r	3,787r	4,612
Chemicals					
Coal	71	155	145	160r	156
Natural gas	1,079	868	968r	938r	783
Petroleum	56	53	30	7r	7
Other (including renewables) *(2)*	352	270	302	353r	335
Total fuel input *(3)*	**1,558**	**1,346**	**1,445r**	**1,458r**	**1,281**
Electricity generated by chemicals *(4)*	**940**	**792**	**759**	**795r**	**836**
(in GWh)	10,931	9,208	8,830	9,248r	9,724
Electricity consumed by chemicals from own generation *(5)*	**687**	**532**	**656**	**617r**	**736**
(in GWh)	7,993	6,188	7,630	7,172r	8,558
Metal products, machinery and equipment					
Coal	-	-	-	-	-
Natural gas	137	48r	83	94r	67
Petroleum	11	6r	6	6	6
Other (including renewables) *(2)*	-	-	-	-	-
Total fuel input *(3)*	**147**	**54**	**89**	**100r**	**73**
Electricity generated by metal products, machinery	**66**	**24**	**38**	**43r**	**32**
and equipment *(4)* (in GWh)	765	274	447	505r	376
Electricity consumed by metal products, machinery	**55**	**22**	**36**	**41r**	**31**
and equipment from own generation *(5)* (in GWh)	636	259	422	475r	362
Food, beverages and tobacco					
Coal	27	20	20	18	16
Natural gas	345	269	322	326r	270
Petroleum	5	5	4	5r	47
Other (including renewables) *(2)*	-	-	-	-	-
Total fuel input *(3)*	**377**	**295**	**347**	**349r**	**333**
Electricity generated by food, beverages and tobacco *(4)*	**183**	**144**	**169**	**170r**	**162**
(in GWh)	2,122	1,679	1,965	1,978r	1,887
Electricity consumed by food, beverages and tobacco	**86**	**83**	**124**	**96**	**143**
from own generation *(5)* (in GWh)	1,005	966	1,438	1,112r	1,659

(1) Industrial categories used are described in Table 1G.
(2) Includes hydro electricity, solid and gaseous renewables and waste.
(3) Total fuels used for generation of electricity. Consistent with figures for fuels used by other generators in Table 5.4.

1.9 Fuels consumed for electricity generation (autogeneration) by main industrial groups[1] (continued)

Thousand tonnes of oil equivalent
(except where shown otherwise)

	2000	2001	2002	2003	2004
Paper, printing and publishing					
Coal	52	45	40	32r	25
Natural gas	629	578	624	842r	829
Petroleum	12	12	9	7	7
Other (including renewables) *(2)*	9	-	-	-	-
Total fuel input *(3)*	**701**	**636**	**673**	**881r**	**861**
Electricity generated by paper, printing and publishing *(4)*	**337**	**296**	**319**	**411r**	**413**
(in GWh)	3,920	3,446	3,708r	4,774r	4,797
Electricity consumed by paper, printing and publishing	**258**	**225**	**210**	**272r**	**278**
from own generation *(5)* *(in GWh)*	3,002	2,619	2,437r	3,159r	3,229
Other industries					
Coal	24	19	14	-r	-
Coke oven gas	5	5	5	7r	24
Natural gas	144	112	153r	201r	183
Petroleum	5	5	5	4	4
Other (including renewables) *(2)*	838	946	1,006	1,187r	1,425
Total fuel input *(3)*	**1,016**	**1,087**	**1,183r**	**1,399r**	**1,636**
Electricity generated by other industries *(4)*	**131**	**96**	**128**	**147r**	**138**
(in GWh)	1,528	1,115	1,484	1,714r	1,607
Electricity consumed by other industries from own	**94**	**52**	**80**	**81r**	**78**
generation *(5)* *(in GWh)*	1,090	609	925r	938r	907
Total					
Coal	877	1,008	969	977r	961
Blast furnace gas	728	481	466	774r	791
Coke oven gas	171	130	128	159r	131
Natural gas	2,409	1,938	2,209r	2,458r	2,193
Petroleum	123	102	72	44r	102
Other (including renewables) *(2)*	1,257	1,271	1,365	1,587r	1,817
Total fuel input *(3)*	**5,564**	**4,929**	**5,209r**	**5,999r**	**5,995**
Electricity generated *(4)*	**2,116**	**1,856**	**1,815r**	**2,040r**	**2,056**
(in GWh)	24,604	21,586	21,104r	23,729r	23,909
Electricity consumed from own generation *(5)*	**1,558**	**1,327**	**1,421r**	**1,431r**	**1,662**
(in GWh)	18,121	15,436	16,524r	16,644r	19,326

(4) Combined heat and power (CHP) generation (i.e. electrical output from Table 6.8) plus non-chp generation, so that the total electricity generated is consistent with the "other generators" figures in Table 5.6.

(5) This is the electricity consumed by the industrial sector from its own generation and is consistent with the other generators final users figures used within the electricity balances (Tables 5.1 and 5.2). These figures are less than the total generated because some of the electricity is sold to the public distribution system and other users.

(6) The figures presented here are consistent with other figures presented elsewhere in this publication as detailed at (3), (4), and (5) above but are further dissaggregated. Overall totals covering all autogenerators can be derived by adding in figures for transport, services and the fuel industries. These can be summarised as follows:

Fuel input	2000	2001	2002	2003	2004
				Thousand tonnes of oil equivalent	
All industry	5,564	4,929	5,209r	5,999r	5,995
Fuel industries	1,159	1,281	1,262r	1,258r	1,103
Transport, Commerce and Administration	440	470	428r	251	267
Services	859	808	1,009	1,053r	1,002
Total fuel input	**8,023**	**7,488**	**7,908r**	**8,561r**	**8,368**
Electricity generated	**3,034**	**2,728**	**2,859r**	**3,083r**	**3,192**
Electricity consumed	**2,211**	**1,848**	**2,091r**	**2,033r**	**2,289**
					GWh
Electricity generated	**35,285**	**31,720**	**33,253r**	**35,857r**	**37,127**
Electricity consumed	**25,714**	**21,495**	**24,319r**	**23,646r**	**26,622**

Chapter 2
Solid fuels and derived gases

Introduction

2.1 This chapter presents figures on the supply and demand for coal and solid fuels derived from coal, and on the production and consumption of gases derived from the processing of solid fuels.

2.2 Balances for coal and manufactured fuels, covering each of the last three years, form the first six tables of this chapter (Tables 2.1 to 2.6). These are followed by a 5 year table showing the supply and consumption of coal as a time series (Table 2.7). Comparable 5 year tables bring together data for coke oven coke, coke breeze and manufactured solid fuels (Table 2.8) and coke oven gas, blast furnace gas, benzole and tars (Table 2.9). As in previous years, tables showing deep mines in production (Table 2.10) and opencast sites in production (Table 2.11) complete the chapter. The long term trends commentary and tables on coal production and stocks, and on coal consumption are on the DTI energy statistics web site at: www.dti.gov.uk/energy/inform/dukes/dukes2005/02longterm.pdf.

2.3 Detailed statistics of imports and exports of solid fuels are in Annex G, also available on the DTI energy statistics web site at: www.dti.gov.uk/energy/inform/dukes/dukes2005/annnexg.pdf.

2.4 Figures for actual consumption of coal are available for all fuel and power producers and for final use by the iron and steel industry. The remaining final users consumption figures are based on information on disposals to consumers by producers and on imports. For further details see the technical notes and definitions section which begins at paragraph 2.32 of this chapter.

Structure of the coal industry

2.5 UK Coal plc (formerly RJB Mining) continues to be the main operator of deep mines. It is also, with H J Banks & Co, one of the largest surface mine operators in England, although production here is in decline owing to increasing difficulty in obtaining necessary planning permissions. This is not as severe a problem in Scotland, where the Scottish Coal Co Ltd, ATH Resources, GM Mining and Kier Minerals are among the larger operators, or in Wales, where Celtic Energy operates the three largest sites working at present. On the deep mine side, 2004 saw the final closure of Hatfield Colliery and of the three remaining mines in the Selby complex, and in early 2005 Ellington colliery was lost to flooding. This leaves 8 larger mines (7 operated by UK Coal plc plus Tower colliery), 5 small mines (Aberpergwm, Blaentillery, Eckington, Hay Royds and Nanthir).

2.6 The deep mines that were in operation at the end of March 2005 are listed in Table 2.10. Opencast coal producers are similarly listed in Table 2.11, as well as those that are developing and are not yet in operation. Further coal and slurry are supplied from recovery operations and shown in the tables under "Other sources".

Commodity balances for coal (Tables 2.1, 2.2 and 2.3)

2.7 These balance tables separately identify the three main types of coal, namely steam coal, coking coal, and anthracite, and show the variation both in the sources of supply and where the various types of coal are mainly used.

2.8 In 2004 86 per cent of coal demand was for steam coal, 10½ per cent was for coking coal and 3 per cent was for anthracite. Electricity generation accounted for 94½ per cent of demand for steam coal and 51 per cent of demand for anthracite. Coking coal was nearly all used in coke ovens (86 per cent), but 14 per cent was directly injected into blast furnaces.

2.9 Only 5 per cent of the total demand for coal was for final consumption, where it was used for steam raising, space or hot water heating or heat for processing. Steam coal accounted for 79 per cent of this final consumption, 62 per cent of which was by industry, where mineral products (eg cement, glass and bricks) and food and beverages were the largest users. The domestic sector accounted for 45 per cent of the final demand for coal, with 58 per cent of this demand being for steam coal and the remainder for anthracite.

2.10   Chart 2.1, below, compares the sources of coal supplies in the UK in 2004, along with a breakdown of consumption by user and serves to illustrate some of the features brought out below.

2.11   In 2004, 20½ per cent of supply was met from deep-mined production, 20 per cent from opencast operations, 59 per cent from net imports and 1 per cent from other sources such as slurry. In 2004 total stock levels were largely unchanged because supply and demand were more or less in balance.

2.12   Recent trends in coal production and consumption are described in paragraphs 2.20 to 2.26.

Chart 2.1: Coal supply and consumption in the UK, 2004

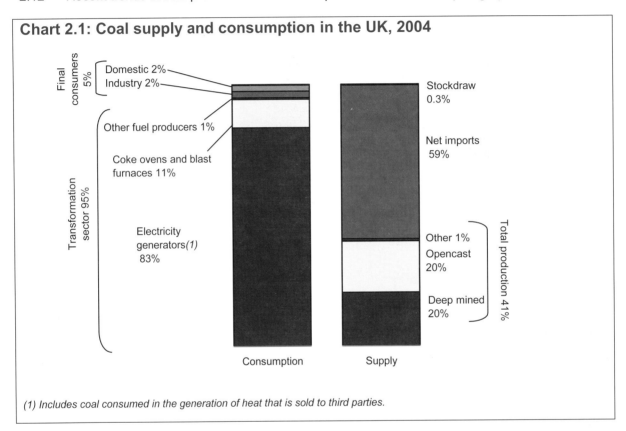

(1) Includes coal consumed in the generation of heat that is sold to third parties.

Commodity balances for manufactured fuels (Table 2.4, 2.5 and 2.6)

2.13   These tables cover fuels manufactured from coal, and gases produced when coal is used in coke ovens and blast furnaces. Definitions of terms associated with coke, breeze and other manufactured solid fuels and manufactured gases are set out in paragraphs 2.44 to 2.48.

2.14   Around 85 per cent of **coke oven coke** is home produced but in 2004 the volume of imports was down slightly from 2003, compared to the sharp rise in imports during the previous year. About 2 per cent of home production was exported. The amount screened out by producers as breeze and fines amounted to about a fifth of production plus imports in 2004, and this appears as transfers in the coke breeze column of the balance. Transfers out of coke oven coke have not always been equal to transfers into coke oven breeze, due to differences arising from the timing, location of measurement and the practise adopted by the Iron and Steel works but since 2000, the Iron and Steel Statistics Bureau have been able to reconcile this data. In 2004, 96 per cent of the demand for coke was at blast furnaces (part of the transformation sector) with most of the remainder going into final consumption in the unclassified sector (eg foundry coke).

2.15   Most of the supply of **coke breeze** is from re-screened coke oven coke with direct production accounting for only 22 per cent of total supply. Some breeze is re-used in coke manufacture or in blast furnaces, but the majority is boiler fuel.

2.16   Patent fuels are manufactured smokeless fuels, produced mainly for the domestic market, as the balances show. A small amount of these fuels (only 2 per cent of total supply in 2004) is imported, but exports generally exceed imports. Imports and exports of manufactured fuels can contain small quantities of non-smokeless fuels.

2.17   Chart 2.2 above shows the sources of coke, breeze and other manufactured solid fuels and a breakdown of their consumption.

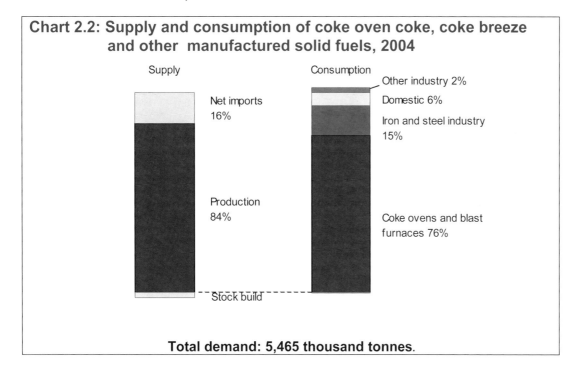

Chart 2.2: Supply and consumption of coke oven coke, coke breeze and other manufactured solid fuels, 2004

Supply

Consumption

Net imports 16%

Production 84%

Stock build

Other industry 2%

Domestic 6%

Iron and steel industry 15%

Coke ovens and blast furnaces 76%

Total demand: 5,465 thousand tonnes.

2.18   The carbonisation and gasification of solid fuels at coke ovens produces **coke oven gas** as a by-product. Some of this (47 per cent in 2004) is used to fuel the coke ovens themselves while at steel works some is piped to blast furnaces and used in the production of steel (10 per cent in 2004). Elsewhere at steel works, the gas is used for electricity generation (17 per cent) or for heat production and for other iron and steel making processes (20 per cent) and the remaining 5 per cent is lost.

2.19   **Blast furnace gas** is a by-product of iron smelting in a blast furnace. A similar product is obtained when steel is made in basic oxygen steel converters, and "BOS" gas is included in this category. Most of this gas is used in other parts of integrated steel works with 58 per cent being used for electricity generation in 2004, 29 per cent being used in coke ovens and blast furnaces themselves, and 1½ per cent being used for general heat production. The remaining 11½ per cent is lost or burned as waste.

Supply and consumption of coal (Table 2.7)

2.20   **Production** - Figures for 2004 show that coal production (including slurry) fell by 12 per cent compared to production in 2003. Deep-mined production fell by 20 per cent while opencast production fell by 1 per cent. Overall demand for coal fell by 2½ per cent in 2004. Imports rose by 13½ per cent in 2004 to make up for declining indigenous production. Longer term trends in production are illustrated in Chart 2.3 below.

2.21   Table 2A shows how production of coal is divided between England, Wales and Scotland on a financial year basis. In 2004/05 59 per cent of coal output was in England, 33 per cent in Scotland, and 8 per cent in Wales.

2.22   Table 2A also shows how numbers employed in the production of coal have changed over the last three years. During 2004/05 total employment, including contractors, was lower by 12 per cent. At 31 March 2005, 73 per cent of the 8,203 people employed in UK coal mining worked in England, while 17 per cent were employed in Scotland and 10 per cent in Wales. The closure of Longannet mine in 2002 brought employment in deep mining for coal in Scotland to an end.

Chart 2.3: Coal production and imports, 1970 to 2004

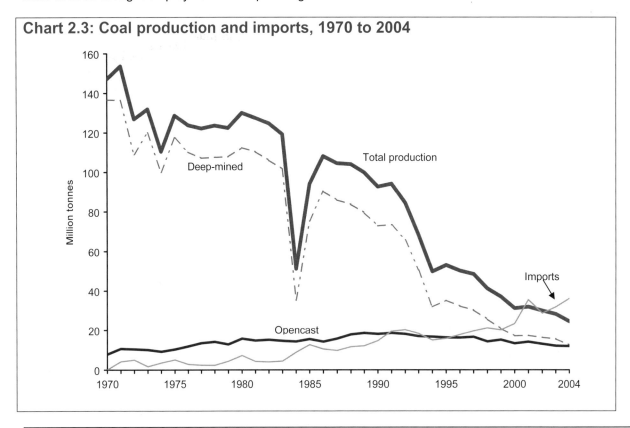

Table 2A: Output from UK coal mines and employment in UK coal mines [1][2]

| | Million tonnes | | | | | Number |
| | Output | | | Employment | | |
	April 2002 to March 2003	April 2003 to March 2004	April 2004 to March 2005	end March 2003	end March 2004	end March 2005
Deep-mined						
England	15.0	14.1	11.1	6,100	6,090	5,284
Wales	0.8	0.6	0.4	577	562	454
Total	15.8	14.7	11.5	6,677	6,652	5,738
Opencast						
England	5.0	3.7	2.7	1,113	1,062	676
Scotland	7.1	6.8	7.6	1,202	1,175	1,411
Wales	1.0	1.2	1.4	297	405	378
Total	13.1	11.6	11.8	2,612	2,642	2,465
Total						
England	20.0	17.8	13.8	7,213	7,152	5,960
Scotland	7.1	6.8	7.6	1,202	1,175	1,411
Wales	1.8	1.7	1.9	874	967	832
Total	28.9	26.3	23.3	9,289	9,294	8,203

Source: The Coal Authority
(1) Output is the tonnage declared by operators to the Coal Authority, including estimated tonnages. It excludes estimates of slurry recovered from dumps, ponds, rivers, etc.
(2) Employment includes contractors and is as declared by licensees to the Coal Authority at 31 March each year.

2.23   **Foreign trade -** Imports of coal and other solid fuel in 2004 rose 13 per cent to a new record of 37.2 million tonnes. Within the total, imports of steam coal rose by 18 per cent – largely due to sharp increases in imports from Australia (up 62 per cent), and Russia (98 per cent).   The EU expanded last year to include 10 new member states.   As a result, imports from the EU have increased significantly, with Poland now a contributor to the EU total. As Table 2B shows, in 2004, 71 per cent of the United Kingdom's imports of coal and other solid fuel came from just three countries: Australia, Russia and South Africa. A further 22½ per cent of coal imports came from four additional countries, Colombia (mainly steam coal), Poland (within the EU) (mainly steam coal), Indonesia (steam coal), USA (mainly coking coal). Steam coal imports came mainly from South Africa (34 per cent), Russia (33 per cent) and Colombia (12½ per cent). All but 2½ per cent of UK coking coal imports came from just three countries, Australia (65 per cent), the USA (21 per cent) and Canada (11 per cent). For more details of imports and exports of solid fuels by country of origin see Annex G on the DTI energy statistics web site at: www.dti.gov.uk/energy/inform/dukes/dukes2005/annnexg.pdf.

2.24   Major power producers have sourced an increasing proportion of their coal from imports over the last four years. In 1999 only 20 per cent of the coal they consumed was imported. This rose to a record level of 56 per cent in 2004.

Table 2B: Imports of coal and other solid fuel in 2004[1]

					Thousand tonnes
	Steam coal	Coking coal	Anthracite	Other solid fuel	Total
European Union [2] [3]	1,500	-	80	199	1,779
Australia	2,035	4,140	-	25	6,200
Canada	25	715	-	18	758
Colombia	3,630	-	-	53	3,683
Indonesia	1,458	-	-	-	1,458
Norway	138	-	-	2	140
People's Republic of China	190	-	43	432	665
Republic of South Africa	10,105	-	39	-	10,144
Russia	9,776	148	8	142	10,074
United States of America	717	1,342	2	-	2,061
Venezuela	39	-	-	-	39
Vietnam	-	-	23	-	23
Other countries	-	-	-	179	179
Total all countries	**29,614**	**6,345**	**194**	**1,051**	**37,203**

Source: H M Revenue and Customs

(1) Country of origin basis.
(2) Includes extra-EU coal routed through the Netherlands.
(3) EU now includes Poland and Latvia

2.25   **Transformation** – The 4 per cent decline in coal consumption during 2004 compared to 2003 reflected a decline across all transformation sectors. This decline of 2 million tonnes was due to prices, which enabled gas fired generation to be more competitive. In addition, UK steel production especially in blast furnace use picked up in 2004 and this led to a rise of 1½ per cent in the use of coal for coke making and for injection at blast furnaces.

2.26   **Consumption** - Consumption by final consumers in 2004 rose by 32 per cent from the low levels of 2003. Industry sector consumption recovered from the low level of 2003 by 57 per cent. Domestic demand increased by 12 per cent from the very low levels of last year, reflecting a slightly colder winter in 2003/04, however demand is still much lower than in 2002.

2.27   Long term trends commentary and tables on the consumption of coal in the UK since 1970 onwards can be found on the DTI energy statistics web site www.dti.gov.uk/energy/inform/dukes/dukes2005/02longterm.pdf.

2.28   **Stocks** – Production and net imports together in 2004 were slightly lower than demand for coal. Consequently total stock levels were only 176 thousand tonnes lower in 2004. Total stocks at the end of 2004 were equivalent to 22 per cent of the year's coal consumption. Stocks held at collieries and opencast sites at the end of 2004 were 432 thousand tonnes lower than a year earlier but stocks at major power stations and coke areas rose by 253 thousand tonnes. The recent changes in coal stocks are illustrated in Chart 2.4 below.

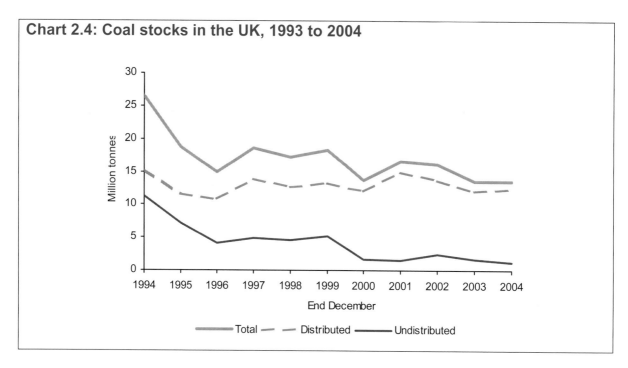

Chart 2.4: Coal stocks in the UK, 1993 to 2004

Y-axis: Million tonnes

X-axis: End December (1994–2004)

Legend: Total — — Distributed ———— Undistributed

Supply and consumption of coke oven coke, coke breeze and other manufactured fuels (Table 2.8)

2.29   This table presents figures for the most recent five years on the same basis as the balance tables. Figures for stocks are also included. Coal used to produce these manufactured fuels is shown in Table 2.7. For **coke oven coke,** demand fell by 7 per cent in 2004 while production fell by 6 per cent. Imports fell by 8 per cent in 2004 from record levels in 2003, whilst exports rose by around 8 per cent. As demand was lower, stock levels rose by 47 per cent in 2004.

2.30   In 2004, the demand for **coke breeze** rose by 7 per cent whilst production and re-screening fell by 5 and 7½ per cent respectively, however, imports rose by nearly three fold. The net effect was a 21 per cent increase in stock. There was a 12 per cent decline in the demand for **other manufactured solid fuels**, mainly because of a 29½ per cent fall in industrial sector demand. UK production was down 19 per cent on 2003 levels.

Supply and consumption of coke oven gas, blast furnace gas, benzole and tars (Table 2.9)

2.31   This table presents figures for the most recent five years on the same basis as the other balance tables. In 2004, production of and demand for **coke oven gas** fell by 5 and 6 per cent respectively. Use in electricity generation, coke ovens, blast furnaces and heat generation fell but demand rose in final consumption terms. Both production and demand for **blast furnace gas** were largely unchanged in 2004 compared to 2003.

Technical notes and definitions

2.32   These notes and definitions are in addition to the technical notes and definitions covering all fuels and energy as a whole in Chapter 1, paragraphs 1.24 to 1.57. For notes on the commodity balances and definitions of the terms used in the row headings see Annex A, paragraphs A.7 to A.42. While the data in the printed and bound copy of this Digest cover only the most recent 5 years, these notes also cover data for earlier years that are available on the DTI web site.

Steam coal, coking coal, and anthracite
2.33   **Steam coal** is coal classified as such by UK coal producers and by importers of coal. It tends to have calorific values at the lower end of the range.

2.34   **Coking coal** is coal sold by producers for use in coke ovens and similar carbonising processes. The definition is not therefore determined by the calorific value or caking qualities of each batch of coal sold, although calorific values tend to be higher than for steam coal.

2.35   **Anthracite** is coal classified as such by UK coal producers and importers of coal. Typically it has a high heat content making it particularly suitable for certain industrial processes and for use as a domestic fuel. Some UK anthracite producers have found a market for their lower calorific value output at power stations.

Coal production
2.36   **Deep-mined** - The statistics cover saleable output from deep mines including coal obtained from working on both revenue and capital accounts. All licensed collieries (and British Coal collieries prior to 1995) are included, even where coal is only a subsidiary product.

2.37   **Opencast** - The figures cover saleable output and include the output of sites worked by operators under agency agreements and licences, as well as the output of sites licensed for the production of coal as a subsidiary to the production of other minerals.

2.38   **Other** - Estimates of slurry etc recovered and disposed of from dumps, ponds, rivers, etc.

Imports and exports of coal and other solid fuels
2.39   Figures are derived from returns made to HM Revenue and Customs and are broken down in greater detail in Annex G on the DTI energy statistics web site at: www.dti.gov.uk/energy/inform/dukes/dukes2005/annnexg.pdf.

2.40   However, in Tables 2.4, 2.5, 2.6 and 2.8, the export figures used for hard coke, coke breeze and other manufactured solid fuels for the years before 1998 (as reported on the DTI web site) are quantities of fuel exported as reported to DTI by the companies concerned, rather than quantities recorded by HM Revenue and Customs in their Trade Statistics.

Allocation of imported coal
2.41   Although data are available on consumption of home produced coal, and also on consumption of imported coal by secondary fuel producers there is only very limited direct information on consumption of imported coal by final users. The DTI carries out surveys of the destination of steam coal imports (excluding those used by electricity generators) from time to time. The most recent was in 1998 and concluded that it was appropriate to allocate 60 per cent of such imports each year to industry, 15 per cent to the public administration sector, and 25 per cent to the domestic sector. This was revised for 2002 and 2003 to 70, 25 and 5 per cent to industry, domestic and public administration respectively. These proportions were revised again in 2004 to 75 per cent to industry, 20 per cent to domestic and 5 per cent to public administration. In addition, 10 per cent of anthracite imports, excluding cleaned smalls, are allocated to industry, with 90 per cent to the domestic sector in all years shown in the tables. From 2000, imports have been allocated within the overall industry sector using the results of the Office for National Statistics Purchases Inquiry. All imports of coking coal and cleaned anthracite smalls are allocated to coke and other solid fuel producers.

Stocks of coal

2.42   Undistributed stocks are those held at collieries and opencast sites. It is not possible to distinguish these two locations in the stock figures. Distributed stocks are those held at power stations and stocking grounds of the major power producing companies (as defined in Chapter 5, paragraph 5.47), coke ovens and low temperature carbonisation plants, and patent fuel plants.

Transformation, energy industry use and consumption of solid fuels

2.43   Annex A of this Digest outlines the principles of energy and commodity balances and defines the activities that fall within these parts of the balances. However, the following additional notes relevant to solid fuels are given below:

Transformation: Blast furnaces - Coking coal injected into blast furnaces is shown separately within the balance tables.

Transformation: Low temperature carbonisation plants and patent fuel plants - Coal used at these plants for the manufacture of domestic coke such as Coalite and of briquetted fuels such as Phurnacite and Homefire.

Consumption: Industry - The statistics comprise sales of coal by the nine main coal producers to the iron and steel industry (excluding that used at coke ovens and blast furnaces) and to other industrial sectors and estimated proportions of anthracite and steam coal imports. The figures exclude coal used for industries' own generation of electricity, which appear separately under transformation.

Consumption: Domestic – Some coal is supplied free of charge or at reduced prices to current and retired miners, officials, etc in the coalfields. The concessionary fuel provided to miners in 2004 is estimated at 146 thousand tonnes. This estimate is included in the domestic steam coal and domestic anthracite figures.

Consumption of coke and other manufactured solid fuels - These are disposals from coke ovens to merchants. The figures also include estimated proportions of coke imports.

Coke oven coke (hard coke) and hard coke breeze

2.44   The statistics cover coke produced at coke ovens owned by Corus plc (formerly British Steel), Coal Products Ltd and other producers. Low temperature carbonisation plants are not included (see paragraph 2.47, below). Breeze (as defined in paragraph 2.45) is excluded from the figures for coke oven coke.

2.45   Breeze can generally be described as coke screened below 19 mm (¾ inch) with no fines removed, but the screen size may vary in different areas and to meet the requirements of particular markets. Coke that has been transported from one location to another is usually re-screened before use to remove smaller sizes, giving rise to further breeze.

2.46   In 1998, an assessment using industry data showed that on average over the last five years 91 per cent of imports have been coke and 9 per cent breeze and it is these proportions that have been used for 1998 and subsequent years in Tables 2.4, 2.5, 2.6 and 2.8.

2.47   Other manufactured solid fuels are mainly solid smokeless fuels for the domestic market for use in both open fires and in boilers. A smaller quantity is exported (although exports are largely offset by similar quantities of imports in most years). Manufacture takes place in patented fuel plants and low temperature carbonisation plants. The brand names used for these fuels include Homefire, Phurnacite, Ancit and Coalite.

Blast furnace gas, coke oven gas, benzole and tars

2.48   The following definitions are used in the tables that include these fuels:

Blast furnace gas - includes basic oxygen steel furnace (BOS) gas. Blast furnace gas is the gas produced during iron ore smelting when hot air passes over coke within the blast ovens. It contains carbon monoxide, carbon dioxide, hydrogen and nitrogen. In a basic oxygen steel furnace the aim is not to introduce nitrogen or hydrogen into the steel making process, so pure oxygen gas and suitable fluxes are used to remove the carbon and phosphorous from the molten pig iron and steel scrap. A similar fuel gas is thus produced.

Coke oven gas - is a gas produced during the carbonisation of coal to form coke at coke ovens.

Synthetic coke oven gas - is mainly natural gas that is mixed with smaller amounts of blast furnace and BOS gas to produce a gas with almost the same qualities as coke oven gas. The transfers row of Tables 2.4, 2.5, 2.6 and 2.8 show the quantities of blast furnace gas used for this purpose and the total input of gases to the synthetic coke oven gas process. There is a corresponding outward transfer from natural gas in Chapter 4, Table 4.1.

Benzole - a colourless, liquid, flammable, aromatic hydrocarbon by-product of the iron and steel making process. It is used as a solvent in the manufacture of styrenes and phenols but can also be used as a motor fuel.

Tars - viscous materials usually derived from the destructive distillation of coal, which are by-products of the coke and iron making processes.

Periods covered

2.49   Figures in this chapter (and figures for earlier years given in the tables on the DTI website) generally relate to periods of 52 weeks or 53 weeks as follows:

Year	52 weeks ended
1999	25 December 1999
	53 weeks ended
2000	30 December 2000
	52 weeks ended
2001	29 December 2001
2002	28 December 2002
2003	27 December 2003
2004	25 December 2004

The 53 week data for 2000 have been adjusted to 52 weeks by omitting data for an average week based on information provided by the largest companies for the first week in April 2000.

2.50   Data for coal used for electricity generation by major power producers follow the electricity industry calendar (see Chapter 5, paragraph 5.58) and coal use by other generators is for the 12 months ending 31 December each year. HM Revenue and Customs data on imports and exports are also for the 12 months ended 31 December each year. Data for coal and coke use in the iron and steel industry, and for gases, benzole and tars produced by the iron and steel industry follow the iron and steel industry calendar (see Chapter 5, paragraph 5.59).

Data collection

2.51   In 2004, aggregate data on coal production were obtained from the Coal Authority. In addition the largest producers (Celtic Energy, Energybuild, Goitre Tower Anthracite, H J Banks, Hall Construction Services Ltd (formerly known as Coal Contractors Limited), J D Flack & Sons Ltd, Scottish Coal Company Ltd and UK Coal plc) have provided data in response to an annual DTI inquiry covering production (deep-mined and opencast), trade, stocks, and disposals. The Iron and Steel Statistics Bureau (ISSB) provides DTI with an annual statement of coke and breeze production and use of coal, coke and breeze within that industry. The ISSB is also the source of data on gases produced by the iron and steel industry (coke oven gas, blast furnace gas and basic oxygen steel furnace gas). DTI directly surveys producers of manufactured fuels other than coke or breeze.

2.52   Trade in solid fuels is also covered by using data from HM Revenue and Customs (see Annex G on DTI energy statistics web site). Consumption of coal for electricity generation is covered by data collected by DTI from electricity generators as described in Chapter 5, paragraphs 5.61 to 5.63.

Monthly and quarterly data

2.53   Monthly data on coal production, foreign trade, consumption and stocks are available on DTI's Energy Statistics web site www.dti.gov.uk/energy/inform/energy_stats/coal/index.shtml in monthly Tables 2.4, 2.5, and 2.6. Quarterly commodity balances for coal; coke oven coke, coke breeze and other manufactured solid fuels; and coke oven gas, blast furnace gas, benzole and tars are published in DTI's quarterly statistical bulletin *Energy Trends* and these balances are also available on DTI's Energy Statistics web site. See Annex C for more information about *Energy Trends* and the DTI energy statistics web site.

Statistical differences

2.54   Tables 2.1 to 2.9 each contain a statistical difference term covering the difference between recorded supply and recorded demand. These statistical differences arise for a number of reasons. First, the data within each table are taken from varied sources, as described above, such as producers, intermediate consumers (such as electricity generators), final consumers (namely the iron and steel industry), and HM Revenue and Customs. Second, some of these industries work to different statistical calendars (see paragraphs 2.49 and 2.50, above), and third, some of the figures are estimated either because data in the required detail are not readily available within the industry or because the methods of collecting the data do not cover the smallest members of the industry.

Contact: Sally Mercer
Energy Markets Information and Analysis
sally.mercer@dti.gsi.gov.uk
020-7215 2717

2.1 Commodity balances 2004
Coal

Thousand tonnes

	Steam coal	Coking coal	Anthracite	Total
Supply				
Production	..	352	..	24,536
Other sources	..	-	..	561
Imports	29,614	6,345	194	36,153
Exports	-440	-9	-172	-621
Marine bunkers	-	-	-	-
Stock change (1)	..	-206	..	+176
Transfers	-	-	-	-
Total supply	..	6,482	..	60,805
Statistical difference (2)	..	+100	..	+126
Total demand	52,387	6,382	1,910	60,679
Transformation	50,063	6,382	1,310	57,755
Electricity generation	49,520	-	983	50,503
Major power producers	47,985	-	983	48,968
Autogenerators	1,535	-	-	1,535
Heat generation	543	-	-	543
Petroleum refineries	-	-	-	-
Coke manufacture	-	5,487	-	5,487
Blast furnaces	-	895	-	895
Patent fuel manufacture and low temperature carbonisation	-	-	327	327
Energy industry use	..	-	..	8
Electricity generation	-	-	-	-
Oil and gas extraction	-	-	-	-
Petroleum refineries	-	-	-	-
Coal extraction	..	-	..	8
Coke manufacture	-	-	-	-
Blast furnaces	-	-	-	-
Patent fuel manufacture	-	-	-	-
Pumped storage	-	-	-	-
Other	-	-	-	-
Losses	-	-	-	-
Final consumption	2,317	-	599	2,916
Industry	1,449	-	33	1,482
Unclassified	-	-	-	-
Iron and steel	-	-	-	-
Non-ferrous metals	..	-	..	233
Mineral products	..	-	..	382
Chemicals	..	-	..	276
Mechanical engineering etc	..	-	..	8
Electrical engineering etc	..	-	..	5
Vehicles	..	-	..	98
Food, beverages etc	..	-	..	182
Textiles, leather, etc	..	-	..	75
Paper, printing etc	..	-	-	162
Other industries	..	-	..	61
Construction	-	-	-	-
Transport	-	-	-	-
Air	-	-	-	-
Rail	-	-	-	-
Road	-	-	-	-
National navigation	-	-	-	-
Pipelines	-	-	-	-
Other	..	-	..	**1,434**
Domestic	793	-	566	1,359
Public administration	..	-	..	52
Commercial	..	-	..	6
Agriculture	..	-	..	9
Miscellaneous	..	-	-	8
Non energy use	-	-	-	-

(1) Stock fall (+), stock rise (-).

(2) Total supply minus total demand.

2.2 Commodity balances 2003
Coal

Thousand tonnes

	Steam coal	Coking coal	Anthracite	Total
Supply				
Production	..	373	..	27,759
Other sources	..	-	..	520r
Imports	25,098	6,474	319	31,891
Exports	-359	-2	-181	-542
Marine bunkers	-	-	-	-
Stock change (1)	..	+62r	..	+2,492r
Transfers	-	-	-	-
Total supply	..	**6,907r**	..	**62,120r**
Statistical difference (2)	..	+296r	..	-183r
Total demand	**53,593r**	**6,611r**	**2,099r**	**62,303r**
Transformation	**52,068r**	**6,611r**	**1,409r**	**60,088r**
Electricity generation	51,451r	-	1,013r	52,464r
Major power producers	49,883r	-	1,013r	50,896r
Autogenerators	1,568r	-	-	1,568r
Heat generation	617r	-	-	617r
Petroleum refineries	-	-	-	-
Coke manufacture	-	5,729r	-	5,729r
Blast furnaces	-	882	-	882
Patent fuel manufacture and low temperature carbonisation	-	-	396	396
Energy industry use	..	-	..	**6**
Electricity generation	-	-	-	-
Oil and gas extraction	-	-	-	-
Petroleum refineries	-	-	-	-
Coal extraction	..	-	..	6
Coke manufacture	-	-	-	-
Blast furnaces	-	-	-	-
Patent fuel manufacture	-	-	-	-
Pumped storage	-	-	-	-
Other	-	-	-	-
Losses	-	-	-	-
Final consumption	**1,520r**	**-**	**689r**	**2,209r**
Industry	**869r**	**-**	**72r**	**941r**
Unclassified	-	-	-	-
Iron and steel	-	-	-	-
Non-ferrous metals	..	-	..	37r
Mineral products	..	-	..	295r
Chemicals	..	-	..	240r
Mechanical engineering etc	..	-	..	4r
Electrical engineering etc	..	-	..	2
Vehicles	..	-	..	44r
Food, beverages etc	..	-	..	112r
Textiles, leather, etc	..	-	..	35r
Paper, printing etc	..	-	..	89r
Other industries	..	-	..	83r
Construction	-	-	-	-
Transport	**-**	**-**	**-**	**-**
Air	-	-	-	-
Rail	-	-	-	-
Road	-	-	-	-
National navigation	-	-	-	-
Pipelines	..	-	..	-
Other	..	**-**	..	**1,268r**
Domestic	589r	-	617r	1,206r
Public administration	..	-	..	42r
Commercial	..	-	..	6
Agriculture	..	-	..	8r
Miscellaneous	..	-	..	6
Non energy use	**-**	**-**	**-**	**-**

(1) Stock fall (+), stock rise (-).

(2) Total supply minus total demand.

2.3 Commodity balances 2002
Coal

Thousand tonnes

	Steam coal	Coking coal	Anthracite	Total
Supply				
Production	..	373	..	29,539
Other sources	..	-	..	450
Imports	21,895	6,315	477	28,687
Exports	-342	-3	-192	-537
Marine bunkers	-	-	-	-
Stock change (1)	..	+162	..	+351
Transfers	-	-	-	-
Total supply	..	**6,847**	..	**58,490**
Statistical difference (2)	..	+314	..	-199r
Total demand	**49,246r**	**6,533**	**2,910**	**58,689r**
Transformation	**47,099r**	**6,533**	**2,075**	**55,707r**
Electricity generation	46,102	-	1,639	47,741
Major power producers	44,506	-	1,639	46,145
Autogenerators	1,596	-	-	1,596
Heat generation	997r	-	-	997r
Petroleum refineries	-	-	-	-
Coke manufacture	-	5,807	-	5,807
Blast furnaces	-	726	-	726
Patent fuel manufacture and low temperature carbonisation	-	-	436	436
Energy industry use	..	-	..	**9**
Electricity generation	-	-	-	-
Oil and gas extraction	-	-	-	-
Petroleum refineries	-	-	-	-
Coal extraction	..	-	..	9
Coke manufacture	-	-	-	-
Blast furnaces	-	-	-	-
Patent fuel manufacture	-	-	-	-
Pumped storage	-	-	-	-
Other	-	-	-	-
Losses	-	-	-	-
Final consumption	**2,139r**	**-**	**834**	**2,973r**
Industry	**1,082r**	**-**	**31**	**1,113r**
Unclassified	-	-	-	-
Iron and steel	-	-	-	-
Non-ferrous metals	..	-	..	151r
Mineral products	..	-	..	401r
Chemicals	..	-	..	119r
Mechanical engineering etc	-	-	-	-
Electrical engineering etc	..	-	..	4
Vehicles	..	-	..	49r
Food, beverages etc	..	-	..	119r
Textiles, leather, etc	..	-	..	62r
Paper, printing etc	..	-	..	162r
Other industries	..	-	..	46r
Construction	-	-	-	-
Transport	-	-	-	-
Air	-	-	-	-
Rail	-	-	-	-
Road	-	-	-	-
National navigation	-	-	-	-
Pipelines	-	-	-	-
Other	..	-	..	**1,860r**
Domestic	999r	-	803	1,802r
Public administration	..	-	..	37r
Commercial	..	-	..	5
Agriculture	..	-	..	8r
Miscellaneous	..	-	..	8
Non energy use	-	-	-	-

(1) Stock fall (+), stock rise (-).

(2) Total supply minus total demand.

2.4 Commodity balances 2004

Manufactured fuels

	Thousand tonnes					Benzole and tars (4)	Coke oven gas	Blast furnace gas
	Coke oven coke	Coke breeze	Other manuf. solid fuel	Total manuf. solid fuel		Benzole and tars (4)	Coke oven gas	Blast furnace gas
Supply								
Production	4,038	298	318	4,654		1,722	9,076	15,770
Other sources	-	-	-	-		-	-	-
Imports	852	193	6	1,051		-	-	-
Exports	-80	-62	-39	-181		-	-	-
Marine bunkers	-	-	-	-		-	-	-
Stock change (1)	-88	-63	+21	-130		-	-	-
Transfers (2)	-1,012	+1,012	-	-		-	+40	-2
Total supply	**3,710**	**1,378**	**306**	**5,394**		**1,722**	**9,116**	**15,768**
Statistical difference (3)	-15	-43	-13	-71		-	+64	-104
Total demand	**3,725**	**1,421**	**319**	**5,465**		**1,722**	**9,052**	**15,872**
Transformation	**3,569**	**602**	**-**	**4,171**		**-**	**2,115**	**9,451**
Electricity generation	-	-	-	-		-	1,522	9,197
Major power producers	-	-	-	-		-	-	-
Autogenerators	-	-	-	-		-	1,522	9,197
Heat generation	-	-	-	-		-	593	254
Petroleum refineries	-	-	-	-		-	-	-
Coke manufacture	-	-	-	-		-	-	-
Blast furnaces	3,569	602	-	4,171		-	-	-
Patent fuel manufacture	-	-	-	-		-	-	-
Low temperature carbonisation	-	-	-	-		-	-	-
Energy industry use	**-**	**-**	**4**	**4**		**-**	**5,274**	**4,570**
Electricity generation	-	-	-	-		-	-	-
Oil and gas extraction	-	-	-	-		-	-	-
Petroleum refineries	-	-	-	-		-	-	-
Coal extraction	-	-	-	-		-	-	-
Coke manufacture	-	-	-	-		-	4,326	297
Blast furnaces	-	-	-	-		-	948	4,273
Patent fuel manufacture	-	-	4	4		-	-	-
Pumped storage	-	-	-	-		-	-	-
Other	-	-	-	-		-	-	-
Losses	**-**	**-**	**-**	**-**		**-**	**783**	**1,557**
Final consumption	**156**	**819**	**315**	**1,290**		**1,722**	**880**	**294**
Industry	**105**	**819**	**12**	**936**		**1,722**	**880**	**294**
Unclassified	83	31	12	126		1,722	178	-
Iron and steel	22	788	-	810		-	702	294
Non-ferrous metals	-	-	-	-		-	-	-
Mineral products	-	-	-	-		-	-	-
Chemicals	-	-	-	-		-	-	-
Mechanical engineering, etc	-	-	-	-		-	-	-
Electrical engineering, etc	-	-	-	-		-	-	-
Vehicles	-	-	-	-		-	-	-
Food, beverages, etc	-	-	-	-		-	-	-
Textiles, leather, etc	-	-	-	-		-	-	-
Paper, printing, etc	-	-	-	-		-	-	-
Other industries	-	-	-	-		-	-	-
Construction	-	-	-	-		-	-	-
Transport	**-**	**-**	**-**	**-**		**-**	**-**	**-**
Other	**51**	**-**	**303**	**354**		**-**	**-**	**-**
Domestic	51	-	303	354		-	-	-
Public administration	-	-	-	-		-	-	-
Commercial	-	-	-	-		-	-	-
Agriculture	-	-	-	-		-	-	-
Miscellaneous	-	-	-	-		-	-	-
Non energy use	**-**	**-**	**-**	**-**		**-**	**-**	**-**

(1) Stock fall (+), stock rise (-).
(2) Coke oven gas and blast furnace gas transfers are for synthetic coke oven gas, see paragraph 2.48.
(3) Total supply minus total demand.
(4) Because of the small number of benzole suppliers, figures for benzole and tars cannot be given separately.

2.5 Commodity balances 2003
Manufactured fuels

	Thousand tonnes				GWh		
	Coke oven coke	Coke breeze	Other manuf. solid fuel	Total manuf. solid fuel	Benzole and tars (4) (5)	Coke oven gas	Blast furnace gas
Supply							
Production	4,286	315	392	4,993	1,773	9,564r	15,790r
Other sources	-	-	-	-	-	-	-
Imports	927r	51r	6	984	-	-	-
Exports	-74r	-64r	-55	-193r	-	-	-
Marine bunkers	-	-	-	-	-	-	-
Stock change (1)	-60	-83	-	-143	-	-	-
Transfers (2)	-1,095r	+1,095r	-	-	-	+86r	-3r
Total supply	3,984r	1,314r	343	5,641r	1,773	9,650r	15,787r
Statistical difference (3)	-23r	-16r	-19	-58	-	+36r	-106r
Total demand	4,007r	1,330r	362	5,699r	1,773	9,614r	15,893r
Transformation	3,716	530	-	4,246	-	2,910r	9,302r
Electricity generation	-	-	-	-	-	1,854r	9,002
Major power producers	-	-	-	-	-	-	-
Autogenerators	-	-	-	-	-	1,854r	9,002
Heat generation	-	-	-	-	-	1,055r	299r
Petroleum refineries	-	-	-	-	-	-	-
Coke manufacture	-	-	-	-	-	-	-
Blast furnaces	3,716	530	-	4,246	-	-	-
Patent fuel manufacture	-	-	-	-	-	-	-
Low temperature carbonisation	-	-	-	-	-	-	-
Energy industry use	-	-	4	4	-	5,630r	4,771r
Electricity generation	-	-	-	-	-	-	-
Oil and gas extraction	-	-	-	-	-	-	-
Petroleum refineries	-	-	-	-	-	-	-
Coal extraction	-	-	-	-	-	-	-
Coke manufacture	-	-	-	-	-	4,466r	432r
Blast furnaces	-	-	-	-	-	1,164r	4,339r
Patent fuel manufacture	-	-	4	4	-	-	-
Pumped storage	-	-	-	-	-	-	-
Other	-	-	-	-	-	-	-
Losses	-	-	-	-	-	457r	1,398r
Final consumption	291r	800r	358	1,449r	1,773	618r	423r
Industry	162r	800r	17	979r	1,773	618r	423r
Unclassified	115r	5r	17	137r	1,773r	53r	-
Iron and steel	23	795	-	818	-r	565r	423r
Non-ferrous metals	24	-	-	24	-	-	-
Mineral products	-	-	-	-	-	-	-
Chemicals	-	-	-	-	-	-	-
Mechanical engineering, etc	-	-	-	-	-	-	-
Electrical engineering, etc	-	-	-	-	-	-	-
Vehicles	-	-	-	-	-	-	-
Food, beverages, etc	-	-	-	-	-	-	-
Textiles, leather, etc	-	-	-	-	-	-	-
Paper, printing, etc	-	-	-	-	-	-	-
Other industries	-	-	-	-	-	-	-
Construction	-	-	-	-	-	-	-
Transport	-	-	-	-	-	-	-
Other	129r	-	341	470r	-	-	-
Domestic	129r	-	341	470r	-	-	-
Public administration	-	-	-	-	-	-	-
Commercial	-	-	-	-	-	-	-
Agriculture	-	-	-	-	-	-	-
Miscellaneous	-	-	-	-	-	-	-
Non energy use	-	-	-	-	-	-	-

(1) Stock fall (+), stock rise (-).
(2) Coke oven gas and blast furnace gas transfers are for synthetic coke oven gas, see paragraph 2.48.
(3) Total supply minus total demand.
(4) Because of the small number of benzole suppliers, figures for benzole and tars cannot be given separately.
(5) From 2000 Iron and steel under final consumption has been reclassified due to additional information being received.

2.6 Commodity balances 2002
Manufactured fuels

	Thousand tonnes						GWh
	Coke oven coke	Coke breeze	Other manuf. solid fuel	Total manuf. solid fuel	Benzole and tars (4) (5)	Coke oven gas	Blast furnace gas
Supply							
Production	4,335	224	430	4,989	1,781	9,549	13,130
Other sources	-	-	-	-	-	-	-
Imports	226	12	18	256	-	-	-
Exports	-272	-46	-67	-385	-	-	-
Marine bunkers	-	-	-	-	-	-	-
Stock change (1)	+261	-14	+14	+261	-	-	-
Transfers (2)	-927	+927			-	+104	-4
Total supply	3,623	1,103	395	5,121	1,781	9,653	13,126
Statistical difference (3)	-35	+28	-28	-35	-	+62	-92
Total demand	3,658	1,075	423	5,156	1,781	9,590	13,218
Transformation	3,224	331	-	3,555	-	2,973r	5,844r
Electricity generation	-	-	-	-	-	1,487	5,422
Major power producers	-	-	-	-	-	-	-
Autogenerators	-	-	-	-	-	1,487r	5,422r
Heat generation	-	-	-	-	-	1,486r	422r
Petroleum refineries	-	-	-	-	-	-	-
Coke manufacture	-	-	-	-	-	-	-
Blast furnaces	3,224	331	-	3,555	-	-	-
Patent fuel manufacture	-	-	-	-	-	-	-
Low temperature carbonisation	-	-	-	-	-	-	-
Energy industry use	17	-	10	27	-	5,321	4,095
Electricity generation	-	-	-	-	-	-	-
Oil and gas extraction	-	-	-	-	-	-	-
Petroleum refineries	-	-	-	-	-	-	-
Coal extraction	-	-	-	-	-	-	-
Coke manufacture	-	-	-	-	-	4,270	510
Blast furnaces	-	-	-	-	-	1,051	3,585
Patent fuel manufacture	17	-	10	27	-	-	-
Pumped storage	-	-	-	-	-	-	-
Other	-	-	-	-	-	-	-
Losses	-	-	-	-	-	387	648
Final consumption	417	744	413	1,574	1,781	909r	2,632r
Industry	239	744	22	1,005	1,781	909r	2,632r
Unclassified	151	44	22	217	1,781r	40r	-
Iron and steel	29	700	-	729	-	869r	2,632r
Non-ferrous metals	59	-	-	59	-	-	-
Mineral products	-	-	-	-	-	-	-
Chemicals	-	-	-	-	-	-	-
Mechanical engineering, etc	-	-	-	-	-	-	-
Electrical engineering, etc	-	-	-	-	-	-	-
Vehicles	-	-	-	-	-	-	-
Food, beverages, etc	-	-	-	-	-	-	-
Textiles, leather, etc	-	-	-	-	-	-	-
Paper, printing, etc	-	-	-	-	-	-	-
Other industries	-	-	-	-	-	-	-
Construction	-	-	-	-	-	-	-
Transport	-	-	-	-	-	-	-
Other	178	-	391	569	-	-	-
Domestic	178	-	391	569	-	-	-
Public administration	-	-	-	-	-	-	-
Commercial	-	-	-	-	-	-	-
Agriculture	-	-	-	-	-	-	-
Miscellaneous	-	-	-	-	-	-	-
Non energy use	-	-	-	-	-	-	-

(1) Stock fall (+), stock rise (-).
(2) Coke oven gas and blast furnace gas transfers are for synthetic coke oven gas, see paragraph 2.48.
(3) Total supply minus total demand.
(4) Because of the small number of benzole suppliers, figures for benzole and tars cannot be given separately.
(5) From 2000 Iron and steel under final consumption has been reclassified due to additional information being received.

2.7 Supply and consumption of coal

Thousand tonnes

	2000	2001	2002	2003	2004
Supply					
Production	30,600	31,513	29,539	27,759	24,536
Deep-mined	17,187	17,347	16,391	15,633	12,543
Opencast	13,412	14,166	13,148	12,126	11,993
Other sources *(3)*	598	417	450	520r	561
Imports	23,446	35,542	28,687	31,891	36,153
Exports	-661	-549	-537	-542	-621
Stock change *(1)*	+4,681	-2,886	+351	+2,492r	+176
Total supply	**58,663**	**64,037**	**58,490**	**62,120r**	**60,805**
Statistical difference *(2)*	-171r	-158r	-199r	-183r	+126
Total demand	**58,833r**	**64,195r**	**58,689r**	**62,303r**	**60,679**
Transformation	**56,136**	**60,074**	**55,707r**	**60,088r**	**57,755**
Electricity generation	46,198	50,932	47,741	52,464r	50,503
Major power producers	44,762	49,291	46,145	50,896r	48,968
Autogenerators	1,436	1,641	1,596	1,568r	1,535
Heat generation	714	750	997r	617r	543
Coke manufacture	8,229	7,132	5,807	5,729r	5,487
Blast furnaces	456	764	726	882	895
Patent fuel manufacture and low temperature carbonisation	540	496	436	396	327
Energy industry use	**12**	**9**	**9**	**6**	**8**
Coal extraction	12	9	9	6	8
Final consumption	**2,684r**	**4,111r**	**2,973r**	**2,209r**	**2,916**
Industry	**702r**	**1,684r**	**1,113r**	**941r**	**1,482**
Unclassified	-	-	-	-	-
Iron and steel	2	1	-	-	-
Non-ferrous metals	58r	197r	151r	37r	233
Mineral products	220r	847r	401r	295r	382
Chemicals	85r	131r	119r	240r	276
Mechanical engineering etc	9r	16r	-	4r	8
Electrical engineering etc	2	9r	4	2	5
Vehicles	44	66r	49r	44r	98
Food, beverages etc	116r	208r	119r	112r	182
Textiles, clothing, leather, etc	34	37r	62r	35r	75
Pulp, paper, printing etc	53r	123r	162r	89r	162
Other industries	79r	49r	46r	83r	61
Construction	-	-	-	-	-
Transport	-	-	-	-	-
Other	**1,982r**	**2,429**	**1,860r**	**1,268r**	**1,434**
Domestic	1,900r	2,361	1,802r	1,206r	1,359
Public administration	60	47	37r	42r	53
Commercial	7	6	5	6	6
Agriculture	7	5	8r	8r	9
Miscellaneous	8	10	8	6	8
Non energy use	-	-	-	-	-
Stocks at end of year *(4)*					
Distributed stocks	12,005	14,954	13,704	12,070	12,325
Of which:					
Major power producers	11,034	13,620	12,542	10,971	11,019
Coke ovens	943	1,309	1,148	1,086	1,291
Undistributed stocks	1,646	1,583	2,482	1,624	1,192
Total stocks	**13,651**	**16,537**	**16,185**	**13,694**	**13,518**

(1) Stock fall (+), stock rise (-).
(2) Total supply minus total demand.
(3) Estimates of slurry etc. recovered from ponds, dumps, rivers, etc.
(4) Excludes distributed stocks held in merchants' yards, etc., mainly for the domestic market, and stocks held by the industrial sector.

2.8 Supply and consumption of coke oven coke, coke breeze and other manufactured solid fuels

	2000	2001	2002	2003	2004
Coke oven coke					
Supply					
Production	6,058	5,306	4,335	4,286	4,038
Imports	421	101	226	927r	852
Exports	-243	-176	-272	-74r	-80
Stock change (1)	-216	+116	+261	-60	-88
Transfers	-827	-982	-927	-1,095r	-1,012
Total supply	**5,193**	**4,365**	**3,623**	**3,984r**	**3,710**
Statistical difference (2)	-108r	-29	-35	-23r	-15
Total demand	**5,301r**	**4,394**	**3,658**	**4,007r**	**3,725**
Transformation	**4,764**	**3,957**	**3,224**	**3,716**	**3,569**
Blast furnaces	4,764	3,957	3,224	3,716	3,569
Energy industry use	**37**	**32**	**17**	**-**	**-**
Final consumption	**500r**	**405**	**417**	**291r**	**156**
Industry	**367r**	**338**	**239**	**162r**	**105**
Unclassified	188r	181	151	115r	83
Iron and steel	19	32	29	23	22
Non-ferrous metals	160	125	59	24	-
Other	**133r**	**67**	**178**	**129r**	**51**
Domestic	133r	67	178	129r	51
Stocks at end of year (3)	**548**	**432**	**171**	**230**	**318**
Coke breeze					
Supply					
Production	148	210	224	315	298
Imports	62	56	12	51r	193
Exports	-138	-143	-46	-64r	-62
Stock change (1)	+22	+8	-14	-83	-63
Transfers	+827	+982	+927	+1,095r	+1,012
Total supply	**921**	**1,113**	**1,103**	**1,314r**	**1,378**
Statistical difference (2)	-112r	-7	+28	-16r	-43
Total demand	**1,033r**	**1,120**	**1,075**	**1,330r**	**1,421**
Transformation	**202**	**313**	**331**	**530**	**602**
Coke manufacture	14	9	-	-	-
Blast furnaces	188	304	331	530	602
Energy industry use	**-**	**-**	**-**	**-**	**-**
Final consumption	**831r**	**807**	**744**	**800r**	**819**
Industry	**831r**	**807**	**744**	**800r**	**819**
Unclassified	38r	16	44	5r	31
Iron and steel	793	791	700	795	788
Stocks at end of year (3)	**207**	**199**	**213**	**296**	**359**
Other manufactured solid fuels					
Supply					
Production	537	487	430	392	318
Imports	14	8	18	6	6
Exports	-79	-75	-67	-55	-39
Stock change (1)	+38	+37	+14	-	+21
Total supply	**510**	**457**	**395**	**343**	**306**
Statistical difference (2)	-22	-38	-28	-19	-13
Total demand	**532**	**495**	**423**	**362**	**319**
Transformation	**-**	**-**	**-**	**-**	**-**
Energy industry use	**11**	**12**	**10**	**4**	**4**
Patent fuel manufacture	11	12	10	4	4
Final consumption	**521**	**483**	**413**	**358**	**315**
Industry	**25**	**37**	**22**	**17**	**12**
Unclassified	25	37	22	17	12
Other	**496**	**446**	**391**	**341**	**303**
Domestic	496	446	391	341	303
Stocks at end of year (3)	**103**	**66**	**52**	**51**	**30**

(1) Stock fall (+), stock rise (-).
(2) Total supply minus total demand.
(3) Producers stocks and distributed stocks.

2.9 Supply and consumption of coke oven gas, blast furnace gas, benzole and tars

GWh

	2000	2001	2002	2003	2004
Coke oven gas					
Supply					
Production	12,661	11,516	9,549	9,564r	9,076
Imports	-	-	-	-	-
Exports	-	-	-	-	-
Transfers (1)	+460	+68	+104	+86r	+40
Total supply	**13,121**	**11,584**	**9,653**	**9,650r**	**9,116**
Statistical difference (2)	-264	+141	+62	+36r	+64
Total demand	**13,385**	**11,443**	**9,590**	**9,614r**	**9,052**
Transformation	**3,797**	**3,365**	**2,973r**	**2,910r**	**2,115**
Electricity generation	1,987	1,490	1,487r	1,854r	1,522
Heat generation	1,810	1,875	1,486r	1,055r	593
Other	-	-	-	-	-
Energy industry use	**6,748**	**6,053**	**5,321**	**5,630r**	**5,274**
Coke manufacture	5,555	4,720	4,270	4,466r	4,326
Blast furnaces	1,193	1,333	1,051	1,164r	948
Other	-	-	-	-	-
Losses	**325**	**231**	**387**	**457r**	**783**
Final consumption	**2,515**	**1,794**	**909r**	**618r**	**880**
Industry	**2,515**	**1,794**	**909r**	**618r**	**880**
Unclassified	200	367	40r	53r	178
Iron and steel	2,315	1,427	869r	565r	702
Blast furnace gas					
Supply					
Production	17,743	14,767	13,130	15,790r	15,770
Imports	-	-	-	-	-
Exports	-	-	-	-	-
Transfers (1)	-17	-3	-4	-3r	-2
Total supply	**17,726**	**14,764**	**13,126**	**15,787r**	**15,768**
Statistical difference (2)	-103	-100	-92	-106r	-104
Total demand	**17,829**	**14,864**	**13,218**	**15,893r**	**15,872**
Transformation	**9,089**	**6,025**	**5,844r**	**9,302r**	**9,451**
Electricity generation (4)	8,470	5,493	5,422r	9,002	9,197
Heat generation	619	532	422r	299r	254
Other	-	-	-	-	-
Energy industry use	**6,034**	**4,709**	**4,095**	**4,771r**	**4,570**
Coke manufacture	1,057	649	510	432r	297
Blast furnaces	4,977	4,060	3,585	4,339r	4,273
Other	-	-	-	-	-
Losses	**1,592**	**965**	**648**	**1,398r**	**1,557**
Final consumption	**1,114**	**3,165**	**2,632r**	**423r**	**294**
Industry	**1,114**	**3,165**	**2,632r**	**423r**	**294**
Unclassified	-	-	-	-	-
Iron and steel (4)	1,114	3,165	2,632r	423r	294
Benzole and tars (3)					
Supply					
Production	2,393	2,115	1,781	1,773	1,722
Final consumption (5)	**2,393**	**2,115**	**1,781**	**1,773**	**1,722**
Unclassified	2,393r	2,115r	1,781r	1,773r	1,722
Iron and steel	-r	-r	-r	-r	-

(1) To and from synthetic coke oven gas, see paragraph 2.48.
(2) Total supply minus total demand.
(3) Because of the small number of benzole suppliers, figures for benzole and tars cannot be given separately
(4) From 2003, a new method of calculating fuel use for CHP in the iron and steel industry has been used (see paragraph 6.33). This results in more blast furnace gas being allocated to electricity generation and less to final consumption than in previous years. It has not been possible to recalculate CHP use for previous years on this new basis.
(5) From 2000 Iron and steel under final consumption has been reclassified due to additional information being received

2.10 Major deep mines in production at 31 March 2005[1]

Licensee	Site	Location
Tower Colliery Ltd	Tower Colliery	Rhondda, Cynon Taff
UK Coal plc	Daw Mill Colliery	Warwickshire
	Harworth Colliery	Nottinghamshire
	Kellingley Colliery	Yorkshire
	Maltby Colliery	Yorkshire
	Rossington Colliery	Yorkshire
	Thoresby Colliery	Nottinghamshire
	Welbeck Colliery	Nottinghamshire

(1) In addition there were 5 smaller deep mines in production at 31 March 2005, viz:

Blaentillery Colliery, owned by Blaentillery Mining Ltd, in Torfaen
Eckington Colliery, owned by Eckington Colliery Partnerships, in Derbyshire
Hay Royds Colliery, owned by Hayroyds Colliery LLP, in Yorkshire
Nanthir Colliery, owned by M & W A Anthracite Ltd, in Neath, Port Talbot
Aberpergwm Colliery, owned by Energybuild in Glyn Neath

Source: The Coal Authority

2.11 Opencast sites in production at 31 March 2005[1]

Licensee	Site Name	Location
Aardvark TMC	Skares Road	Cumnock, East Ayrshire
(trading as ATH Resources)	Skares Road Extension	Cumnock, East Ayrshire
ATH Garleffan Ltd	Garleffan	New Cumnock, East Ayrshire
Brymbo Developments Ltd	Brymbo Steelworks	Wrexham
Bryn Bach Coal Ltd	Cwm Yr Onen Colliery Reclamation	Neath, Port Talbot
Celtic Energy Ltd	Margam Opencast	Bridgend
	Nant Helen Extension	Powys
	Selar	Neath & Port Talbot
CRE Energy Ltd	Climpy	South Lanarkshire
Ecosse Regeneration Ltd	Polkemmet	West Lothian
Energybuild Ltd	Nant Melyn	Neath, Port Talbot
G M Mining	Drumshangie	North Lanarkshire
	Kingslaw Site	Kirkcaldy, Fife
H J Banks & Company Ltd	Bankrigg Ltd.	Falkirk
	Delhi Site	Stannington, Northumberland
	Woodhead Site	Barnsley, Yorkshire
H J Banks (Mining) Ltd	Cave Lane	Yorkshire
Hall Construction Services Ltd	Albion Extension	Moira, Leicestershire
	Earlseat OCCS	East Wemys, Fife
	Rosebank	East Wemys, Fife
I & H Brown Ltd	Begg Farm	Kirkcaldy, Fife
Minerals (UK) Ltd	Bwlch Ffos Mining Site	Neath, Port Talbot
Parkhill Estates Ltd	Caughley Quarry	Shropshire
Scottish Coal Company Ltd	Broken Cross & Extension	Lanark, South Lanarkshire
	Chalmerston	East Ayrshire
	Chalmerston North	East Ayrshire
	Glentaggart	South Lanarkshire
	Greenbank (St Ninians)	Nr Kelty, Fife
	House of Water	New Cumnock, East Ayrshire
	Newbigging Farm	Midlothian
	Pennyvenie	Dalmellington, East Ayrshire
	Pennyvenie Area L Deep	Dalmellington, East Ayrshire
	Powharnal	East Ayrshire
	Spireslack	Cumnock, East Ayrshire
Shires Development Ltd	Roundwood Colliery Reclamation Scheme	Yorkshire
UK Coal Mining Ltd	Arkwright	Chesterfield, Derbyshire
	Barugh Bridge	Barnsley, Yorkshire
	Maiden's Hall Extension	Morpeth, Northumberland
	Orgreave	Treeton, Rotherham, Yorkshire
	Southfield Resub	Durham
	Stobswood East	Stobswood, Northumberland

(1) There were 41 opencast sites as at 31 March 2005.

Source: The Coal Authority

.

Chapter 3
Petroleum

Introduction

3.1   This chapter contains commodity balances covering the supply and disposal of primary oils (crude oil and natural gas liquids), feedstocks (including partly processed oils) and petroleum products in the UK in the period 2002 to 2004. These balances are given in Tables 3.1 to 3.6. Additional data have been included in supplementary tables on areas not covered by the format of the balances. This extra information includes details on refinery capacities and aggregates for refinery operations, and extra detail on deliveries into consumption, including breakdowns by country, sector and industry.

3.2   Statistics of imports and exports of crude oil, other refinery feedstocks and petroleum products, refinery receipts, refinery throughput and output and deliveries of petroleum products are obtained from the United Kingdom oil industry and the Department of Trade and Industry's Petroleum Production Reporting System.

3.3   The annual figures relate to calendar years or the ends of calendar years. In the majority of tables the data cover the United Kingdom.

3.4   Information on long-term trends (Tables 3.1.1 and 3.1.2) and the annex on the oil and gas resources of the UK (Annex F) are now only available on DTI's energy statistics web site www.DTI.gov.uk/energy/inform/dukes/dukes2005/03longterm.pdf and www.DTI.gov.uk/energy/inform/dukes/dukes2005/annexf.pdf. This information is included to provide a more complete picture of the UK oil and gas production sector.

Commodity balances for primary oil (Tables 3.1, 3.2 and 3.3)

3.5   These tables show details of the production, supply and disposals of primary oils (crude oil and natural gas liquids (NGLs)) and feedstocks in 2004, 2003 and 2002. The upper half of the table (supply) equates to the upstream oil industry, covering the supply chain from the production of oil and NGLs, recorded by individual oil terminals and oil fields, to their disposal to export or to UK refineries (see Annex F, Table F.2 on DTI's energy statistics web site). The lower half of the table covers the use of these primary oils, including the amount used as a fuel during the extraction process (ie burned to provide power for drilling and pumping operations) and as inputs into refineries, as recorded by the refineries. The statistical difference in the tables thus represents the differences between data reported by these different sources and the sites of production and consumption.

3.6   Gross production of crude oil and NGLs in 2004 was 95 million tonnes, a decline of 10 per cent on 2003 and 30 per cent lower than the peak production level of 137 million tonnes in 1999. Over two-thirds of the United Kingdom's primary oil production in 2004 was exported, and imported crude oil accounted for 70 per cent of UK requirements. Feedstocks (including partly processed oils) made up 11 per cent of total imports of oil in 2004. Total oil imports in 2004 were 15 per cent higher than in 2003. Exports of primary oils and feedstocks in 2004 were 65 million tonnes or 14 per cent lower than those recorded in 2003. Exports in 2004 were 3 per cent higher than imports and made a significant contribution to the UK economy (see Annex G on DTI's energy statistics web site). This is down from previous years where exports were 38 per cent higher than imports in 2003 and 53 per cent higher in 2002. Further declines in exports and increases in imports will be seen as indigenous production declines. Chart 3.1 illustrates recent trends in production, imports and exports of crude oil, NGLs and feedstocks.

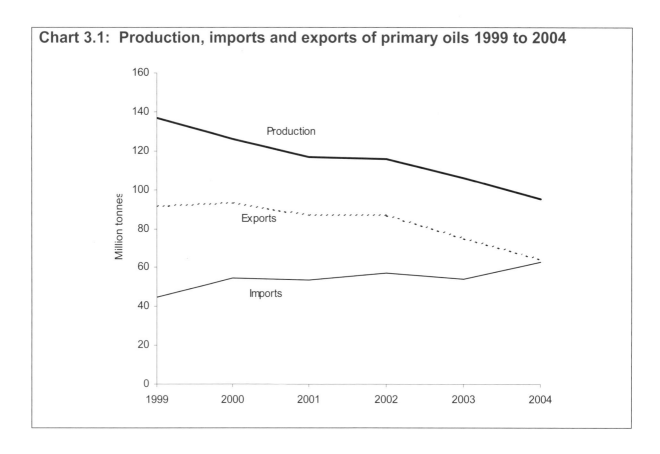

Chart 3.1: Production, imports and exports of primary oils 1999 to 2004

3.7   Although the UK currently produces enough crude oil to meet its own needs, it still imports crude oil. There are various reasons why this makes commercial sense. Primarily refineries consider the type of crude oil rather than its source origin. Most UK refineries use North Sea 'type' crude and do not differentiate between the UK and Norwegian sectors of the North Sea. Indeed, some UK refiners have production interests in both UK and Norwegian waters so the company may own the imported crude at the point of production. The close proximity of some UK and Norwegian oil fields mean that they may use the same pipeline infrastructure, for example the Norpipe oil terminal in Teesside receives both UK and Norwegian crude from the North Sea. Some crude oils are specifically imported for the heavier hydrocarbons which they contain as these are needed for the manufacture of various petroleum products such as bitumen and lubricating oils. This is in contrast to most North Sea type crude which contains a higher proportion of the lighter hydrocarbon fuels resulting in higher yields of products such as motor spirit and other transport fuels.

3.8   Chart 3.2 compares the level of imports and exports of crude oil, NGLs and feedstocks with those for petroleum products over the period 1999 to 2004. Production from the United Kingdom Continental Shelf peaked in 1999 and has subsequently gradually declined in recent years. As would be expected, crude oil exports have followed a similar path to production albeit that they initially levelled off between 1999 and 2000 before slowly declining. Crude oil imports have steadily increased to substantially narrow the gap with exports although the UK remains a net exporter of crude. Exports of petroleum products declined from 1998 to 2001 but have subsequently increased while imports of products have followed a similar pattern to that of crude imports by steadily increasing. The UK is still a net exporter of petroleum products and the significant refinery infrastructure suggests that it will continue to be so for sometime. Additional analysis of the exports and imports of oil products is given in paragraphs 3.14 to 3.18 and the long term trends internet section (3.1.2-3.1.9) and additional details about trends in UK oil production are given in Annex F on DTI's energy statistics web site.

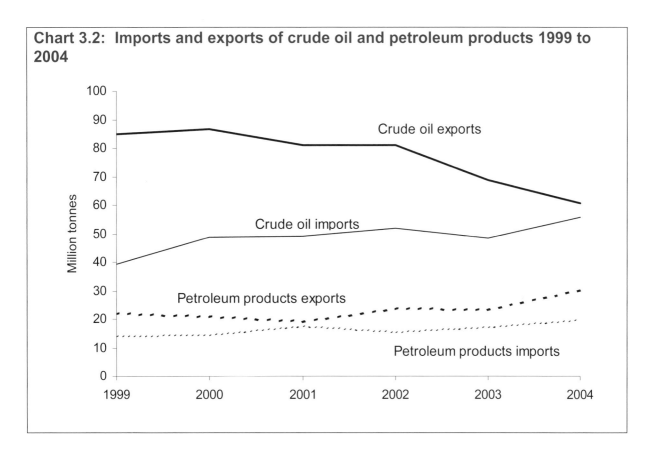

Chart 3.2: Imports and exports of crude oil and petroleum products 1999 to 2004

3.9   It will be seen from the balances in Table 3.1 that the overall statistical difference in the primary oil balance for 2004 is minus 111 thousand tonnes. This means that the total quantities of crude oil and NGLs reported as being produced by the individual UK production fields are 111 thousand tonnes less than the totals reported by UK oil companies as being received by refineries or going for export. The reasons for this are discussed later in paragraphs 3.35 to 3.39.

Commodity balances - Petroleum products (Tables 3.4 to 3.6)

3.10   These tables show details of the production, supply and disposals of petroleum products into the UK market in 2004, 2003 and 2002. The upper half of the table (supply) covers details of the overall availability of these products in the UK as calculated by observing production at refineries, and adding in the impact of trade (imports and exports), stock changes, product transfers and deliveries to international marine bunkers. The lower half of the table covers the uses made of these products, including the uses made within refineries as fuels in the refining process, and details of the amounts reported by oil companies within the UK as delivered for final consumption.

Supply of petroleum products

3.11   Total petroleum products output from UK refineries in 2004 was 90 million tonnes, which was 6 per cent higher than the level in 2003 (itself ½ per cent higher than 2002).

3.12   In terms of output of individual products, production of aviation turbine fuel increased by 6½ per cent in 2004 compared to 2003 and production of motor spirit and gas oil/diesel both increased (by 8½ and 4 per cent respectively). The tightness of the US gasoline market probably encouraged UK refineries to run at higher capacity and increase exports.

3.13 In recent years, the trend in the production of aviation turbine fuel has been downwards. This was primarily due to the fact that aviation turbine fuel and gas oil/diesel are extracted from the same fraction of crude oil (middle distillates), though to different quality criteria. Therefore, as the demand for gas oil/diesel and other middle distillates has increased, there is less of this fraction of the crude oil processed at refineries available for production of aviation turbine fuel. However, production rose in 2004 because refiners were running at higher capacity, see paragraph 3.12 above. More information on refinery capacity in the UK and refinery capacity utilisation is given in paragraphs 3.40 and 3.41.

3.14   The UK has been a net exporter of oil products every year since 1974, with the exception of 1984 due to the effects of the industrial action in the coal-mining sector. Exports of petroleum products were 30 million tonnes in 2004, 30 per cent higher than in 2003 and 29 per cent higher than in 2002. Imports of oil products into the UK were 19 million tonnes in 2004, which were 13 per cent higher than in 2003 and 28 per cent higher than in 2002. Overall, the UK net exports increased to 11 million tonnes in 2004, up from the 6 million tonnes reported in 2003 and higher than the 8 million tonnes in 2002.

3.15   The United States remains one of the key markets for UK exports of oil products, with 5¼ million tonnes being exported there in 2004. These exports made up 17 per cent of total UK exports of oil products in 2004, with the other main countries receiving UK exports of petroleum products being Belgium, France, Ireland, the Netherlands, and Spain. The main sources of the UK's imports of petroleum products in 2004 were France, Germany, Kuwait, the Netherlands, Saudi Arabia and the UAE (source: IEA).

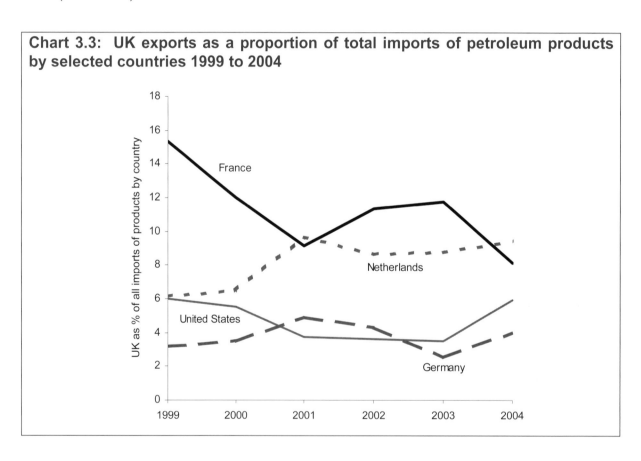

Chart 3.3:   UK exports as a proportion of total imports of petroleum products by selected countries 1999 to 2004

3.16 Chart 3.3 shows how the UK has penetrated selected overseas markets for its petroleum products. UK supplied 6 per cent of the total volume of US imports of petroleum products in 2004 (mostly in the form of motor spirit) and 8, 9 and 4 per cent respectively of the total imports of petroleum products into France, the Netherlands and Germany (mostly as gas oil for heating, motor spirit and fuel oil). The UK regularly supplies the vast majority of total oil products imported into Ireland (mostly motor spirit and DERV fuel for transport, and gas oil and burning oil for heating).

3.17   Differences in product types explain why the UK imports petroleum products when it has a surplus available for export. Exports in 2004 were mainly made up of motor spirit (7 million tonnes), gas oil/diesel (6½ million tonnes) and fuel oil (9 million tonnes). Imports were made up of aviation turbine fuel (7½ million tonnes), motor spirit (2 million tonnes) and gas oil/diesel (4 million tonnes). The make up of refinery structure in the UK is such that it contains a surplus of capacity for some petroleum products such as motor spirit, leading to a surplus availability within the UK for export. Imports take place to cover specific periods of heavy demand within the UK, such as around the time of the Budget or during the summer, or cover production shortfalls in the refinery shutdowns for maintenance.

3.18   Similarly for gas oil/diesel, exports from the UK tend to be of lower grades of gas oil/diesel for use as heating fuels, while imports tend to be of higher-grade gas oil/diesel with a low sulphur content. With the introduction of low sulphur DERV fuel and motor spirit into the UK market (see paragraph 3.51 below) and the required increased production capacity at UK refineries for these fuels, UK imports of these products increased to meet the shortfall. Aviation turbine fuel is imported simply because the UK cannot make enough of it to meet demand. It is derived from the same sort of hydrocarbons as gas oil/diesel, and as such there is a physical limit to how much can be made from the amount of oil processed in the UK.

3.19   More information on the structure of refineries in the UK and trends in imports and exports of crude oil and oil products is given in the long-term trends section on DTI's energy statistics web site (Table 3.1.1).

3.20   In 2004, 8 per cent of UK production of fuel oil and 3 per cent of gas oil/diesel production went into international marine bunkers, totalling 2 million tonnes of products, 2½ per cent of total UK refinery production in the year. These are sales of fuels that are destined for consumption on ocean going vessels. As such the products cannot be classified as being consumed within the UK, and these quantities are thus treated in a similar way to exports in the commodity balances. It should be noted that these quantities do not include deliveries of fuels for use in UK coastal waters, which are counted as UK consumption and the figures given in the transport section of the commodity balances.

3.21   Details are given in the balances of stocks of products held within the UK either at refineries or oil distribution centres such as coastal oil terminals (undistributed stocks).   In addition, some information is available on stocks of oil products held by major electricity generators (distributed stocks). However, these figures exclude any details of stocks held by distributors of fuels or stocks held at retail sites, such as petrol stations. The figures for stocks in the balances also solely relate to those stocks currently present in the UK and as such exclude any stocks that might be held by UK oil companies in other countries under bilateral agreements.

3.22   In order for the UK to be prepared for any oil emergency, the UK Government places an obligation on companies supplying oil products into final consumption in the UK to maintain a certain level of stocks of oil products used as fuels. As part of this, oil companies are allowed to hold stocks in other EU countries subject to bilateral agreements between governments, and count these stocks towards their stocking obligations. The stocks figures in Table 3.10 take account of these bilateral stocks (see paragraphs 3.65 to 3.68) to give a true picture of the amount of stocks available to the UK.

Consumption of petroleum products

3.23   To help users gain the maximum information from the commodity balances, the text in the following section examines the data given on the consumption of oil products in the period 2002 to 2004. The main sectors of consumers will be looked at first (going down the tables) and then the data for individual products will be looked at (going across the tables).

3.24   Table 3.4 shows how overall deliveries of petroleum products into consumption in the UK in 2004, including those used by the UK refining industry as fuels within the refining process and all other uses, totalled 80 million tonnes. This was 3 per cent higher than in 2003 and 4½ per cent higher than in 2002. Between 1996 and 2002, deliveries have been on a declining trend, which since 2002 has turned upwards.

3.25   From the tables, one of the most significant changes in deliveries of products in recent years has been the decline in use for electricity generation. (See long term trends, Table 3.1.2 on DTI's energy statistics web site). This change is primarily a result of the move away by major electricity producers from oil-based fuels towards using natural gas as their fuel of choice for electricity generation. This trend is also reflected in the declining level of usage by auto-producers of electricity over the period, despite the growth in auto-generation of electricity by industry as a whole, and in the significant declining use in heat generation. However, compared with 2003, oil products used for electricity generation in 2004 bucked this downward trend and increased from 538 thousand tonnes to 631 thousand tonnes. This increase was probably due to the high level of gas prices in 2004. Whilst the 17½ per cent increase appears significant, use of oil products for fuel generation in 2004 was still 35 per cent below the level seen in 2001.

3.26   The data included under the blast furnaces heading of the Transformation sector represents fuel oil used in the manufacture of iron and steel which is directly injected into blast furnaces, as opposed to being used as a fuel to heat the blast furnaces. The fuel used for the latter (mostly gas oil) is included under the blast furnaces heading of the Energy Industry Use sector.

3.27   Other figures in the Energy Industry Use sector relate to uses within the UK refining industry in the manufacture of oil products. These are products either used as fuels during refining processes or products used by the refineries themselves as opposed to being sold to other consumers, but excluding any fuels used for the generation of electricity.   These amounts are included in the Transformation sector totals. Given the interest in the total amounts of fuels used within refineries, Table 3.7 includes data on total refinery fuel usage (ie including that used in the generation of electricity) over the period 2000 to 2004. The data under the other headings of the Energy Industry Use sector represent fuels used by the gas supply industry.

3.28   Final consumption of oil products in 2004, ie excluding any uses by the energy industries themselves or for transformation purposes, amounted to 74 million tonnes, 2 million tonnes higher than in 2003 and 4 million tonnes higher than in 2002.   Chart 3.4 shows the breakdown of consumption for energy uses by each sector in 2004.

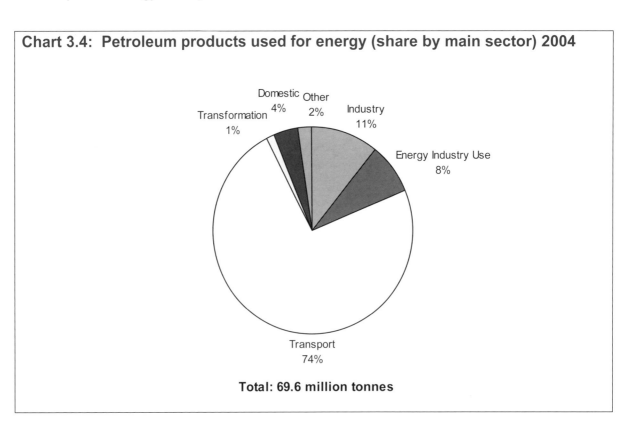

Chart 3.4: Petroleum products used for energy (share by main sector) 2004

Domestic 4%
Other 2%
Transformation 1%
Industry 11%
Energy Industry Use 8%
Transport 74%

Total: 69.6 million tonnes

3.29   The total amount of oil products used by industry was in decline in the middle-1990s due to industry moving away from the use of oil products as an energy source. In the three-year period 1998 to 2000 oil use by industry was fairly constant. In 2001 industrial use of oil products increased by 1 million tonnes to 6½ million tonnes and fell back ½ million tonnes to 6 million tonnes in 2002. More recently industrial usage has grown again to reach to almost 7 million tonnes in 2003, and 7½ million tonnes in 2004.

3.30   Transport sector consumption in 2004 was 2½ per cent higher than in 2003 and 4 per cent higher than in 2002. This was due to higher usage for air transport in 2004 compared to 2003 (up 10 per cent) and higher consumption of road fuels (up 1 per cent). Within road fuels, motor spirit decreased by 2 per cent but this was partly offset by an increase in use of DERV fuel (up 4½ per cent). In 2004, transport usage totalled 51 million tonnes and accounted for 70 per cent of total final consumption of oil products. Consumption by sectors other than transport and industry decreased by 3½ per cent in 2004 compared with 2003.

3.31   Consumption of non-energy products increased to 10½ million tonnes in 2004, up by 2 per cent when compared to 2003. In 2004, non-energy products made up 14½ per cent of final consumption of oil products, compared with 14 per cent in 2003. More detail on the non-energy uses of oil products, by product and by type of use where such information is available, is given in Table 3C and paragraphs 3.57 to 3.63 later in this text.

3.32   Looking at the final consumption of individual products, 76 per cent of total final consumption in 2004 was made up of consumption of just three products; aviation turbine fuel, motor spirit and gas oil/diesel, ie predominantly transport products (some gas oil is used for power generation). Consumption of aviation turbine fuel increased by 10 per cent in 2004 to 11 million tonnes. Changes in the consumption of aviation fuel are discussed in more detail in paragraphs 3.54 to 3.56 below. More detailed information on consumption of motor spirit and gas oil/diesel over the period 2000 to 2004 is given in Table 3.8 and discussed in paragraphs 3.42 to 3.53.

3.33   In 2004 total final consumption of fuel oil was 2 million tonnes, up by 35 per cent on 2003. This was mainly due to an increase in industrial usage of 40 per cent. Whilst fuel oil used for electricity generation increased by 22 per cent between 2003 and 2004, this was largely offset by a fall in fuel oil used for heat generation for sale to third parties, down 52 per cent. Further detail on the consumption of fuel oil broken down by grade is given in Table 3.8.

3.34   Tables 3.4 to 3.6 include estimates for the use of gas for road vehicles. These estimates were based on information on the amounts of duty received by HM Revenue and Customs from the tax on gas used as a road fuel. It is estimated that some 112 thousand tonnes of gas (mostly butane or propane) was used in road vehicles in the UK in 2004. While a very small use when compared to overall consumption of these fuels and the consumption of fuels for road transport as a whole, the consumption of these gases for road transport in 2004 has risen five-fold since 2001.

Supply and disposal of products (Table 3.7)

3.35   This table brings together the commodity balances for primary oils and for petroleum products into a single overall balance table.

3.36   The statistical difference for primary oils in the table includes own use in onshore terminals and gas separation plants, losses, platform and other field stock changes. Another factor is the time lag that can exist between production and loading onto tankers being reported at an offshore field and the arrival of these tankers at onshore refineries and oil terminals. This gap is usually minimal and works such that any effect of this at the start of a month is balanced by a similar counterpart effect at the end of a month. However, there can be instances where the length of this interval can be significant and, if it happens at the end of a year, significant effects on the statistical differences seen for the years involved can result.

3.37   With the downstream sector, the statistical differences can similarly be used to assess the validity and consistency of the data. From the tables, these differences are generally a very small proportion of the totals involved.

3.38   Paragraphs 3.73 to 3.84 provide details on the reasons why statistical differences occur for the upstream and downstream sectors.

3.39   The downstream oil data reporting system was reviewed in late 2001 and early 2002 after some discrepancies in the reporting of refinery production data were identified. It was noticed that potential losses within the refining system could be incorrectly reported elsewhere. Given the impact of these factors on the statistical differences, corrections were incorporated in the "Losses in refining process" line in Table 3.7 for the years affected, ie 1999 to 2002. Further work has been done since, including the testing of a new data collection system in the latter half of 2004, designed to enhance the quality of collected data. The new system replaced its predecessor in full at the beginning of 2005.

Refinery capacity

3.40   Data for refinery capacity as at the end of 2004 are presented in Table 3A, with the location of these refineries illustrated in Map 3A. These figures are collected annually by the Department of Trade and Industry from individual oil companies. Capacity per annum for each refinery is derived by applying the rated capacity of the plant per day when on-stream by the number of days the plant was on stream during the year. Fluctuations in the number of days the refinery is active are usually the main reasons for annual changes in the level of capacity. Reforming capacity covers catalytic reforming, and cracking/conversion capacity covers processes for upgrading residual oils to lighter products, eg catalytic, thermal or hydro-cracking, visbreaking and coking.

Table 3A: UK refinery processing capacity as at end 2004 [1]

| | Million tonnes per annum | | |
(Symbols relate to Map 3A)	Distillation	Reforming	Cracking and Conversion
Shell UK Ltd			
❶ Stanlow	11.5	1.5	3.8
ExxonMobil Co. Ltd			
❷ Fawley	16.2	2.9	4.1
BP Ltd			
❸ Coryton	8.8	1.8	3.4
❹ Grangemouth	10.0	1.9	3.3
Total (BP)	18.8	3.7	6.7
Total (UK)			
❺ Lindsey Oil Refinery Ltd South Killingholme	10.9	1.5	4.1
Texaco Refining Co. Ltd			
❻ Pembroke	10.1	1.5	6.1
Conoco Ltd			
❼ Killingholme	10.2	2.2	9.2
Total (UK) / Murco Pet. Ltd			
❽ Milford Haven	6.9	1.1	2.5
Petroplus International Ltd			
❾ North Tees	5.0	-	-
Petrochem Carless Ltd			
① Harwich	0.7	-	-
Eastham Refinery Ltd			
② Eastham	1.1	-	-
Nynas UK AB			
③ Dundee (Camperdown)	0.7	-	-
Total all refineries	92.0	14.2	36.5

(1) Rated design capacity per day on stream multiplied by the average number of days on stream.

Map 3A: Distribution of UK refineries active as at end 2004
Symbols relate to refinery details given in Table 3A

3.41 At the end of 2004 the UK had 9 major refineries operating, with three minor refineries in existence. Distillation capacity in the UK at the end of 2004 was 92 million tonnes, 1.7 million tonnes higher than at the end of 2003. Total UK reforming capacity at the end of 2004 was 14.2 million tonnes and cracking and conversion capacity was 0.3 million tonnes higher at 36.5 million tonnes.

Additional information on inland deliveries of selected products (Table 3.8)

3.42 This table gives details for consumption of motor spirit, gas oil/diesel and fuel oils given in the main commodity balance tables for the period 2000 to 2004. It includes information on retail and commercial deliveries of motor spirit and DERV fuel that cannot be accommodated within the structure of the commodity balances, but which are of interest. The table also includes additional details of the quantities of motor spirit and DERV fuel sold collectively by hypermarket and supermarket companies in the UK.

3.43 Motor spirit deliveries in 2004 were 2 per cent down compared to 2003, and 6½ per cent lower than in 2002. In contrast, deliveries of DERV fuel were 4½ per cent higher in 2004 compared to 2003, which in turn was 4½ per cent higher than in 2002.

3.44 Several factors are behind the differing trends seen for motor spirit and DERV fuel. For a number of years, there has been a sustained year-on-year increase in the number of diesel-engined vehicles in use in the UK. Diesel vehicles are more fuel-efficient than their petrol equivalents. In the National Travel Survey carried out by the Department for Transport, diesel-engined cars averaged 39 miles per gallon of fuel, compared with 30 miles per gallon for petrol-engined cars. Traditionally the greater fuel-efficiency of diesel vehicles had been at the expense of higher purchase prices and a performance deficit when compared to petrol-engined equivalents. More recently, the purchase prices for diesel and petrol engined vehicles have become more similar and improved technology has substantially reduced the performance deficit.

3.45   The price differential between DERV fuel and motor spirit has affected the relative demands for the two road fuels. In the early 1990s there was a significant price differential that worked in favour of using DERV fuel. For example, the average retail price for a litre of 4-star petrol in 1990 was 44.87 pence compared to 40.48 pence for a litre of DERV fuel, representing a 10 per cent saving. By December 2004, average retail prices for a litre of the most common grade of motor spirit purchased (ultra low sulphur petrol (ULSP)) and DERV fuel were 82.41 and 85.93 pence per litre respectively. In the mid 1990s, the policy on DERV taxation was changed for environmental reasons and the level of tax was increased to remove the favourable price differential. It is thought that the removal of the favourable differential significantly reduced the rate of transfer from petrol to diesel engine vehicles in recent years compared to what would have otherwise occurred.

3.46   Chart 3.5 shows how the share of total motor spirit deliveries accounted for by unleaded fuel has increased from 72 per cent in 1997 to effectively 100 per cent in 2004. It should be noted that, since 1st January 2000, retails sales of leaded petrol ceased as a result of the implementation of a European strategy to reduce pollution from road traffic (known as the Auto-Oil Directive). Since 2000 effectively all petrol sold has been unleaded. Prior to 2002, super premium unleaded accounted for about 2 per cent of total motor spirit deliveries but this has since grown to over 4 per cent in 2004. It is suspected that the recent increase in the use of this fuel is due to the declining availability of lead replacement petrol (LRP) but there has also been recent growth in the marketing of super premium unleaded as a high performance product that will have increased sales.

3.47   Since 1990 there has been an overall trend of a reduction in the consumption of motor spirit in the UK. Consumption in 2004 was 19 per cent lower than the peak of 24 million tonnes of motor spirit in 1990. Chart 3.5 shows the drop in the level of consumption of leaded fuel caused by motorists switching to using unleaded petrol in their vehicles.

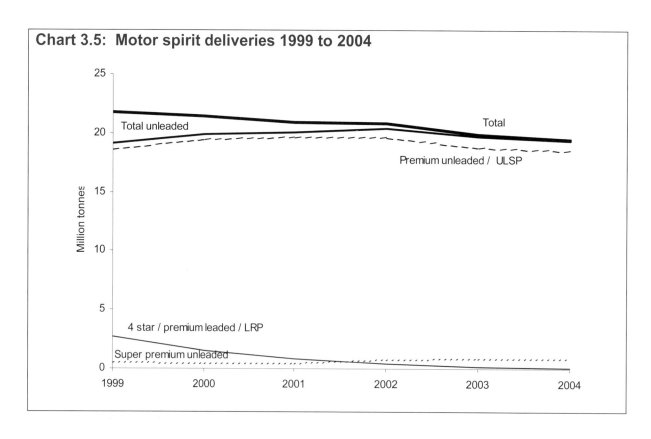

3.48   As mentioned above and as illustrated in Chart 3.6, the large differential between the price of a litre of leaded and unleaded motor spirit helped encourage motorists to switch from leaded to unleaded petrol. In addition, the implementation of the Auto-Oil Directive banned the general sale of leaded petrol (4-star) from 1st January 2000 giving a final push for motorists to switch to unleaded fuels.

3.49   The switch to unleaded petrol provided an impetus for people to change their vehicles to newer ones.   The resultant reduction in the age of the vehicle stock has probably further reduced overall motor spirit consumption, as newer vehicles tend to be more fuel efficient due to improved technology.

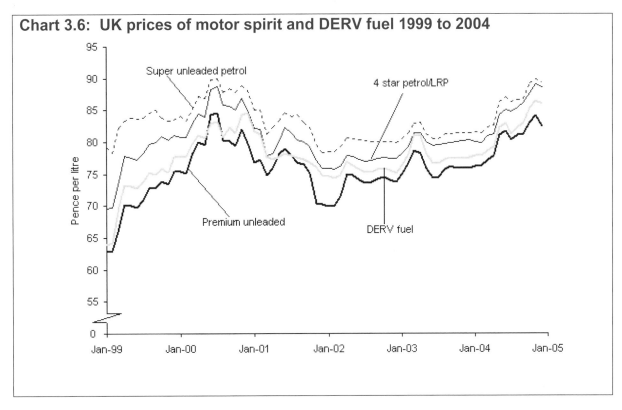

Chart 3.6: UK prices of motor spirit and DERV fuel 1999 to 2004

3.50   Chart 3.6 illustrates the large differential that existed between the price of 4-star leaded petrol and DERV fuel, with the latter being priced at similar levels to premium grade unleaded petrol. As with the differential between leaded and unleaded petrol, this price differential also worked to encourage motorists to convert to diesel-engined vehicles.   Chart 3.7 contains details of vehicle licence registrations for private cars during each year for the period 1994 to 2004, broken down by type of engine. Whilst the number of petrol-engined vehicles licensed only grew by 11 per cent, the number of diesel-engined vehicles licensed has increased nearly 250 percent in the same period.

3.51   Although not specifically covered by the statistics included in this Digest, differential duty rates have been used to encourage the switch to low sulphur road fuels, specifically Ultra Low Sulphur Diesel fuel (ULSD) and Ultra Low Sulphur Petrol (ULSP). This extra differential has mostly been used to allow producers to cover the additional costs of providing the ULSD and ULSP, through both covering the extra cost of importing these low sulphur products and through funding changes in refinery processes. By mid 2002, 100 per cent of UK refinery capacity for the production of premium grade unleaded petrol (the grade replaced by ULSP) had been converted over to produce ULSP. The introduction of duty differentials has had a significant effect on moving consumers over to what are regarded as more environmentally friendly fuels.

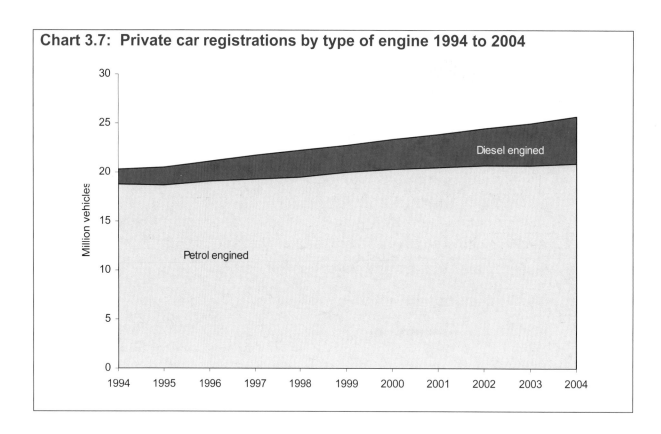

Chart 3.7: Private car registrations by type of engine 1994 to 2004

3.52   Sales by super/hypermarkets have taken an increasing share of retail deliveries (ie deliveries to dealers) of motor spirit and DERV fuel in recent years as Table 3B shows. These figures have been derived from a survey of super/hypermarket companies to collect details of their sales of motor spirit and DERV fuel. The share of total deliveries (ie including deliveries direct to commercial consumers) is shown in brackets.

Table 3B: Super/hypermarkets share of retail deliveries, 2000 to 2004

per cent

	Motor spirit		DERV fuel	
2000	26.9	(26)	19.6	(9)
2001	28.2	(27)	20.8	(10)
2002	29.3	(29)	22.7	(11)
2003	30.7	(30)	23.6	(12)
2004	32.9	(32)	26.0	(13)

Figures in brackets are shares of total deliveries.

3.53 The increases seen in recent years represent an increase in sales by super/hypermarket companies although the percentage shares are also affected by the decline in the overall deliveries of motor spirit in the UK seen in these years as mentioned earlier. Hypermarket deliveries of motor spirit increased by 3½ per cent from 2003 and their DERV deliveries increased by 16 per cent. For motor spirit in particular, the hypermarkets are being noticeably successful at increasing or at least maintaining their sales as overall consumption declines.

Aviation fuel

3.54   Data in Tables 3.4 to 3.6 show the changing amounts of aviation turbine fuel (ATF) kerosene being consumed in the UK between 2002 and 2004. The long-term trends section on the Internet discusses the trend seen since 1970 in the use of ATF kerosene in the UK. Overall, deliveries in the UK in 2004 were 10 per cent higher than in 2003.

3.55   Chart 3.8 shows annual deliveries of ATF kerosene in the UK over the last decade. ATF consumption increased steadily until 1997 and then rapidly until 2000. The September 11th terrorist attacks on the United States had a significant impact on the global aviation industry and reversed the trend for a period lasting more than twelve months. The increase in ATF deliveries since 2002 illustrates the subsequent recovery the global aviation industry.

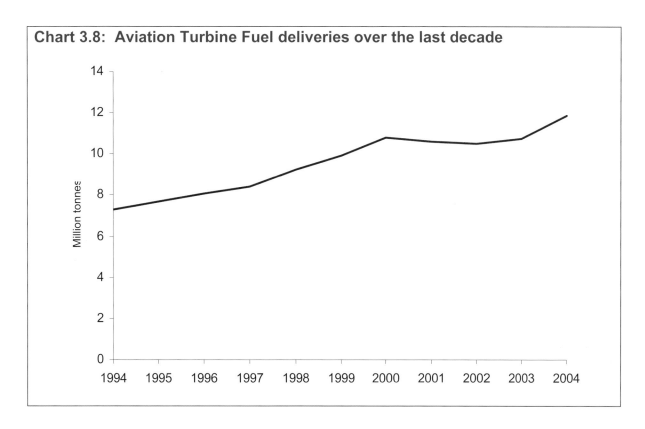

Chart 3.8: Aviation Turbine Fuel deliveries over the last decade

3.56   Chart 3.9 shows the aviation industry's activities over the last ten years split by the domestic and international passenger uplifts and cargo delivery categories. It is clear to see that the events of September 11th 2001 had varied effects on the different sections of the industry. International air passenger movements suffered a fall in the rate of growth, while domestic flights appear to be largely unaffected. The most significant effect however is clearly visible within the cargo division of the industry, which saw a fall of 21 per cent in 2001. The differing ways in which the demand for the industry's separate services reacted to the terrorist attack implies that rather than causing a reluctance of passengers in the UK to fly, the negative effect on the economy, causing cargo demand to fall, had the greatest impact. Since 2001 the cargo division has steadily grown and in 2004 was similar to the level seen in 2000.

Chart 3.9: Aviation Turbine Fuel usage over the last decade by type

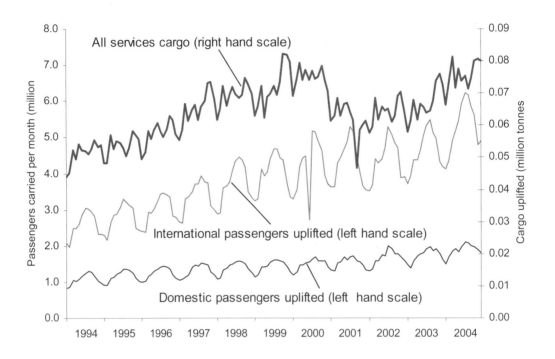

Additional information on inland deliveries for non-energy uses

3.57 Table 3C below summarises additional data on the non–energy uses made of the total deliveries of oil products included as the bottom line in the commodity balances in Tables 3.4 to 3.6. It provides extra information on the uses of lubricating oils and greases by use, and details of products used as petro-chemical feedstocks.

3.58 All inland deliveries of lubricating oils and petroleum coke have been classified as going for non-energy uses only. However, some deliveries are used for energy purposes though it is difficult to estimate energy use figures for these products with any degree of accuracy, hence no such estimates appear in the commodity balance tables.

3.59 For lubricating oils, about 50 per cent of inland deliveries each year are lost as a film on manufactured goods, lost due to evaporation, consumed during use (ie burnt within engines) or for products like process oils and white oils, the oil becomes part of the product. Work done by the Department for Environment, Food and Rural Affairs (Defra) suggests that each year about 50 per cent of inland deliveries become available as waste or used lubricating oil. Some 85 per cent of the waste/used lubricating oil (ie some 388 thousand tonnes) is centrally collected and processed for reuse as Recovered Fuel Oil. The remaining 15 per cent of the waste is probably burnt locally in small space heaters. Studies have shown that the UK's 85 per cent collection rate of used lubricating oils is one of the highest in Europe.

3.60 For petroleum coke, more information is available allowing more accurate estimates to be made. It has been possible to analyse the data available for the imports of petroleum coke to identify which type of company is importing the product. This work has shown that a significant proportion of petroleum coke imports each year are made by energy companies, such as power generators or fuels merchants, with another substantial proportion being imported by cement manufacturers. Whilst it cannot be certain that these imports are being used as a fuel, information on the use of petroleum coke in cement manufacture suggests that it is.

Table 3C: Additional information on inland deliveries for non-energy uses, 2002 to 2004

Thousand tonnes

	2002	2003	2004
Feedstock for petroleum chemical plants:			
Propane	883	835	1,106
Butane	584	789	680
Other gases	1,881	1,810	1,661
Total gases	3,348	3,434	3,447
Naphtha (LDF)	1,592	2,332	2,029
Middle Distillate Feedstock (MDF)	205	287	249
Other products	-	-	-
Total feedstock	5,145	6,053	5,725
Lubricating oils and grease:			
Aviation	3	3	3
Industrial	545	522	560
Marine	31	40	28
Motors	240	288	310
Agricultural	11	15	14
Fuel oil sold as lubricant	-	-	-
Total lubricating oils and grease	829	868	914
Other non-energy products:			
Industrial spirit	32	33	131
White spirit	125	114	150
Bitumen	2,002	1,959	1,991
Petroleum wax	51	57	50
Petroleum coke	893	880	1,146
Miscellaneous products	596	449	476
Total non-energy use	9,673	10,411	10,584

3.61   Using imports data, estimates have been constructed which show that around 1 million tonnes of petroleum coke were imported for inland deliveries in 2004 compared to around 830 thousand tonnes in 2003.   Around 320 thousand tonnes of petroleum coke were estimated to have been imported in 2002 for energy uses (for electricity generation, use as a fuel in the manufacture of cement, sold as a solid fuel or to be used in the manufacture of other solid fuels). In 2003, the level for energy use fell to 263 thousand tonnes. Estimates of imports for energy uses rose to 2004 to 343 thousand tonnes or 32 per cent of total supplies.

3.62   Analysis of the data on the quantity and value of imports of petroleum coke into the UK from HM Revenue and Customs provides some estimates for the cost of imports and gives some indication of the prices being paid. These are only indicative of the prices being paid in the port of importation, and do not include the extra transport costs from the port to the final destination that would be part of more rigorous price estimate. Details of these estimates are included in Annex G on trade in fuels, as part of Table G.3 on the DTI energy statistics website.   A breakdown has been made by grade of petroleum coke and type of use for imports into the UK, which is given in Table 3D below. Calcined petroleum coke is virtually pure carbon, and as such is more valuable than non-calcined (otherwise known as "green") petroleum coke, as shown by the higher price per tonne it commands and the fact that it is not used simply as a fuel.

Table 3D: Estimated £ per tonne for imports of petroleum coke into the UK

	Non-calcined ("green") petroleum coke			Calcined petroleum coke
	Energy	Non-energy	Total	Non-energy
2002	18.0	37.9	26.2	131.0
2003	22.2	28.9	25.9	122.7
2004	22.5	35.0	29.9	120.6

3.63 Petroleum coke is a relatively low energy content fuel, having a calorific value of 35.8 GJ per tonne, compared with an average for petroleum products of 45.9 GJ per tonne, and 43.5 GJ per tonne for fuel oil. It is however higher than coal (27.2 GJ per tonne) and in certain areas is competing with coal as a fuel. It has the advantage of being a very cheap fuel, since it is often regarded as a waste product rather than a specific output from the refining process. Compared to imports of coal, prices of petroleum coke per GJ were about 60 per cent lower in 2004.

Inland deliveries by country (Table 3.9)

3.64 This table shows deliveries in England and Wales, Scotland, and Northern Ireland for 2002 to 2004. The figures for deliveries for energy use show increases in use for Scotland, Northern Ireland and England and Wales. The 5½ per cent increase in energy use in Northern Ireland between 2003 and 2004 reflects an increase in deliveries of DERV of 22 per cent while motor spirit deliveries were flat. The overall increase probably reflects success in tackling illegal cross-border smuggling from the Republic of Ireland into Northern Ireland. Partly due to a 4½ per cent increase in DERV deliveries, energy deliveries in England and Wales rose 3½ per cent between 2003 and 2004, despite motor spirit being down by 2 per cent. A 4 per cent rise in Scotland occurred despite a 4 per cent decrease in motor spirit deliveries. Scotland and Northern Ireland experienced differing patterns in deliveries of burning oil, down by 17 per cent and up by 9½ per cent respectively. Non-energy use deliveries fell in England and Wales by 2½ per cent but rose in Scotland by 13½ per cent, which was driven by demand for feedstock in the petrochemical industry. Non-energy use in Northern Ireland is substantially lower than other parts of the UK due to lack of a significant local petrochemical industry.

Stocks of oil (Table 3.10)

3.65 This table shows stocks of crude oil, feedstocks (including partly processed oils) and products (in detail) at the end of each year. Stocks of crude oil and feedstocks decreased in 2004, with decreases in stocks held at offshore facilities and oil terminals offsetting an increase in stocks held at refineries.

3.66 The UK holds emergency stocks of oil to help reduce the adverse impact on the UK of any disruptions of supplies of oil arising from domestic or international incidents. EU legislation (EC Directive 98/93) requires EU member states to hold oil stocks equivalent to 90 days worth of average daily consumption calculated from the previous calendar year. These stocks are held purely to deal with oil supply emergencies, not to manage or affect prices. The UK, as a producer, receives a derogation of 25 per cent on its obligation and is only required to hold stocks equivalent to 67½ days of consumption.

3.67 To meet this obligation the UK government requires companies supplying oil products into final consumption in the UK to maintain a certain level of emergency stocks of oil products as fuels. As part of this, oil companies are allowed to hold stocks in other EU countries subject to bilateral agreements between governments, and count these stocks towards their stocking obligations. The stock figures in Table 3.10 take account of these stocks to give a true picture of the amount of stocks available to the UK.

3.68 Stocks of petroleum products at the end of 2004 were 6½ per cent lower than a year earlier. The total stocks of crude oil and products held by UK companies at the end of 2004 were equivalent to approximately 78.6 days of UK consumption.

Technical notes and definitions

3.69   These notes and definitions are in addition to the technical notes and definitions covering all fuels and energy as a whole in Chapter 1, paragraphs 1.24 to 1.56. For notes on the commodity balances and definitions of the terms used in the row headings see the Annex A, paragraphs A.7 to A.42. While the data in the printed and bound copy of this Digest cover only the most recent 5 years, these notes also cover data for earlier years that are available on the DTI web site.

Indigenous production
3.70   The term indigenous is used throughout this chapter and includes oil from the UK Continental Shelf both offshore and onshore.

Deliveries
3.71   These are deliveries into consumption, as opposed to being estimates of actual consumption or use. They are split between inland deliveries and deliveries to marine bunkers. Inland deliveries will not necessarily be consumed in the United Kingdom (eg aviation fuels).

Sources of data
3.72   The majority of the data included in the text and tables of this chapter are derived from the UK Petroleum Industry Association (UKPIA) data collection system. Data relating to the inland operations of the UK oil industry (ie information on the supply, refining and distribution of oil in the UK) are collected from companies. The data format and coverage have been designed to meet most of the needs of both government and the industry itself. Each member of UKPIA provides returns on its refining activities and deliveries of various products to the internal UK market. This information is supplemented whenever necessary to allow for complete coverage within the statistics, with separate exercises carried out on special topics (for example, the work on super/hypermarkets referred to in paragraph 3.52).

Statistical differences
3.73   In Tables 3.1 to 3.7, there are headings titled "statistical differences". These are differences between the separately observed figures for production and delivery of crude oil and products during the path of their movement from the point of production to the point of consumption.

3.74   These headings listed in the primary oil commodity balances (Tables 3.1 to 3.3) are differences between the separately observed and reported figures for production from onshore or offshore fields and supply to the UK market that cannot be accounted for by any specific factors. Primarily they result from inaccuracies in the meters at various points along offshore pipelines. These meters vary slightly in their accuracy within accepted tolerances, giving rise to both losses and gains when the volumes of oil flowing are measured. Errors may also occur when non-standard conditions are used to meter the oil flow.

3.75   Another technical factor that can contribute to the statistical differences relates to the recording of quantities at the producing field (which is the input for the production data) and at oil terminals and refineries, since they are in effect measuring different types of oil. Terminals and refineries are able to measure a standardised, stabilised crude oil, ie with its water content and content of NGLs at a standard level and with the amounts being measured at standard conditions. However, at the producing field they are dealing with a "live" crude oil that can have a varying level of water and NGLs within it. While offshore companies report live crude at field, the disposals from oil terminals and offshore loading fields are reported as stabilised crude oil. This effectively assumes that terminal disposals are stabilised crude production figures. These changes were introduced in the 2002 edition of this Digest.

3.76   Part of the overall statistical difference may also be due to problems with the correct reporting of individual NGLs at the production site and at terminals and refineries. It is known that there is some mixing of condensate and other NGLs in with what might otherwise be stabilised crude oil before it enters the pipeline. This mixing occurs as it removes the need for separate pipeline systems for transporting the NGLs and it also allows the viscosity of the oil passing down the pipeline to be varied as necessary. While the quantity figures recorded by terminals are in terms of stabilised crude oil, with the NGL component removed, there may be situations where what is being reported does not comply with this requirement.

3.77 Refinery data are collated from details of individual shipments received and made by each refinery and terminal operating company. Each year there are thousands of such shipments, which may be reported separately by two or three different companies involved in the movement. Whilst intensive work is carried out to check these returns, it is possible that some double counting of receipts might be occurring.

3.78 Temperature, pressure and natural leakage also contribute to the statistical differences. In addition, small discrepancies can occur between the estimated calorific values used at the field and the more accurate values measured at the onshore terminal where data are shown on an energy basis. The statistical differences can also be affected by rounding or clerical errors or unrecorded losses, such as leakage. Other contributory factors are inaccuracies in the reporting of the amounts being disposed of to the various activities listed, including differences between the quantities reported as going to refineries and the actual amounts passing through refineries.

3.79 Similarly, the data under these headings in Tables 3.4 to 3.6 are the differences between the deliveries of petroleum products to the inland UK market reported by the supplying companies and estimates for such deliveries. These estimates are calculated by taking the output of products reported by refineries and then adjusting it by the relevant factors (such as imports and exports of the products, changes in the levels of stocks etc.).

3.80 It may be thought that such differences should not exist as the data underlying both the observed deliveries into the UK market and the individual components of the estimates (ie production, imports, exports, stocks) come from the same source (the oil companies). While it is true that each oil company provides data on its own activities in each area, there are separate areas of operation within the companies that report their own part of the overall data. Table 3E below illustrates this.

Table 3E: Sources of data within oil companies

Area covered	Source
Refinery production	Refinery
Imports and exports	Refinery, logistics departments, oil traders
Stocks	Refinery, crude and product terminals, major storage and distribution sites
Final deliveries	Sales, marketing and accounts departments

3.81 Each individual reporting source will have direct knowledge of its own data. For example, refineries will know what they produce and how much leaves the refinery gate as part of routine monitoring of the refinery operations. Similarly other data such as sales to final consumers or imports and exports will be closely monitored. Companies will ensure that each component set of data reported is as accurate as possible but their reporting systems may not be integrated, meaning that internal consistency checks across all reported data cannot be made. Each part of a company may also work to different timings as well, which may further add to the degree of differences seen.

3.82 The main area where there is known to be a problem is with the "Transfers" heading in the commodity balances. The data reported under this heading have two components. Firstly there is an allowance for reclassification of products within the refining process. For example, butane can be added to motor spirit to improve the octane rating, aviation turbine fuel could be reclassified as domestic kerosene if its quality deteriorates, and much of the fuel oil imported into the UK is further refined into other petroleum products. Secondly, and in addition to these inter-product transfers, the data also include an allowance to cover the receipt of backflows of products from petrochemical plants. Such plants are often very closely integrated with refineries (for example, BP's refinery at Grangemouth is right next to the petrochemical plant). A deduction for these backflows thus needs to be included under the "Transfers" heading so that calculated estimates reflect net output and are thus more comparable with the basis of the observed deliveries data.

3.83 However, there is scope for error in the recording of these two components. With inter-product transfers, the data are recorded within the refinery during the refining and blending processes where the usual units used to record the changes are volumes rather than masses. Different factors apply

78

for each product when converting from a volume to mass basis, as shown by the conversion factors given in Annex A of this Digest. Thus, a balanced transfer in volume terms may not be equivalent when converted to a mass basis. This is thought to be the main source of error within the individual product balances.

3.84   With the backflows data, as the observed deliveries data are derived from sales data on a "net" basis and will therefore exclude the element of backflows, it is thought that there is significant scope for error in the recording of the backflows when received at a refinery.   For example, these could be seen simply as an input of fuel oils to be used as a feedstock, and thus recorded as an input without their precise nature being recorded – in effect a form of double-counting.   It is this relationship between the petrochemical sector and refineries that is thought to be the main source of error in the overall oil commodity balances.

Imports and exports
3.85   The information given under the headings "imports" and "exports" in this chapter are the figures recorded by importers and exporters of oil. They thus differ in some cases from the import and export figures provided by HM Revenue and Customs that are given in Annex G on the Internet. These differences may arise since whilst the trader's figures are a record of actual movements in the period, for non-EU trade, HM Revenue and Customs figures show the trade as declared by exporters on documents received during the period stated. The Customs figures also include re-exports. These are products that may have originally entered the UK as imports from another country and been stored in the UK prior to being exported back out of the UK, as opposed to having been actually produced in the UK.

Marine bunkers
3.86   This covers deliveries to ocean going and coastal vessels under international bunker contracts. Other deliveries to fishing, coastal and inland vessels are excluded.

Crude and process oils
3.87   These are all feedstocks, other than distillation benzene, for refining at refinery plants. Gasoline feedstock is any process oil whether clean or dirty which is used as a refinery feedstock for the manufacture of gasoline or naphtha.   Other refinery feedstock is any process oil used for the manufacture of any other petroleum products.

Refineries
3.88   Refineries distilling crude and process oils to obtain petroleum products.   This excludes petrochemical plants, plants only engaged in re-distilling products to obtain better grades, crude oil stabilisation plants and gas separation plants.

Products used as fuel (energy use)
3.89   The following paragraphs define the product headings used in the text and tables of this chapter. The products are used for energy in some way, either directly as a fuel or as an input into electricity generation.

Refinery fuel - Petroleum products used as fuel at refineries.

Ethane - An ethane (C_2H_6) rich gas in natural gas and refinery gas streams. Primarily used, or intended to be used, as a chemical feedstock.

Propane - Hydrocarbon containing three carbon atoms, gaseous at normal temperature but generally stored and transported under pressure as a liquid. Used mainly for industrial purposes, but also as transport LPG, and some domestic heating and cooking.

Butane - Hydrocarbon containing four carbon atoms, otherwise as for propane. Additionally used as a constituent of motor spirit to increase vapour pressure and as a chemical feedstock.

Naphtha (Light distillate feedstock) - Petroleum distillate boiling predominantly below 200°C.

Aviation spirit - All light hydrocarbon oils intended for use in aviation piston-engine power units, including bench testing of aircraft engines.

Motor spirit - Blended light petroleum components used as fuel for spark-ignition internal-combustion engines other than aircraft engines:

(i)   Premium unleaded grade - all finished motor spirit, with an octane number (research method) not less than 95.

(ii)   Super premium unleaded grade - finished motor spirit, with an octane number (research method) not less than 97.

(iii)   Lead Replacement Petrol (LRP) – finished motor spirit with an octane number (research method) not less than 97. This is usually Super Premium Unleaded containing a valve seat protection additive.

Aviation turbine fuel (ATF) - All other turbine fuel intended for use in aviation gas-turbine power units and including bench testing of aircraft engines.

Burning oil (kerosene or "paraffin") - Refined petroleum fuel, intermediate in volatility between motor spirit and gas oil, used primarily for heating. White spirit and kerosene used for lubricant blends are excluded.

Gas oil/automotive diesel - Petroleum fuel having a distillation range immediately between kerosene and light-lubricating oil:

(i)   **DERV (Diesel Engined Road Vehicle) fuel** - automotive diesel fuel for use in high speed, compression ignition engines in vehicles subject to Vehicle Excise Duty.

(ii)   **Gas oil** - used as a burner fuel in heating installations, for industrial gas turbines and as for DERV (but in vehicles not subject to Vehicle Excise Duty eg Agriculture vehicles, fishing vessels, construction equipment).

(iii)   **Marine diesel oil** - heavier type of gas oil suitable for heavy industrial and marine compression-ignition engines.

Fuel oil - Heavy petroleum residue blends used in atomising burners and for heavy duty marine diesel engines (marine bunkers, etc.) the heavier requiring pre-heating before combustion, but excluding fuel oil for grease making or lubricating oil and fuel oil sold as such for road making.

Products not used as fuel (non-energy use)

3.90 The following paragraphs define the product headings used in the text and tables of this chapter, which are used for non-energy purposes.

Feedstock for petroleum chemical plants - All petroleum products intended for use in the manufacture of petroleum chemicals. This includes middle distillate feedstock of which there are several grades depending on viscosity. The boiling point ranges between 200°C and 400°C. (A deduction has been made from these figures equal to the quantity of feedstock used in making the conventional petroleum products that are produced during the processing of the feedstock. The output and deliveries of these conventional petroleum products are included elsewhere as appropriate.)

White spirit - A highly refined distillate with a boiling range of about 150°C to 200°C used as a paint and commercial solvent.

Industrial spirit - Refined petroleum fractions with boiling ranges up to 200°C dependent on the use to which they are put - eg seed extraction, rubber solvents, perfume etc.

Lubricating oils (and grease) - Refined heavy distillates obtained from the vacuum distillation of petroleum residues. Includes liquid and solid hydrocarbons sold by the lubricating oil trade, either alone or blended with fixed oils, metallic soaps and other organic and/or inorganic bodies. A certain percentage of inland deliveries are re-used as a fuel (see paragraphs 3.57 to 3.63).

Bitumen - The residue left after the production of lubricating oil distillates and vacuum gas oil for upgrading plant feedstock. Used mainly for road making and building construction purposes. Includes other petroleum products, creosote and tar mixed with bitumen for these purposes and fuel oil sold as such for road making.

Petroleum wax - Includes paraffin wax, which is a white crystalline hydrocarbon material of low oil content normally obtained during the refining of lubricating oil distillate, paraffin scale, slack wax, microcrystalline wax and wax emulsions. Used for candle manufacture, polishes, food containers, wrappings etc.

Petroleum cokes - Carbonaceous material derived from hydrocarbon oils, uses for which include metallurgical electrode manufacture. Quantities of imports of this product are used as a fuel, primarily in the manufacture of cement (see paragraphs 3.57 to 3.63).

Miscellaneous products - Includes aromatic extracts, defoament solvents and other minor miscellaneous products.

Main classes of consumer

3.91 The following are definitions of the main groupings of users of petroleum products used in the text and tables of this chapter.

Electricity generators - Petroleum products delivered for use by major power producers and other companies for electricity generation including those deliveries to the other industries listed below which are used for autogeneration of electricity (Tables 3.4 to 3.6). This includes petroleum products used to generate electricity at oil refineries and is recorded in the Transformation sector, as opposed to other uses of refinery fuels which are recorded in the Energy Industry Use sector. Because delivered fuel may be put to stock and not used immediately and because generators may consume stocks rather than order new deliveries of petroleum products, these numbers may not necessarily be the same as those reported in the **Electricity** chapter (Chapter 5) which gives **consumption** of petroleum products by electricity generators.

Agriculture - Deliveries of fuel oil and gas oil/diesel for use in agricultural power units, dryers and heaters. Burning oil for farm use.

Iron and steel - Deliveries of petroleum products to steel works and iron foundries. This is now based on information from the Iron and Steel Statistics Bureau.

Other industries - The industries covered correspond to the industrial groups shown in Table 1E excluding Iron and Steel of Chapter 1.

National navigation - Fuel oil and gas oil/diesel delivered, other than under international bunker contracts, for fishing vessels, UK oil and gas exploration and production, coastal and inland shipping and for use in ports and harbours.

Railways - Deliveries of fuel oil, gas oil/diesel and burning oil to railways.

Air transport - Total inland deliveries of aviation turbine fuel and aviation spirit. The figures cover deliveries of aviation fuels in the United Kingdom to international and other airlines, British and foreign governments (including armed services) and for private flying. In order to compile the UK Greenhouse Gas Inventory, the National Environmental Technology Centre (NETCEN) need to estimate how aviation fuel usage splits between domestic and international consumption. Information from NETCEN suggests that virtually all aviation spirit is used domestically while just 6 per cent of civilian aviation turbine fuel use is for domestic consumption.

Road transport - Deliveries of motor spirit and DERV fuel for use in road vehicles of all kinds. Again as part of their work to compile the UK emissions inventory, NETCEN has constructed estimates for the consumption of road transport fuels by different vehicle classes, and these are shown in Table 3F. The table shows the increasing share of DERV used by cars and light goods vehicles (vans).

Table 3F: Estimated consumption of road transport fuels by vehicle class

	1990	1995	2000	2003
Motor spirit:				
Cars and taxis	90%	92%	95%	96%
Light goods vehicles	9%	7%	5%	3%
Motor cycles etc	1%	1%	1%	1%
DERV:				
Cars and taxis	6%	14%	19%	21%
Light goods vehicles	15%	20%	23%	25%
Heavy goods vehicles	64%	55%	51%	47%
Buses and coaches	14%	10%	7%	6%

Source: NETCEN

As part of the Energy White remit to provide more regional data, DTI commissioned NETCEN in early 2005 to provide estimates for regional and local use of road transport fuels for 2003. This work was published in the June 2005 edition of Energy Trends: www.dti.gov.uk/energy/inform/energy_stats/.

Domestic - Fuel oil and gas oil delivered for central heating of private houses and other dwellings and deliveries of kerosene (burning oil) and liquefied petroleum gases for domestic purposes (see Tables 3.4 to 3.6).

Public services - Deliveries to national and local government premises (including educational, medical and welfare establishments and British and foreign armed forces) of fuel oil and gas oil for central heating and of kerosene (burning oil).

Miscellaneous - Deliveries of fuel oil and gas oil for central heating in premises other than those classified as domestic or public.

Monthly and quarterly data

3.92 Monthly or quarterly aggregate data for certain series presented in this chapter are available. This information can be obtained free of charge by following the links given at the Energy Statistics section of the DTI web site, at: www.dti.gov.uk/energy/inform/energy_stats/.

Contact: *Martin Young*
martin.young@dti.gsi.gov.uk
020-7215 5184

Clive Evans
clive.evans@dti.gsi.gov.uk
020-7215 5189

Gregory Haigh
greg.haigh@dti.gsi.gov.uk
020-7215 2712

3.1 Commodity balances 2004[(1)]

Primary oil

Thousand tonnes

	Crude oil	Ethane	Propane	Butane	Condensate	Total NGL	Feedstock	Total primary oil
Supply								
Production	87,516	1,473	2,441	1,863	2,081	7,858	-	95,374
Other sources	-	-	-	-	-	-	-	-
Imports	55,858	-	-	-	-	-	6,659	62,516
Exports	-60,724	-10	-1,265	-639	-774	-2,688	-1,091	-64,504
Marine bunkers	-	-	-	-	-	-	-	-
Stock change (2)	-136	..	..	..	..	-53	+55	-133
Transfers	-	-1,417	-828	-645	-835	-3,724	+181	-3,543
Total supply	**82,513**	..	..	..	..	**1,392**	**5,804**	**89,710**
Statistical difference (3)(4)	+341	..	..	..	..	+35	-487	-111
Total demand (4)	**82,173**	..	..	..	..	**1,357**	**6,291**	**89,821**
Transformation (4)	**82,173**	..	..	..	..	**1,357**	**6,291**	**89,821**
Electricity generation	-	-	-	-	-	-	-	-
Major power producers	-	-	-	-	-	-	-	-
Autogenerators	-	-	-	-	-	-	-	-
Heat generation	-	-	-	-	-	-	-	-
Petroleum refineries	82,173	..	..	..	..	1,357	6,291	89,821
Coke manufacture	-	-	-	-	-	-	-	-
Blast furnaces	-	-	-	-	-	-	-	-
Patent fuel manufacture	-	-	-	-	-	-	-	-
Other	-	-	-	-	-	-	-	-
Energy industry use	**-**	**-**	**-**	**-**	**-**	**-**	**-**	**-**
Electricity generation	-	-	-	-	-	-	-	-
Oil & gas extraction	-	-	-	-	-	-	-	-
Petroleum refineries	-	-	-	-	-	-	-	-
Coal extraction	-	-	-	-	-	-	-	-
Coke manufacture	-	-	-	-	-	-	-	-
Blast furnaces	-	-	-	-	-	-	-	-
Patent fuel manufacture	-	-	-	-	-	-	-	-
Pumped storage	-	-	-	-	-	-	-	-
Other	-	-	-	-	-	-	-	-
Losses	**-**	**-**	**-**	**-**	**-**	**-**	**-**	**-**

(1) As there is no use made of primary oils and feedstocks by industries other than the oil and gas extraction and petroleum refining industries, other industry headings have not been included in this table. As such, this table is a summary of the activity of what is known as the Upstream oil industry.

(2) Stock fall (+), stock rise (-).

(3) Total supply minus total demand.

(4) Figures for total demand for the individual NGLs (and thus for the statistical differences as well) are not available.

3.2 Commodity balances 2003[(1)]

Primary oil

Thousand tonnes

	Crude oil	Ethane	Propane	Butane	Condensate	Total NGL	Feedstock	Total primary oil
Supply								
Production	97,835	1,531	2,578	1,999	2,130	8,238	-	106,073
Other sources	-	-	-	-	-	-	-	-
Imports	48,589	-	-	-	-	-	5,588	54,177
Exports	-68,823	-24	-1,785	-917	-978	-3,703	-2,372	-74,898
Marine bunkers	-	-	-	-	-	-	-	-
Stock change (2)	+486	..	..	..	..	-5	-11	+469
Transfers	-	-1,509	-628	-524	-	-2,661	+1,653	-1,008
Total supply	**78,086**	..	..	..	..	**1,869**	**4,859**	**84,814**
Statistical difference (3)(4)	**+778**	..	..	..	..	**+596**	**-1,145**	**+229**
Total demand (4)	**77,309**	..	..	..	..	**1,273**	**6,004**	**84,585**
Transformation (4)	**77,309**	..	..	..	..	**1,273**	**6,004**	**84,585**
Electricity generation	-	-	-	-	-	-	-	-
Major power producers	-	-	-	-	-	-	-	-
Autogenerators	-	-	-	-	-	-	-	-
Heat generation	-	-	-	-	-	-	-	-
Petroleum refineries	77,309	..	..	..	..	1,273	6,004	84,585
Coke manufacture	-	-	-	-	-	-	-	-
Blast furnaces	-	-	-	-	-	-	-	-
Patent fuel manufacture	-	-	-	-	-	-	-	-
Other	-	-	-	-	-	-	-	-
Energy industry use	**-**	**-**	**-**	**-**	**-**	**-**	**-**	**-**
Electricity generation	-	-	-	-	-	-	-	-
Oil & gas extraction	-	-	-	-	-	-	-	-
Petroleum refineries	-	-	-	-	-	-	-	-
Coal extraction	-	-	-	-	-	-	-	-
Coke manufacture	-	-	-	-	-	-	-	-
Blast furnaces	-	-	-	-	-	-	-	-
Patent fuel manufacture	-	-	-	-	-	-	-	-
Pumped storage	-	-	-	-	-	-	-	-
Other	-	-	-	-	-	-	-	-
Losses	**-**	**-**	**-**	**-**	**-**	**-**	**-**	**-**

(1) As there is no use made of primary oils and feedstocks by industries other than the oil and gas extraction and petroleum refining industries, other industry headings have not been included in this table. As such, this table is a summary of the activity of what is known as the Upstream oil industry.

(2) Stock fall (+), stock rise (-).

(3) Total supply minus total demand.

(4) Figures for total demand for the individual NGLs (and thus for the statistical differences as well) are not available.

3.3 Commodity balances 2002[(1)]

Primary oil

Thousand tonnes

	Crude oil	Ethane	Propane	Butane	Condensate	Total NGL	Feedstock	Total primary oil
Supply								
Production	107,430	1,596	2,728	2,071	2,118	8,514	-	115,944
Other sources	-	-	-	-	-	-	-	-
Imports	52,042	-	-	-	-	-	4,926	56,968
Exports	-81,198	-10	-1,909	-888r	-1,022	-3,830	-2,116	-87,144
Marine bunkers	-	-	-	-	-	-	-	-
Stock change (2)	+33	..	..	..	..	+34	+75	+143
Transfers	-	-1,578	-670	-1,046	-	-3,294	+1,739	-1,555
Total supply	**78,306**	..	..	..	..	**1,424**	**4,625**	**84,356**
Statistical difference (3)(4)	+506	..	..	..	..	-143	-791	-428
Total demand (4)	**77,801**	..	..	..	..	**1,567**	**5,416**	**84,784**
Transformation (4)	**77,801**	..	..	..	..	**1,567**	**5,416**	**84,784**
Electricity generation	-	-	-	-	-	-	-	-
Major power producers	-	-	-	-	-	-	-	-
Autogenerators	-	-	-	-	-	-	-	-
Heat generation	-	-	-	-	-	-	-	-
Petroleum refineries	77,801	..	..	..	..	1,567	5,416	84,784
Coke manufacture	-	-	-	-	-	-	-	-
Blast furnaces	-	-	-	-	-	-	-	-
Patent fuel manufacture	-	-	-	-	-	-	-	-
Other	-	-	-	-	-	-	-	-
Energy industry use	-	-	-	-	-	-	-	-
Electricity generation	-	-	-	-	-	-	-	-
Oil & gas extraction	-	-	-	-	-	-	-	-
Petroleum refineries	-	-	-	-	-	-	-	-
Coal extraction	-	-	-	-	-	-	-	-
Coke manufacture	-	-	-	-	-	-	-	-
Blast furnaces	-	-	-	-	-	-	-	-
Patent fuel manufacture	-	-	-	-	-	-	-	-
Pumped storage	-	-	-	-	-	-	-	-
Other	-	-	-	-	-	-	-	-
Losses	-	-	-	-	-	-	-	-

(1) As there is no use made of primary oils and feedstocks by industries other than the oil and gas extraction and petroleum refining industries, other industry headings have not been included in this table. As such, this table is a summary of the activity of what is known as the Upstream oil industry.

(2) Stock fall (+), stock rise (-).

(3) Total supply minus total demand.

(4) Figures for total demand for the individual NGLs (and thus for the statistical differences as well) are not available.

3.4 Commodity balances 2004

Petroleum products

Thousand tonnes

	Ethane	Propane	Butane	Other gases	Naphtha	Aviation spirit	Motor spirit	Industrial spirit	White spirit	Aviation turbine fuel	Burning oil
Supply											
Production	15	1,794	376	3,012	3,176	31	24,589	20	80	5,615	3,613
Other sources	1,417	828	645	-	835	-	-	-	-	-	-
Imports	-	245	245	34	871	19	2,175	132	77	7,658	360
Exports	-	-621	-411	-	-2,940	-8	-7,334	-22	-40	-758	-413
Marine bunkers	-	-	-	-	-	-	-	-	-	-	-
Stock change (1)	-	-15	-19	-	-109	+1	-40	+1	+1	-112	-58
Transfers	-	-37	42	-1	+79	-	-11	-	+23	-345	+413
Total supply (2)	1,432	2,193	879	3,045	1,911	44	19,380	131	142	12,059	3,915
Statistical difference (3)	-7	-26	-36	+59	-125	-6	-105	-	-8	+197	-35
Total demand	1,439	2,219	914	2,987	2,036	49	19,484	131	150	11,862	3,950
Transformation	-	-	-	145	-	-	-	-	-	-	-
Electricity generation	-	-	-	145	-	-	-	-	-	-	-
Major power producers	-	-	-	-	-	-	-	-	-	-	-
Autogenerators	-	-	-	145	-	-	-	-	-	-	-
Heat generation	-	-	-	-	-	-	-	-	-	-	-
Petroleum refineries	-	-	-	-	-	-	-	-	-	-	-
Coke manufacture	-	-	-	-	-	-	-	-	-	-	-
Blast furnaces	-	-	-	-	-	-	-	-	-	-	-
Patent fuel manufacture	-	-	-	-	-	-	-	-	-	-	-
Other	-	-	-	-	-	-	-	-	-	-	-
Energy industry use	15	19	-	2,528	7	-	-	-	-	-	-
Electricity generation	-	-	-	-	-	-	-	-	-	-	-
Oil & gas extraction	-	-	-	-	-	-	-	-	-	-	-
Petroleum refineries	15	19	-	2,528	7	-	-	-	-	-	-
Coal extraction	-	-	-	-	-	-	-	-	-	-	-
Coke manufacture	-	-	-	-	-	-	-	-	-	-	-
Blast furnaces	-	-	-	-	-	-	-	-	-	-	-
Patent fuel manufacture	-	-	-	-	-	-	-	-	-	-	-
Pumped storage	-	-	-	-	-	-	-	-	-	-	-
Other	-	-	-	-	-	-	-	-	-	-	-
Losses	-	-	-	-	-	-	-	-	-	-	-
Final consumption	1,424	2,200	914	313	2,029	49	19,484	131	150	11,862	3,950
Industry	76	592	190	-	-	-	-	-	-	-	1,465
Unclassified	76	592	190	-	-	-	-	-	-	-	1,465
Iron & steel	-	-	-	-	-	-	-	-	-	-	-
Non-ferrous metals	-	-	-	-	-	-	-	-	-	-	-
Mineral products	-	-	-	-	-	-	-	-	-	-	-
Chemicals	-	-	-	-	-	-	-	-	-	-	-
Mechanical engineering, etc	-	-	-	-	-	-	-	-	-	-	-
Electrical engineering, etc	-	-	-	-	-	-	-	-	-	-	-
Vehicles	-	-	-	-	-	-	-	-	-	-	-
Food, beverages, etc	-	-	-	-	-	-	-	-	-	-	-
Textiles, leather, etc	-	-	-	-	-	-	-	-	-	-	-
Paper, printing etc	-	-	-	-	-	-	-	-	-	-	-
Other industries	-	-	-	-	-	-	-	-	-	-	-
Construction	-	-	-	-	-	-	-	-	-	-	-
Transport	-	112	-	-	-	49	19,484	-	-	11,862	12
Air	-	-	-	-	-	49	-	-	-	11,862	-
Rail	-	-	-	-	-	-	-	-	-	-	12
Road	-	112	-	-	-	-	19,484	-	-	-	-
National navigation	-	-	-	-	-	-	-	-	-	-	-
Pipelines	-	-	-	-	-	-	-	-	-	-	-
Other	-	391	45	-	-	-	-	-	-	-	2,472
Domestic	-	285	45	-	-	-	-	-	-	-	2,448
Public administration	-	-	-	-	-	-	-	-	-	-	12
Commercial	-	-	-	-	-	-	-	-	-	-	-
Agriculture	-	106	-	-	-	-	-	-	-	-	12
Miscellaneous	-	-	-	-	-	-	-	-	-	-	-
Non energy use	1,348	1,106	680	313	2,029	-	-	131	150	-	-

(1) Stock fall (+), stock rise (-).
(2) Incorporates an extra adjustment for what are thought to be refinery losses. These data are the subject of ongoing investigations.
(3) Total supply minus total demand.

86

3.4 Commodity balances 2004 (continued)
Petroleum products

Thousand tonnes

Gas oil	Marine diesel oil	Fuel oils	Lubri-cants	Bitu-men	Petroleum wax	Petroleum coke	Misc. products	Total Products	
									Supply
28,773	66	12,988	1,136	2,196	94	1,645	607	89,828	Production
-	-	-	-	-	-	-	-	3,724	Other sources
4,216	-	1,552	530	227	29	1,081	32	19,485	Imports
-6,623	-	-8,936	-750	-336	-41	-598	-438	-30,270	Exports
942	131	1,012	-	-	-	-	-	2,085	Marine bunkers
-268	-	-46	-14	-11	-2	+31	+370	-289	Stock change (1)
-576	+183	-19	-3	+22	-36		+63	-203	Transfers (2)
24,581	**117**	**4,527**	**900**	**2,098**	**44**	**2,160**	**634**	**80,191**	**Total supply (2)**
-30	-	-159	-15	+108	-7	+2	+158	-35	**Statistical difference (3)**
24,611	**118**	**4,685**	**914**	**1,991**	**50**	**2,157**	**476**	**80,226**	**Total demand**
67	-	**793**	-	-	-	-	-	**1,006**	**Transformation**
59	-	427	-	-	-	-	-	631	Electricity generation
11	-	136	-	-	-	-	-	147	Major power producers
48	-	291	-	-	-	-	-	484	Autogenerators
9	-	69	-	-	-	-	-	78	Heat generation
-	-	-	-	-	-	-	-	-	Petroleum refineries
-	-	-	-	-	-	-	-	-	Coke manufacture
-	-	297	-	-	-	-	-	297	Blast furnaces
-	-	-	-	-	-	-	-	-	Patent fuel manufacture
-	-	-	-	-	-	-	-	-	Other
192	-	**1,681**	-	-	-	**1,012**	-	**5,455**	**Energy industry use**
-	-	-	-	-	-	-	-	-	Electricity generation
-	-	-	-	-	-	-	-	-	Oil & gas extraction
192	-	1,680	-	-	-	1,012	-	5,453	Petroleum refineries
-	-	-	-	-	-	-	-	-	Coal extraction
-	-	1	-	-	-	-	-	1	Coke manufacture
-	-	-	-	-	-	-	-	-	Blast furnaces
-	-	-	-	-	-	-	-	-	Patent fuel manufacture
-	-	-	-	-	-	-	-	-	Pumped storage
-	-	-	-	-	-	-	-	-	Other
-	-	-	-	-	-	-	-	-	Losses
24,352	**117**	**2,211**	**914**	**1,991**	**50**	**1,146**	**476**	**73,765**	**Final Consumption**
3,488	-	**1,814**	-	-	-	-	-	**7,626**	**Industry**
-	-	-	-	-	-	-	-	2,324	Unclassified
2	-	31	-	-	-	-	-	33	Iron & steel
27	-	13	-	-	-	-	-	39	Non-ferrous metals
171	-	15	-	-	-	-	-	186	Mineral products
116	-	3	-	-	-	-	-	120	Chemicals
90	-	18	-	-	-	-	-	108	Mechanical engineering etc
22	-	3	-	-	-	-	-	26	Electrical engineering etc
79	-	12	-	-	-	-	-	91	Vehicles
261	-	58	-	-	-	-	-	319	Food, beverages etc
58	-	10	-	-	-	-	-	68	Textiles, leather, etc
27	-	28	-	-	-	-	-	55	Paper, printing etc
2,492	-	1,622	-	-	-	-	-	4,113	Other industries
143	-	-	-	-	-	-	-	143	Construction
19,399	**117**	**266**	-	-	-	-	-	**51,301**	**Transport**
-	-	-	-	-	-	-	-	11,911	Air
158	-	-	-	-	-	-	-	170	Rail
18,514	-	-	-	-	-	-	-	38,110	Road
727	117	266	-	-	-	-	-	1,110	National navigation
-	-	-	-	-	-	-	-	-	Pipelines
1,216	-	**130**	-	-	-	-	-	**4,254**	**Other**
10	-	-	-	-	-	-	-	2,788	Domestic
394	-	30	-	-	-	-	-	435	Public administration
341	-	44	-	-	-	-	-	385	Commercial
122	-	5	-	-	-	-	-	245	Agriculture
350	-	51	-	-	-	-	-	401	Miscellaneous
249	-	-	**914**	**1,991**	**50**	**1,146**	**476**	**10,584**	**Non energy use**

3.5 Commodity balances 2003
Petroleum products

	Ethane	Propane	Butane	Other gases	Naphtha	Aviation spirit	Motor spirit	Industrial spirit	White spirit	Aviation turbine fuel	Burning oil
Supply											
Production	11	1,620	679	2,891	3,516	26	22,627	6	98	5,277	3,521
Other sources	1,509	628	524	-	-	-	-	-	-	-	-
Imports	-	194	172	-	782	12	2,022	27	7	7,346	327
Exports	-	-328	-16	-7	-2,461	-5	-5,603	-	-	-587	-556
Marine bunkers	-	-	-	-	-	-	-	-	-	-	-
Stock change (1)	-	+5	+22	+1	-74	-1	-88	-	+4	-100	+36
Transfers	-9	-254	-703	-196	+742	-1	+454	-	-	-1,347	+151
Total supply (2)	**1,510**	**1,865**	**679**	**2,688**	**2,506**	**31**	**19,412**	**33**	**108**	**10,588**	**3,479**
Statistical difference (3)	-60r	-180r	-311r	-40	+161r	-15	-506	-	-6	-176	-90r
Total demand	**1,571r**	**2,046r**	**990r**	**2,729**	**2,345r**	**46**	**19,918**	**33**	**114**	**10,765**	**3,569r**
Transformation	-	**1r**	-	**158r**	-	-	-	-	-	-	-
Electricity generation	-	-	-	158r	-	-	-	-	-	-	-
Major power producers	-	-	-	-	-	-	-	-	-	-	-
Autogenerators	-	-	-	158r	-	-	-	-	-	-	-
Heat generation	-	1r	-	-	-	-	-	-	-	-	-
Petroleum refineries	-	-	-	-	-	-	-	-	-	-	-
Coke manufacture	-	-	-	-	-	-	-	-	-	-	-
Blast furnaces	-	-	-	-	-	-	-	-	-	-	-
Patent fuel manufacture	-	-	-	-	-	-	-	-	-	-	-
Other	-	-	-	-	-	-	-	-	-	-	-
Energy industry use	**9**	**19r**	-	**2,248r**	**13r**	-	-	-	-	-	-
Electricity generation	-	-	-	-	-	-	-	-	-	-	-
Oil & gas extraction	-	-	-	-	-	-	-	-	-	-	-
Petroleum refineries	9	19r	-	2,248r	13r	-	-	-	-	-	-
Coal extraction	-	-	-	-	-	-	-	-	-	-	-
Coke manufacture	-	-	-	-	-	-	-	-	-	-	-
Blast furnaces	-	-	-	-	-	-	-	-	-	-	-
Patent fuel manufacture	-	-	-	-	-	-	-	-	-	-	-
Pumped storage	-	-	-	-	-	-	-	-	-	-	-
Other	-	-	-	-	-	-	-	-	-	-	-
Losses	-	-	-	-	-	-	-	-	-	-	-
Final consumption	**1,562r**	**2,027r**	**990r**	**323**	**2,332r**	**46**	**19,918**	**33**	**114**	**10,765**	**3,569r**
Industry	**75r**	**690**	**154**	-	-	-	-	-	-	-	**839**
Unclassified	75r	690	154	-	-	-	-	-	-	-	839
Iron & steel	-	-	-	-	-	-	-	-	-	-	-
Non-ferrous metals	-	-	-	-	-	-	-	-	-	-	-
Mineral products	-	-	-	-	-	-	-	-	-	-	-
Chemicals	-	-	-	-	-	-	-	-	-	-	-
Mechanical engineering, etc	-	-	-	-	-	-	-	-	-	-	-
Electrical engineering, etc	-	-	-	-	-	-	-	-	-	-	-
Vehicles	-	-	-	-	-	-	-	-	-	-	-
Food, beverages, etc	-	-	-	-	-	-	-	-	-	-	-
Textiles, leather, etc	-	-	-	-	-	-	-	-	-	-	-
Paper, printing etc	-	-	-	-	-	-	-	-	-	-	-
Other industries	-	-	-	-	-	-	-	-	-	-	-
Construction	-	-	-	-	-	-	-	-	-	-	-
Transport	-	**104**	-	-	-	**46**	**19,918**	-	-	**10,765**	**12**
Air	-	-	-	-	-	46	-	-	-	10,765	-
Rail	-	-	-	-	-	-	-	-	-	-	12
Road	-	104	-	-	-	-	19,918	-	-	-	-
National navigation	-	-	-	-	-	-	-	-	-	-	-
Pipelines	-	-	-	-	-	-	-	-	-	-	-
Other	-	**397**	**48**	-	-	-	-	-	-	-	**2,717r**
Domestic	-	294	47	-	-	-	-	-	-	-	2,693r
Public administration	-	-	-	-	-	-	-	-	-	-	12
Commercial	-	-	-	-	-	-	-	-	-	-	-
Agriculture	-	103	-	-	-	-	-	-	-	-	12
Miscellaneous	-	-	-	-	-	-	-	-	-	-	-
Non energy use	**1,487r**	**835r**	**789r**	**323**	**2,332r**	-	-	**33**	**114**	-	-

(1) Stock fall (+), stock rise (-).
(2) Incorporates an extra adjustment for what are thought to be refinery losses. These data are the subject of ongoing investigations.
(3) Total supply minus total demand.

3.5 Commodity balances 2003 (continued)
Petroleum products

Thousand tonnes

Gas oil	Marine diesel oil	Fuel oils	Lubri -cants	Bitu -men	Petroleum wax	Petroleum coke	Misc. products	Total Products	
									Supply
27,579	-	11,517	576	1,925	460	1,630	569	84,529	Production
-	-	-	-	-	-	-	-	2,661	Other sources
3,503	-	1,208	570	249	21	834	13	17,286	Imports
-5,528	-	-6,385	-678	-329	-46	-566	-228	-23,323	Exports
861	36	867	-	-	-	-	-	1,764	Marine bunkers
-27	-	-3	+46	-9	+3	17	-94	-262	Stock change (1)
-779	+155	+136	+454	+43	-375	-22	-100	-1,652	Transfers (2)
23,887	119	5,606	968	1,879	64	1,893	160	77,475	**Total supply (2)**
-195	-36	+1,231	+101	-80r	+7	-5r	-289	-491r	**Statistical difference (3)**
24,082	155	4,374r	868	1,959r	57	1,898r	449	77,966r	**Total demand**
47	-	714r	-	-	-	-	-	920r	**Transformation**
29	-	350r	-	-	-	-	-	538r	Electricity generation
17	-	83	-	-	-	-	-	100	Major power producers
12	-	267r	-	-	-	-	-	438r	Autogenerators
18	-	133r	-	-	-	-	-	152r	Heat generation
-	-	-	-	-	-	-	-	-	Petroleum refineries
-	-	1	-	-	-	-	-	1	Coke manufacture
-	-	229	-	-	-	-	-	229	Blast furnaces
-	-	-	-	-	-	-	-	-	Patent fuel manufacture
-	-	-	-	-	-	-	-	-	Other
200	-	2,022r	-	-	-	1,018r	-	5,528r	**Energy industry use**
-	-	-	-	-	-	-	-	-	Electricity generation
-	-	-	-	-	-	-	-	-	Oil & gas extraction
199	-	2,022r	-	-	-	1,018r	-	5,528r	Petroleum refineries
-	-	-	-	-	-	-	-	-	Coal extraction
-	-	-	-	-	-	-	-	-	Coke manufacture
-	-	-	-	-	-	-	-	-	Blast furnaces
-	-	-	-	-	-	-	-	-	Patent fuel manufacture
-	-	-	-	-	-	-	-	-	Pumped storage
-	-	-	-	-	-	-	-	-	Other
-	-	-	-	-	-	-	-	-	**Losses**
23,835	155	1,638r	868	1,959r	57	880r	449	71,518r	**Final Consumption**
3,657	-	1,296r	-	-	-	-	-	6,711r	**Industry**
-	-	-	-	-	-	-	-	1,758r	Unclassified
1	-	17	-	-	-	-	-	19	Iron & steel
21	-	38	-	-	-	-	-	59	Non-ferrous metals
206	-	37	-	-	-	-	-	243	Mineral products
111	-	263r	-	-	-	-	-	374r	Chemicals
113	-	142	-	-	-	-	-	255	Mechanical engineering etc
13	-	39	-	-	-	-	-	52	Electrical engineering etc
69	-	45	-	-	-	-	-	114	Vehicles
154	-	153	-	-	-	-	-	306	Food, beverages etc
78	-	135	-	-	-	-	-	212	Textiles, leather, etc
21	-	97	-	-	-	-	-	118	Paper, printing etc
2,576	-	328	-	-	-	-	-	2,904	Other industries
293	-	3	-	-	-	-	-	295	Construction
18,945	155	50	-	-	-	-	-	49,995	**Transport**
-	-	-	-	-	-	-	-	10,810	Air
302	-	-	-	-	-	-	-	314	Rail
17,712	-	-	-	-	-	-	-	37,735	Road
930	155	50	-	-	-	-	-	1,135	National navigation
-	-	-	-	-	-	-	-	-	Pipelines
947	-	292	-	-	-	-	-	4,401r	**Other**
163	-	6	-	-	-	-	-	3,204r	Domestic
283	-	185	-	-	-	-	-	479	Public administration
258	-	83	-	-	-	-	-	341	Commercial
173	-	4	-	-	-	-	-	292	Agriculture
70	-	14	-	-	-	-	-	84	Miscellaneous
287	-	-	868	1,959r	57	880r	449	10,411r	**Non energy use**

3.6 Commodity balances 2002
Petroleum products

	Ethane	Propane	Butane	Other gases	Naphtha	Aviation spirit	Motor spirit	Industrial spirit	White spirit	Aviation turbine fuel	Burning oil
Supply											
Production	50	1,620	529	2,928	3,174	28	22,944	6	115	5,365	3,506
Other sources	1,578	670	1,047	-	-	-	-	-	-	-	-
Imports	-	82	110	-	96	9	2,307	38	7	6,700	299
Exports	-	-448	-377	-	-2,077	-6	-5,532	-2	-	-588	-402
Marine bunkers	-	-	-	-	-	-	-	-	-	-	-
Stock change (1)	-	+80	-11	-3	+20	-4	+273	-	+2	+269	-8
Transfers	-83	-259	-483	+42	+743	+3	+499	-	-	-1,972	+150
Total supply (2)	1,546	1,744	815	2,966	1,956	30	20,490	42	124	9,773	3,545
Statistical difference (3)	-173r	-87r	+84r	+63	+344r	-19	-319	+10	-2	-746	-33r
Total demand	1,718r	1,832r	731r	2,903	1,612r	50	20,808	32	125	10,519	3,578r
Transformation	-	-	-	228	-	-	-	-	-	-	-
Electricity generation	-	-	-	228	-	-	-	-	-	-	-
Major power producers	-	-	-	-	-	-	-	-	-	-	-
Autogenerators	-	-	-	228	-	-	-	-	-	-	-
Heat generation	-	-	-	-	-	-	-	-	-	-	-
Petroleum refineries	-	-	-	-	-	-	-	-	-	-	-
Coke manufacture	-	-	-	-	-	-	-	-	-	-	-
Blast furnaces	-	-	-	-	-	-	-	-	-	-	-
Patent fuel manufacture	-	-	-	-	-	-	-	-	-	-	-
Other	-	-	-	-	-	-	-	-	-	-	-
Energy industry use	50r	10r	-	2,390	20r	-	-	-	-	-	-
Electricity generation	-	-	-	-	-	-	-	-	-	-	-
Oil & gas extraction	-	-	-	-	-	-	-	-	-	-	-
Petroleum refineries	50r	10r	-	2,390	20r	-	-	-	-	-	-
Coal extraction	-	-	-	-	-	-	-	-	-	-	-
Coke manufacture	-	-	-	-	-	-	-	-	-	-	-
Blast furnaces	-	-	-	-	-	-	-	-	-	-	-
Patent fuel manufacture	-	-	-	-	-	-	-	-	-	-	-
Pumped storage	-	-	-	-	-	-	-	-	-	-	-
Other	-	-	-	-	-	-	-	-	-	-	-
Losses	-	-	-	-	-	-	-	-	-	-	-
Final consumption	1,668r	1,822r	731r	284	1,592r	50	20,808	32	125	10,519	3,578r
Industry	72r	484	99	-	-	-	-	-	-	-	807
Unclassified	72r	474	99	-	-	-	-	-	-	-	807
Iron & steel	-	10	-	-	-	-	-	-	-	-	-
Non-ferrous metals	-	-	-	-	-	-	-	-	-	-	-
Mineral products	-	-	-	-	-	-	-	-	-	-	-
Chemicals	-	-	-	-	-	-	-	-	-	-	-
Mechanical engineering, etc	-	-	-	-	-	-	-	-	-	-	-
Electrical engineering, etc	-	-	-	-	-	-	-	-	-	-	-
Vehicles	-	-	-	-	-	-	-	-	-	-	-
Food, beverages, etc	-	-	-	-	-	-	-	-	-	-	-
Textiles, leather, etc	-	-	-	-	-	-	-	-	-	-	-
Paper, printing etc	-	-	-	-	-	-	-	-	-	-	-
Other industries	-	-	-	-	-	-	-	-	-	-	-
Construction	-	-	-	-	-	-	-	-	-	-	-
Transport	-	86	-	-	-	50	20,808	-	-	10,519	12
Air	-	-	-	-	-	50	-	-	-	10,519	-
Rail	-	-	-	-	-	-	-	-	-	-	12
Road	-	86	-	-	-	-	20,808	-	-	-	-
National navigation	-	-	-	-	-	-	-	-	-	-	-
Pipelines	-	-	-	-	-	-	-	-	-	-	-
Other	-	369	48	-	-	-	-	-	-	-	2,759r
Domestic	-	271	48	-	-	-	-	-	-	-	2,735r
Public administration	-	-	-	-	-	-	-	-	-	-	12
Commercial	-	-	-	-	-	-	-	-	-	-	-
Agriculture	-	98	-	-	-	-	-	-	-	-	12
Miscellaneous	-	-	-	-	-	-	-	-	-	-	-
Non energy use	1,597r	883r	584r	284	1,592r	-	-	32	125	-	-

(1) Stock fall (+), stock rise (-).
(2) Incorporates an extra adjustment for what are thought to be refinery losses. These data are the subject of ongoing investigations.
(3) Total supply minus total demand.

3.6 Commodity balances 2002 (continued)
Petroleum products

Thousand tonnes

Gas oil	Marine diesel oil	Fuel oils	Lubri -cants	Bitu -men	Petroleum wax	Petroleum coke	Misc. products	Total Products	
									Supply
28,393	-	10,551	509	1,918	430	1,543	389	83,996	Production
-	-	-	-	-	-	-	-	3,295	Other sources
3,219	-	927	422	232	18	790	13	15,269	Imports
-6,352	-	-5,780	-521	-261	-59	-541	-497	-23,444	Exports
1,108	36	769	-	-	-	-	-	1,913	Marine bunkers
+194	-	-32	-16	+24	-4	16	427	1,226	Stock change (1)
-722	-	+235	+442	+50	-324	-1	-59	-1,740	Transfers (2)
23,624	**-36**	**5,132**	**836**	**1,963**	**61**	**1,806**	**273**	**76,689**	**Total supply (2)**
+588	-76	+996	+7	-39r	+10	-188r	-334	+86r	**Statistical difference (3)**
23,036	**39**	**4,136**	**829**	**2,002r**	**51**	**1,995r**	**607**	**76,603r**	**Total demand**
52	-	**828**	-	-	-	-	-	**1,108**	**Transformation**
29	-	414	-	-	-	-	-	671	Electricity generation
10	-	108	-	-	-	-	-	119	Major power producers
18	-	306	-	-	-	-	-	552	Autogenerators
23	-	227	-	-	-	-	-	250	Heat generation
-	-	-	-	-	-	-	-	-	Petroleum refineries
-	-	1	-	-	-	-	-	1	Coke manufacture
-	-	186	-	-	-	-	-	186	Blast furnaces
-	-	-	-	-	-	-	-	-	Patent fuel manufacture
-	-	-	-	-	-	-	-	-	Other
50	-	**2,045**	-	-	-	**1,102r**	**11**	**5,677r**	**Energy industry use**
-	-	-	-	-	-	-	-	-	Electricity generation
-	-	-	-	-	-	-	-	-	Oil & gas extraction
49	-	2,045	-	-	-	1,102r	11	5,677r	Petroleum refineries
-	-	-	-	-	-	-	-	-	Coal extraction
-	-	-	-	-	-	-	-	-	Coke manufacture
-	-	-	-	-	-	-	-	-	Blast furnaces
-	-	-	-	-	-	-	-	-	Patent fuel manufacture
-	-	-	-	-	-	-	-	-	Pumped storage
-	-	-	-	-	-	-	-	-	Other
									Losses
-	-	-	-	-	-	-	-	-	
22,935	**39**	**1,263**	**829r**	**2,002r**	**51**	**893r**	**596**	**69,818r**	**Final Consumption**
3,305	-	**1,051**	-	-	-	-	-	**5,818r**	**Industry**
-	-	-	-	-	-	-	-	1,452r	Unclassified
2	-	66	-	-	-	-	-	77	Iron & steel
41	-	39	-	-	-	-	-	80	Non-ferrous metals
213	-	31	-	-	-	-	-	244	Mineral products
129	-	185	-	-	-	-	-	314	Chemicals
155	-	108	-	-	-	-	-	263	Mechanical engineering etc
21	-	30	-	-	-	-	-	51	Electrical engineering etc
151	-	37	-	-	-	-	-	188	Vehicles
180	-	128	-	-	-	-	-	308	Food, beverages etc
79	-	102	-	-	-	-	-	181	Textiles, leather, etc
35	-	74	-	-	-	-	-	109	Paper, printing etc
1,864	-	248	-	-	-	-	-	2,112	Other industries
435	-	2	-	-	-	-	-	437	Construction
17,826	**39**	**42**	-	-	-	-	-	**49,382**	**Transport**
-	-	-	-	-	-	-	-	10,568	Air
334	-	-	-	-	-	-	-	346	Rail
16,926	-	-	-	-	-	-	-	37,821	Road
566	39	42	-	-	-	-	-	647	National navigation
-	-	-	-	-	-	-	-	-	Pipelines
1,599	-	**170**	-	-	-	-	-	**4,945r**	**Other**
202	-	4	-	-	-	-	-	3,260r	Domestic
602	-	96	-	-	-	-	-	710	Public administration
315	-	56	-	-	-	-	-	371	Commercial
395	-	3	-	-	-	-	-	509	Agriculture
85	-	11	-	-	-	-	-	96	Miscellaneous
205	-	-	**829**	**2,002r**	**51**	**893r**	**596**	**9,673r**	**Non energy use**

3.7 Supply and disposal of petroleum$^{(1)}$

Thousand tonnes

	2000	2001	2002	2003	2004
Primary oils (Crude oil, NGLs and feedstocks)					
Indigenous production *(2)*	126,245	116,678	115,944	106,073	95,374
Imports	54,387	53,551	56,968	54,177	62,516
Exports *(3)*	-92,918	-86,930	-87,144	-74,898	-64,504
Transfers - Transfers to products *(4)*	-3,383	-3,575	-3,294	-2,661	-3,724
Product rebrands *(5)*	+3,493	+4,328	+1,739	+1,653	+181
Stock change *(6)* - Offshore	+550	-378	+68	+12	-43
Oil terminals	+548	-236	+75	+457	-90
Use during production *(7)*	-295	-	-	-	-
Calculated refinery throughput *(8)*	88,627	83,438	84,356	84,814	89,710
Overall statistical difference *(9)*	+613	+96	-428	+229	-111
Actual refinery throughput	**88,014**	**83,343**	**84,784**	**84,585**	**89,821**
Petroleum products					
Losses in refining process	-168	+1,261	+788	+56r	+301
Refinery gross production *(10)*	86,341	82,109	83,996	84,529	89,828
Transfers - Transfers to products *(4)*	+3,383	+3,575	+3,295	+2,661	+3,724
Product rebrands *(5)*	-3,493	-4,328	-1,740	-1,652	-203
Imports	14,212	17,466	15,269	17,286	19,485
Exports *(11)*	-20,677	-19,088	-23,444	-23,323	-30,270
Marine bunkers	-2,079	-2,274	-1,913	-1,764	-2,085
Stock changes *(6)* - Refineries	-425	+613	-1,214	+291	-84
Power generators	+94	-15	-12	-29	-57
Calculated total supply	77,397	76,863	75,025r	78,055r	80,640
Statistical difference *(9)*	+201	+217	+86r	-491r	-35
Total demand *(4)*	**77,197**	**76,646**	**76,603r**	**77,966r**	**80,226**
Of which:					
Energy use	67,142	67,759	66,928r	67,555r	69,642
Of which, for electricity generation *(12)*	978	971	671	538r	631
total refinery fuels *(12)*	5,603	5,059	5,677r	5,528r	5,453
Non-energy use	10,055	8,887	9,673r	10,411r	10,584

(1) Aggregate monthly data on oil production, trade, refinery throughput and inland deliveries are available - see paragraph 3.92 and Annex C.

(2) Crude oil plus condensates and petroleum gases derived at onshore treatment plants.

(3) Includes NGLs, process oils and re-exports.

(4) Disposals of NGLs by direct sale (excluding exports) or for blending.

(5) Product rebrands (inter-product blends or transfers) represent petroleum products received at refineries/ plants as process for refinery or cracking unit operations.

(6) Impact of stock changes on supplies. A stock fall is shown as (+) as it increases supplies, and vice-versa for a stock rise (-).

(7) Own use in onshore terminals and gas separation plants. These figures ceased to be available from January 2001 with the advent of the new PPRS system.

(8) Equivalent to the total supplies reported against the upstream transformation sector in Tables 3.1 to 3.3.

(9) Supply greater than (+) or less than (-) recorded throughput or disposals.

(10) Includes refinery fuels.

(11) Excludes NGLs.

(12) Figures cover petroleum used to generate electricity by all major power producers and by all other generators, including petroleum used to generate electricity at refineries. These quantities are also included in the totals reported as used as refinery fuel, so there is thus some overlap in these figures.

3.8 Additional information on inland deliveries of selected products$^{(1)(2)(3)}$

Thousand tonnes

	2000	2001	2002	2003	2004
Motor spirit					
Retail deliveries *(4)*					
Super/hypermarkets *(5)*					
Leaded premium / Lead Replacement Petrol *(6)*	339	213	138	92	66
Super premium unleaded	9	24	33	39	53
Premium unleaded	5,260	5,498	5,764	5,803	6,019
Total super/hypermarkets	5,608	5,735	5,934	5,935	6,138
Refiners/other traders					
Leaded premium / Lead Replacement Petrol *(6)*	1,123	624	263	91	8
Super premium unleaded	395	396	673	822	757
Premium unleaded	13,748	13,602	13,404	12,488	11,776
Total Refiners/other traders	15,265	14,622	14,340	13,400	12,541
Total retail deliveries					
Leaded premium / Lead Replacement Petrol *(6)*	1,462	838	401	183	74
Super premium unleaded	403	420	706	861	810
Premium unleaded	19,008	19,100	19,167	18,291	17,795
Total retail deliveries	20,873	20,358	20,274	19,335	18,679
Commercial consumers *(7)*					
Leaded premium / Lead Replacement Petrol *(6)*	44	34	19	19	14
Super premium unleaded	6	9	17	22	26
Premium unleaded	480	538	499	542	765
Total commercial consumers	530	581	535	583	805
Total motor spirit	**21,403**	**20,939**	**20,809**	**19,918**	**19,484**
Unleaded as % of total motor spirit	93.0	95.8	98.0	99.0	99.5
Gas oil/diesel oil					
DERV fuel:					
Retail deliveries *(4)* :					
Super/hypermarkets *(5)*	1,411	1,633	1,854	2,135	2,474
Refiners/other traders	5,770	6,214	6,300	6,922	7,043
Total retail deliveries	7,181	7,846	8,153	9,057	9,517
Commercial consumers *(7)*	8,451	8,213	8,774	8,655	8,997
Total DERV fuel	15,632	16,059	16,927	17,712	18,514
Gas oil	7,487	6,834	6,060	6,172	5,905
Marine diesel oil	41	126	39	155	117
Total gas oil/diesel oil	**23,160**	**23,019**	**23,026**	**24,039**	**24,536**
Fuel oils *(8)*					
Light	45	55	84	169	214
Medium	390	663	779	927	1,450
Heavy	1,685r	2,087	1,226	1,256r	1,340
Total fuel oils	**2,119r**	**2,806**	**2,088**	**2,352r**	**3,004**

(1) Aggregate monthly data for inland deliveries of oil products are available - see paragraph 3.92 and Annex C.

(2) The end use section analyses are based partly on recorded figures and on estimates made by the Institute of. Petroleum and the Department of Trade and Industry and are intended to be for general guidance only. See also the notes in the main text of this chapter.

(3) For a full breakdown of the end-uses of all oil products, see Commodity Balances in Tables 3.4 to 3.6.

(4) Retail deliveries - deliveries to garages, etc. mainly for resale to final consumers.

(5) Data for sales by super and hypermarket companies are collected via a separate reporting system, but are consistent with the main data collected from UKPIA member companies - see paragraph 3.72.

(6) Sales of Leaded Petrol ceased on 31 December 1999 - see paragraphs 3.46 to 3.48.

(7) Commercial consumers - direct deliveries for use in consumer's business.

(8) Inland deliveries excluding that used as a fuel in refineries, but including that used for electricity generation by major electricity producers and other industries.

3.9 Inland deliveries by country[1]

	England and Wales (2)			Scotland			Northern Ireland		
	2002	2003	2004	2002	2003	2004	2002	2003	2004
Energy use									
Gases for gasworks and other uses									
Butane and propane	880	1,186	1,090	91	80	97	29	23	30
Other gases	132r	80r	64	168r	153r	157	-	-	-
Aviation spirit	48	41	35	2	3	12	-	1	2
Motor spirit:									
Dealers	18,854r	17,962r	17,352	1,059r	1,026r	980	361r	347r	348
Commercial consumers	473	518	738	38	40	42	23	25	25
Total motor spirit	19,327r	18,480r	18,090	1,097r	1,066r	1,022	384r	372r	373
Kerosenes									
Aviation turbine fuel	9,971	10,102	11,091	476	592	691	72	71	79
Burning oil	2,491r	2,352	2,698	309	298	247	778r	918r	1,004
Gas oil/diesel oil									
DERV fuel	15,607r	16,310r	17,064	1,062r	1,110r	1,094	257r	292r	356
Other (3)	4,707r	4,872r	4,727	719	693	620	468	474	427
Fuel oils	1,757	2,011	2,426	197	205	437	135	135	141
Total products used as energy (4)	**55,007r**	**55,539r**	**57,397**	**4,120r**	**4,200r**	**4,378**	**2,123r**	**2,287r**	**2,413**
Non-energy use									
Feedstock for petroleum chemical plants	3,992r	4,829r	4,402	2,640	2,552	2,945	2	-	-
Industrial spirit	32	33	131	-	-	-	-	-	-
White spirit	125	114	150	-	-	-	-	-	-
Lubricating oils	798	835	878	27	29	32	3	4	5
Bitumen	1,680r	1,634r	1,684	210	217	199	111	108	107
Petroleum wax	51	57	50	-	-	-	-	-	-
Total products used as non-energy (5)	**6,679r**	**7,501r**	**7,296**	**2,877r**	**2,798r**	**3,176**	**116**	**111**	**112**
Total all products	**60,577r**	**62,121r**	**63,687**	**6,998r**	**6,999r**	**7,554**	**2,239r**	**2,399r**	**2,524**

(1) Excludes products used as a fuel within refineries that are included in Tables 3.4 to 3.6.
(2) Includes the Channel Islands and the Isle of Man.
(3) Includes deliveries of marine diesel oil.
(4) Includes deliveries of LPG road transport fuel.
(5) Includes deliveries of miscellaneous products and petroleum coke.

3.10 Stocks of crude oil and petroleum products at end of year[1]

Thousand tonnes

	2000	2001	2002	2003	2004
Crude and process oils					
Refineries (2)	3,917	4,183	4,508	4,670	4,440
Terminals (3)	2,556	2,526	2,126	1,509	1,261
Offshore (4)	450	828	760	741	736
Total crude and process oils (5)	6,992	7,637	7,504	7,140	6,648
Petroleum products					
Ethane	6	6	6	6	6
Propane	162	188	108	103	119
Butane	88	105	117	95	113
Other petroleum gases	-	-	2	2	1
Naphtha	428	424	404	478	575
Aviation spirit	4	4	2	3	2
Motor spirit	1,078	1,375	1,280	1,487	1,503
Industrial spirit	14	12	11	11	11
White spirit	21	23	22	18	18
Aviation turbine fuel	487	779	510	610	759
Burning oil	414	292	300	265	310
Gas oil (6)	1,908	2,232	2,363	2,765	2,721
Marine diesel oil	-	-	-	-	-
Fuel oils	1,122	1,180	1,196	1,237	987
Lubricating oils	199	202	214	166	182
Bitumen	165	215	192	212	205
Petroleum wax	1	9	15	12	12
Petroleum coke	291	318	302	285	254
Miscellaneous products	1,031	1,097	670	778	197
Total all products	7,419	8,461	7,712	8,533	7,975
Of which : net bilateral stocks (7)	77	514	1,008	1,500	1,545

(1) Aggregate monthly data on the level of stocks of crude oil and oil products are available - see paragraph 3.92 and Annex C.

(2) Stocks of crude oil, NGLs and process oils at UK refineries.

(3) Stocks of crude oil and NGLs at UKCS pipeline terminals.

(4) Stocks of crude oil in tanks and partially loaded tankers at offshore fields.

(5) Includes process oils held abroad for UK use approved by bilateral agreements.

(6) Includes middle distillate feedstock.

(7) The difference between stocks held abroad for UK use under approved bilateral agreements and the equivalent stocks held in the UK for foreign use.

Chapter 4
Natural gas

Introduction

4.1   This chapter presents figures on the production, transmission and consumption of natural gas and colliery methane. Three tables are presented and a map showing the gas transmission system in Great Britain is included (page 107). The commodity balances for natural gas and colliery methane form the first table (Table 4.1). This is followed by a 5 year table showing the supply, transmission and consumption of these gases as a time series (Table 4.2). A more detailed examination of the various stages of natural gas from gross production through to consumption is given in Table 4.3. Long term trends commentary and table on production and consumption of gas back to 1970 is to be found on the DTI Energy Statistics web site at:
www.dti.gov.uk/energy/inform/dukes/dukes2005/04longterm.pdf.

4.2   Petroleum gases are covered in Chapter 3. Gases manufactured in the coke making and iron and steel making processes (coke oven gas and blast furnace gas) appear in Chapter 2. Biogases (landfill gas and sewage gas) are part of Chapter 7. Details of net selling values of gas for the domestic sector are to be found in Chapter 1.

The gas supply industry Great Britain

4.3   When British Gas was privatised in 1986, it was given a statutory monopoly over supplies of natural gas (methane) to premises taking less than 732,000 kWh (25,000 therms) a year. Under the Oil and Gas (Enterprise) Act 1982, contract customers taking more than this were able to buy their gas from other suppliers but no other suppliers entered the market until 1990.

4.4   In 1991, the Office of Fair Trading (OFT) followed up an examination of the contract market by the Monopolies and Mergers Commission (MMC) that had taken place in 1988. It reviewed progress towards a competitive market and found that the steps taken in 1988 had been ineffective in encouraging self-sustaining competition. British Gas undertook in March 1992 to allow competitors to take by 1995 at least 60 per cent of the contract market above 732,000 kWh (25,000 therms) a year (subsequently redefined as 45 per cent of the market above 73,200 kWh (2,500 therms)); to release to competitors the gas necessary to achieve this; and to establish a separate transport and storage unit with regulated charges. At the same time, the Government took powers in the 1992 Competition and Service (Utilities) Act to reduce or remove the tariff monopoly, and in July 1992 it lowered the tariff threshold to 73,200 kWh.

4.5   Difficulties in implementing the March 1992 undertakings led to further references to the MMC. As a result of the new recommendations made by the MMC in 1993, the President of the Board of Trade decided in December 1993 to require full internal separation of British Gas's supply and transportation activities, but not divestment, and to accelerate removal of the tariff monopoly to April 1996, with a phased opening of the domestic market by the regulator over the following two years.

4.6   In November 1995 the Gas Bill received Royal Assent, clearing the way for the extension of competition into the domestic gas supply market on a phased basis between 1996 and 1998. This was carried out in stages between April 1996 and May 1998. By December 2004, just over 8½ million gas consumers (42 per cent) were no longer supplied by British Gas. Table 4A gives market penetration in more detail, by local distribution zone (LDZ). For all types of domestic customer it is in the markets in Northern England that new suppliers have had most success. At the end of Q4 2004, British Gas had lost around 37 per cent of the credit and 50 per cent of the direct debit market compared to 29 per cent of the pre-payment market, although it should be noted that British Gas's pre-payment prices are below the average of new suppliers. At the end of 2004, 21 suppliers were licensed to supply gas to domestic customers.

Table 4A: Domestic gas market penetration (in terms of percentage of customers supplied) by local distribution zone and payment type, fourth quarter of 2004

Region	British Gas Trading			Non-British Gas		
	Credit	Direct Debit	Prepayment	Credit	Direct Debit	Prepayment
Northern	52	37	57	48	63	43
Wales	53	48	46	47	52	54
North East	59	47	78	41	53	22
East Midlands	60	48	67	40	52	33
North West	62	50	77	38	50	23
South East	62	43	67	38	57	33
North Thames	63	53	81	37	47	19
Scotland	63	47	71	37	53	29
Eastern	65	50	70	35	50	30
Southern	67	52	72	33	48	28
South West	68	63	81	32	37	19
West Midlands	71	56	76	29	44	24
Great Britain	63	50	71	37	50	29

4.7   Following the 1995 Act, the business of British Gas was fully separated into two corporate entities. The supply and shipping businesses were devolved to a subsidiary, British Gas Trading Limited, while the transportation business (Transco) remained within British Gas plc. In February 1997, Centrica plc was demerged from British Gas plc (which was itself renamed as BG plc) completing the division of the business into two independent entities. Centrica became the holding company for British Gas Trading, British Gas Services, the Retail Energy Centres and the company producing gas from the North and South Morecambe fields. BG plc comprised the gas transportation and storage business of Transco, along with British Gas's other exploration and production, international downstream, research and technology and property activities. In October 2000 BG plc demerged into two separately listed companies, of which Lattice Group plc was the holding company for Transco, while BG Group plc included the international and gas storage businesses. On 21 October 2002 Transco and the National Grid Company merged to form National Grid Transco.

4.8   From 1 October 2001, under the Utilities Act, gas pipeline companies have been able to apply for their own national Gas Transporter Licences so that they can compete with Transco. In some areas low pressure spur networks had already been developed by new transporters competing with Transco to bring gas supplies to new customers (mainly domestic). In addition, some very large loads (above 60 GWh) are serviced by pipelines operated independently, some by North Sea producers.

4.9   By the end of 1994, competitors had exceeded the target 45 per cent of the market above 73,200 kWh (2,500 therms), but virtually all of this was in the firm gas market. From 1995 British Gas's competitors made inroads into the interruptible market but in 2004 Centrica's share of the industrial and commercial market remained at 11 per cent. At the end of 2004, there were about 40 suppliers active in the UK gas market, but some companies own or part own more than one supplier. The structure of the gas industry in Great Britain as it stood at the end of 2004 is shown in Chart 4.1.

Chart 4.1: Structure of the gas industry in Great Britain in 2004

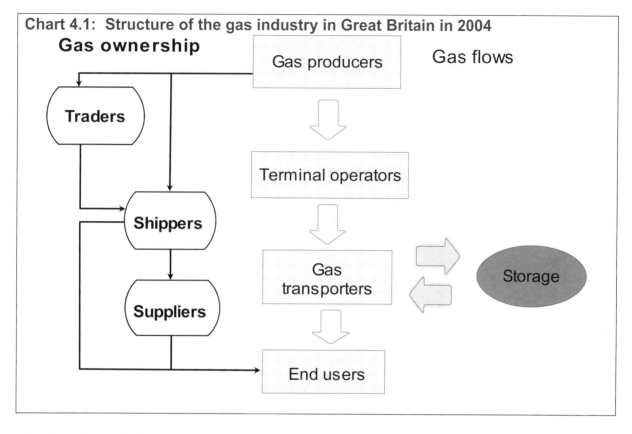

Regional analysis

4.10   Table 4B gives the number of consumers with a gas demand below 73,200 kWh per year in 2003 and the total number of gas consumers. It covers customers receiving gas from the national transmission system.   The below 73,200 kWh category covers both domestic and small business customers and it was this section of the market that was progressively opened up to competition between April 1996 and May 1998. In previous years the regions shown in the table were Transco's 13 local distribution zones (LDZs), but data are now available for Government Office Regions and so this information has been substituted, but note that the data are for 2003.

Table 4B: Consumption by gas customers by region in 2003

Government Office Region	Consumption by customers below 73,200 kWh (2,500 therms) annual demand		Consumption by all customers	
	Number of consumers (thousands)	Gas sales 2003 (GWh)	Number of consumers (thousands)	Gas sales 2003 (GWh)
Wales	992	20,278	1,008	41,287
Scotland	1,661	34,200	1,696	63,149
North East	992	20,706	1,008	34,864
North West	2,656	54,280	2,708	96,771
Yorkshire and the Humber	1,913	38,384	1,952	75,097
East Midlands	1,538	31,201	1,566	54,066
West Midlands	1,911	38,526	1,949	68,168
East of England	1,776	36,333	1,812	60,575
Greater London	2,858	56,074	2,927	90,459
South East	2,831	58,159	2,895	93,076
South West	1,554	27,806	1,583	46,231
Great Britain	20,683	415,948	21,105	723,743

Source: National Grid Transco

4.11   In December 2004, DTI published in Energy Trends and on the DTI web site (www.dti.gov.uk/energy/inform/energy_trends/2004/dec_04.pdf) gas consumption data at both regional and local level. The local level data are at "NUTS4" level (see article in December 2004 Energy Trends for definition) and the regional data at "NUTS1" level. Data for 2001, 2002 and 2003 were presented and domestic sector sales were shown separately from commercial and industrial sales. Numbers of consumers were also given. The 2001 and 2002 data replaced figures for those years that had been published in December 2003. It is planned to update the analysis to cover 2004 and publish a further article in Energy Trends by December 2005.

Northern Ireland

4.12   Before 1997, Northern Ireland did not have a public natural gas supply. The construction of a natural gas pipeline from Portpatrick in Scotland to Northern Ireland was completed in 1996 and provided the means of establishing such a system. The primary market is Ballylumford power station, which was purchased by British Gas in 1992 and converted from oil to gas firing (with a heavy fuel oil back up). The onshore line has been extended to serve wider industrial, commercial and domestic markets and this extension is continuing. In 2004, 77 per cent of all gas supplies in Northern Ireland were used to generate electricity.

Competition

4.13   Paragraphs 4.3 to 4.12 above referred to the developments in recent years in opening up the non-domestic market to competition. About three-quarters of this market (by volume) in the United Kingdom was opened to competition at the end of 1982, and the remainder in August 1992 (with the reduction in the tariff threshold). As mentioned above, however, no other suppliers entered the market until 1990. After 1990 there was a rapid increase in the number of independent companies supplying gas, although from 1999 there were signs of some consolidation and in recent years sales of gas have become more concentrated in the hands of the largest companies in the domestic, industrial and commercial sectors. This has come about through larger companies absorbing smaller suppliers and through mergers between already significant suppliers. The three largest suppliers now jointly account for 79 per cent of sales to domestic customers whereas in 2003 the proportion was 75 per cent. For the industrial sector the share of the largest three suppliers rose from 53 per cent in 2003 to 63 per cent in 2004. For commercial sector sales, in 2004 the three largest suppliers accounted for 69 per cent of sales, up from 62 per cent in 2003.

Commodity balances for gas (Table 4.1)

4.14   In 2004, for the first time since 1996 production of natural gas was less than supply because imports were larger than exports. However, net imports of natural gas were not large in absolute terms, amounting to only 1 per cent of total production in 2004. Imports and exports of natural gas are described in greater detail below in paragraph 4.19.

4.15   Although demand for natural gas is traditionally less than supply because of the various measurement differences described in paragraphs 4.44 to 4.47, in 2004 they broadly balanced each other, the difference being only 0.1 per cent.

4.16   In 2004, 30 per cent of natural gas demand was for electricity generation (transformation sector), ¾ per cent more than in 2003. A further 8 per cent was consumed for heating purposes within the energy industries. A half per cent was accounted for by distribution losses within the gas network. (For an explanation of the items included under losses, see paragraphs 4.44 to 4.47.) Of the remaining 61½ per cent, 3 per cent was transformed into heat for sale to a third party, 13 per cent was accounted for by the industrial sector with the chemicals industry (excluding natural gas for petrochemical feedstocks), food and paper making industries being the largest consumers. The chemicals sector accounted for over a quarter of the industrial consumption of natural gas.

4.17   Sales of gas to households (domestic sector) produced 35 per cent of gas demand, while public administration (including schools and hospitals) consumed 4 per cent of total demand, which was more than was sold to the chemicals sector. The commercial, agriculture and miscellaneous sectors together took up 5½ per cent. Non energy use of gas accounted for the remaining 1 per cent. As Table 4C, below, shows, non-energy use of gas is small (and decreasing in proportion terms) relative to total use (see the technical notes section, paragraph 4.37, for more details on non-energy use of gas).

Table 4C: Non-energy use: share of natural gas demand

	Continental shelf and onshore natural gas
2000	1.2%
2001	1.0%
2002	1.0%
2003	0.9%
2004	0.9%

4.18   Care should be exercised in interpreting the figures for individual industries in these commodity balance tables. As companies switch contracts between gas suppliers, it has not been possible to ensure consistent classification between and within industry sectors and across years. The breakdown of final consumption includes a substantial amount of estimated data. For about 7 per cent of consumption the allocation to consuming sector is estimated.

4.19   Imports of natural gas from the Norwegian sector of the North Sea began to decline in the late 1980s as output from the Frigg field tailed off. The interconnector linking the UK's transmission network with Belgium via a Bacton to Zeebrugge pipeline began to operate in October 1998. Since 1998 there was an increase in imports brought about by inflows through the Bacton to Zeebrugge interconnector (although the UK has been a net exporter through this interconnector since it began operation). In 2003, imports added about 12 per cent to UK production. Exports to mainland Europe from the United Kingdom's share of the Markham field began in 1992 with Windermere's output being added in 1997. Exports to the Republic of Ireland began in 1995. In 2004, exports accounted for 10 per cent of UK production. Exports of natural gas exceeded imports for the first time in 1997 and grew rapidly to 2000, fell by 5½ per cent in 2001, but rose for the second consecutive year to a new peak in 2003 before falling by 35½ per cent in 2004 to a lower level than imports.

4.20   Chart 4.2 shows the increase in indigenous production and consumption of natural gas over the past five years and relative size of net exports.

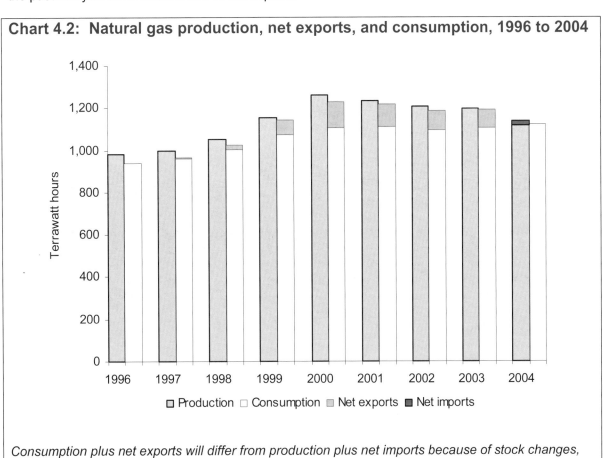

Chart 4.2: Natural gas production, net exports, and consumption, 1996 to 2004

☐ Production ☐ Consumption ▨ Net exports ■ Net imports

Consumption plus net exports will differ from production plus net imports because of stock changes, losses and the statistical difference item.

Supply and consumption of natural gas and colliery methane (Table 4.2)

4.21   This table summarises the production and consumption of gas from these sources in the United Kingdom over the last 5 years.

4.22   As Chart 4.3 shows, the growth in consumption for electricity generation has dominated the growth in natural gas consumption over the last 10 years. Most of this gas was used in Combined Cycle Gas Turbine (CCGT) stations, although the use of gas in dual fired conventional steam stations was a growth area in 1997 and 1998. However, gas use for electricity generation fell by 4½ per cent in 2001 as higher gas prices made it more difficult for gas fired stations to compete with large coal fired stations. This was reversed by a 5½ per cent growth in 2002 when gas prices eased but fell again in 2003 by 1½ per cent. Higher gas prices again meant that at times some generators found it more profitable to sell gas than use it for generation, particularly given plentiful supplies of inexpensive coal. In 2004 gas use for generation rose by 4½ per cent as newly built power stations came on stream. In 2004 the transformation sector as a whole accounted for 33 per cent of gas demand – a percentage point higher than in any of the previous 4 years.

4.23   Since 2000, industrial use of gas has been on a downward trend apart from a small recovery in 2003. The decline in 2004 was particularly marked at 13 per cent with all major industrial sectors showing a decline, but the chemicals sector showing the largest reduction. At the same time there was a large increase in 2004 in gas used for heat that was then sold to other companies and such sales are particularly marked in the chemicals sector. If heat use and total industrial use are combined then the decrease in gas use in 2004 is only 5 per cent (and only 4 per cent in the chemicals sector). Use by the public administration sector and the commercial sector were 3 and 4 per cent higher, respectively, in 2004 than in 2003 but consumption in the energy industries other than electricity (and heat) generation fell by 1½ per cent.

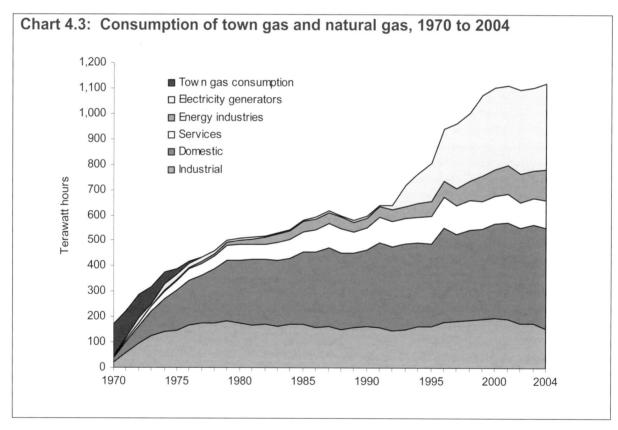

Chart 4.3: Consumption of town gas and natural gas, 1970 to 2004

4.24   Gas use in the domestic sector is particularly dependent on winter temperatures and in 2004 the average temperature over the winter months was slightly lower than in 2003. This helped domestic sector demand to increase by 2½ a per cent in 2004 to a new peak level. Although demand from the domestic sector increased by 7 per cent between 2000 and 2004, its share of total demand rose less sharply from 33 per cent to 35 per cent.

4.25   Maximum daily demand for natural gas through the National Transmission System in winter 2003/04 was 4,606 GWh on 24th February 2005. On that day natural gas demand in Northern Ireland was 23 GWh. This total maximum daily demand was 7 per cent lower than January 2003's record level.

4.26   It is estimated that sales of gas supplied on an interruptible basis accounted for around 20 per cent of total gas sales in 2004; an increase of around 6 percentage points on 2003.

UK continental shelf and onshore natural gas (Table 4.3)

4.27   Table 4.3 shows the flows for natural gas from production through transmission to consumption. The footnotes to the table give more information about each table row. This table departs from the standard balance methodology and definitions in order to maintain the link with past data and with monthly data given at DTI's energy statistics web site (see paragraph 4.43). The relationship between total UK gas consumption shown in this table and total demand for gas given in the balance tables (4.1 and 4.2) is illustrated for 2004 as follows:

		GWh
Total UK consumption (Table 4.3)		1,035,560
plus Producers' own use		76,899
plus Operators' own use		6,560
equals		
"Consumption of natural gas" (see paragraph 4.33)		1,119,019
plus Other losses and metering differences (upstream)		-
plus Downstream losses - leakage assessment	5,413)	8,036
- own use gas	437)	
- theft	2,186)	
plus Metering differences (transmission)		137
equals		
Total demand for natural gas (Tables 4.1 and 4.2)		1,127,193

4.28   Gross production rose steadily and peaked in 2000 at 1.26 TWh but fell for the fourth consecutive year in 2004 to stand at slightly less than the level in 1999 (1.12TWh). Gas available at UK terminals has remained fairly constant over this period mainly because of the changes in exports and imports described in paragraph 4.19. Producers' and operators' own use of gas have tended to change in proportion to the volumes of gas produced and transmitted. Output from the transmission system increased by 0.2 per cent between 2000 and 2004, while total UK consumption of natural gas increased by 0.3 per cent. Consumption increased by more than the output from the transmission system because distribution losses and metering differences have been reduced as a proportion of consumption over these four years.

4.29   For a discussion of the various losses and statistical differences terms in this table, see paragraphs 4.44 to 4.47 in the technical notes and definitions section below. The statistical difference between output from the National Transmission System and total UK consumption has been disaggregated using information obtained from Transco on leakage from local distribution zone pipes, theft and use regarded as own use by pipeline operators. The convention used is set out in paragraph 4.47.

4.30   Losses and metering differences attributable to the information provided on the upstream gas industry are zero from 2001 onwards because these data are no longer reported in the revised Petroleum Production Reporting System. This simplified system for reporting the production of crude oil, NGLs and natural gas in the UK was implemented from 1st January 2001; it reduced the burden on the respondents and improved the quality of data reported on gas production.

4.31   Table 4.3 now includes two rows showing gas stocks and gas storage capacity at the end of the year. Storage data are not currently available before 2004. The 2004 stocks and storage data have been sourced from National Grid Transco's weekly brief and 2004 Ten Year Statement.

Technical notes and definitions

4.32   These notes and definitions are in addition to the technical notes and definitions covering all fuels and energy as a whole in Chapter 1, paragraphs 1.24 to 1.57. For notes on the commodity balances and definitions of the terms used in the row headings see Annex A, paragraphs A.7 to A.42. While the data in the printed and bound copy of this Digest cover only the most recent 5 years, these notes also cover data for earlier years that are available on the DTI web site.

Definitions used for production and consumption

4.33   **Natural gas** production in Tables 4.1 and 4.2 relates to the output of indigenous methane at land terminals and gas separation plants (includes producers' and processors' own use). For further explanation, see Annex F, paragraph F.19 on DTI's Energy Statistics web site under 'Production of oil and gas' - www.dti.gov.uk/energy/inform/dukes/dukes2005/annexf.pdf.   Output of the Norwegian share of the Frigg and Murchison fields is included under imports. A small quantity of onshore produced methane (other than colliery methane) is also included.

4.34   Table 4.3 shows production, transmission and consumption figures for UK continental shelf and onshore natural gas. Production includes waste and own use for drilling, production and pumping operations, but excludes gas flared. Gas available in the United Kingdom excludes waste, own use for drilling etc, stock change, and includes imports net of exports. Gas transmitted (input into inland transmission systems) is after stock change, own use, and losses at inland terminals. The amount consumed in the United Kingdom differs from the total gas transmitted by the gas supply industry, because of losses in transmission, differences in temperature and pressure between the points at which the gas is measured, delays in reading meters and consumption in the works, offices, shops, etc of the undertakings. The figures include an adjustment to the quantities billed to consumers to allow for the estimated consumption remaining unread at the end of the year.

4.35   **Colliery methane** production is colliery methane piped to the surface and consumed at collieries or transmitted by pipeline to consumers. As the output of deep-mined coal declines so does the production of colliery methane, unless a use can be found for gas that was previously vented. The supply of methane from coal measures that are no longer being worked or from drilling into coal measures is licensed under the same legislation as used for offshore gas production.

4.36   **Transfers** of natural gas include natural gas use within the iron and steel industry for mixing with blast furnace gas to form a synthetic coke oven gas. For further details see paragraph 2.48 in Chapter 2.

4.37   **Non-energy gas**: Non-energy use is gas used as feedstock for petrochemical plants in the chemical industry as raw material for the production of ammonia (an essential intermediate chemical in the production of nitrogen fertilisers) and methanol. The contribution of liquefied petroleum gases (propane and butane) and other petroleum gases is shown in Tables 3.4 to 3.6 of Chapter 3. Firm data for natural gas are not available, but estimates for 2000 to 2004 are shown in Table 4.2 and estimates for 2002 to 2004 in Table 4.1 Estimates for the years up to 2003 have been obtained from the National Atmospheric Emissions Inventory (NAEI); 2004 data are DTI extrapolations.

Sectors used for sales/consumption

4.38   For definitions of the various sectors used for sales and consumption analyses see Chapter 1 paragraphs 1.52 to 1.56 and Annex A, paragraphs A.31 to A.42. However, **miscellaneous** has a wider coverage than in the commodity balances of other fuels. This is because some gas supply companies are unable to provide a full breakdown of the services sector and the gas they supply to consumers is allocated to miscellaneous when there is no reliable basis for allocating it elsewhere. See also paragraph 4.41, below, for information on the source of the sectoral data for consumption of gas.

Data collection

4.39   Production figures are generally obtained from returns made under the Department of Trade and Industry's Petroleum Production Reporting System (PPRS) and from other sources. DTI obtain data on the transmission of natural gas from National Grid Transco (who operate the National Transmission System) and from other pipeline operators. Data on consumption are based on returns from gas suppliers and UKCS producers who supply gas directly to customers.

4.40   The production data are for the United Kingdom (including natural gas from the UKCS - offshore and onshore). The restoration of a public gas supply to parts of Northern Ireland in 1997 (see paragraph 4.12 means that all tables in this chapter (except Tables 4A and 4B) cover the UK.

4.41   DTI carry out an annual survey of gas suppliers to obtain details of gas sales to the various categories of consumer. Estimates are included for the suppliers with the smallest market share since the DTI inquiry covers only the largest suppliers (ie those with more than about a ½ per cent share of the UK market up to 1997 and those known to supply more than 1,750 GWh per year for 1998 onwards). For 2000 and subsequent years, gas consumption for the iron and steel sector is based on data provided by the Iron and Steel Statistics Bureau (ISSB) rather than gas suppliers since gas suppliers were over estimating their sales to this sector. The difference between the ISSB and gas suppliers figures has been re-allocated to other sectors using the results of the Office for National Statistics' Purchases Inquiry.

Period covered
4.42   Figures generally relate to years ended 31 December. However, before 2004 data for natural gas for electricity generation relate to periods of 52 weeks as set out in Chapter 5, paragraphs 5.58 and 5.59.

Monthly and quarterly data
4.43   Monthly data on natural gas production and supply are available from the DTI's Energy Statistics web site www.dti.gov.uk/energy/inform/energy_stats/ in monthly Table 4.2. A quarterly commodity balance for natural gas (which includes consumption data) is published in DTI's quarterly statistical bulletin *Energy Trends* and is also available from quarterly Table 4.1 at DTI's Energy Statistics web site. See Annex C for more information about *Energy Trends* and the DTI Energy Statistics web site.

Statistical and metering differences
4.44   In Table 4.3 there are several headings that refer to statistical or metering differences. These arise because measurement of gas flows, in volume and energy terms, takes place at several points along the supply chain. The main sub-headings in the table represent the instances in the supply chain where accurate reports are made of the gas flows at that particular key point in the supply process. It is possible to derive alternative estimates of the flow of gas at any particular point by taking the estimate for the previous point in the supply chain and then applying the known losses and gains in the subsequent part of the supply chain. The differences seen when the actual reported flow of gas at any point and the derived estimate are compared are separately identified in the table wherever possible, under the headings statistical or metering differences.

4.45   The differences arise from several factors:-

• Limitations in the accuracy of meters used at various points of the supply chain. While standards are in place on the accuracy of meters, there is a degree of error allowed which, when large flows of gas are being recorded, can become significant.

• Differences in the methods used to calculate the flow of gas in energy terms. For example, at the production end, rougher estimates of the calorific value of the gas produced are used which may be revised only periodically, rather than the more accurate and more frequent analyses carried out further down the supply chain. At the supply end, although the calorific value of gas shows day-to-day variations, for the purposes of recording the gas supplied to customers a single calorific value is used. Until 1997 this was the lowest of the range of calorific values for the actual gas being supplied within each LDZ, resulting in a "loss" of gas in energy terms. In 1997 there was a change to a "capped flow-weighted average" algorithm for calculating calorific values resulting in a reduction in the losses shown in the penultimate row of Table 4.3. This change in algorithm, along with improved meter validation and auditing procedures, also reduced the level of the "metering differences" row within the downstream part of Table 4.3.

• Differences in temperature and pressure between the various points at which gas is measured. Until February 1997 British Gas used "uncorrected therms" on their billing system for tariff customers when converting from a volume measure of the gas used to an energy measure. This made their supply figure too small by a factor of 2.2 per cent, equivalent to about 1 per cent of the wholesale market.

- Differences in the timing of reading meters. While National Transmission System meters are read daily, customers' meters are read less frequently (perhaps only annually for some domestic customers) and profiling is used to estimate consumption. Profiling will tend to underestimate consumption in a strongly rising market.
- Other losses from the system, for example, theft through meter tampering by consumers.

4.46   The headings in Table 4.3 show where, in the various stages of the supply process, it has been possible to identify these metering differences as having an effect. Usually they are aggregated with other net losses as the two factors cannot be separated. Whilst the factors listed above can give rise to either losses or gains, losses are more common. However, the negative downstream gas metering difference within the transmission system in 2003 was an anomaly that was investigated by National Grid Transco during 2004. They concluded that this unaccounted for element of National Transmission System shrinkage was due to an exceptional run of monthly negative figures between February and June 2003 within what is usually a variable but mainly positive series. However, after a comprehensive investigation of this exceptional period no causal factors were identified. It is probable that the meter error or errors that caused this issue were corrected during the validation of metering. The investigation has enabled the size of the negative metering difference in 2003 to be reduced compared with that reported here last year.

4.47   The box below shows how in 2004 the wastage, losses and metering differences figures in Table 4.3 are related to the losses row in the balance Tables 4.1 and 4.2. It should be noted that losses from 2001 onwards are lower than in earlier years because figures for losses and metering differences in the upstream gas industry are no longer available (see above):

Table 4.3	GWh
Upstream gas industry:	
Other losses and metering differences	-
Downstream gas industry:	
Transmission system metering differences	137
Leakage assessment	5,413
Own use gas	437
Theft	2,186
Tables 4.1 and 4.2	
Losses	8,174

Similarly the statistical difference row in Tables 4.1 and 4.2 is made up of the following components in 2004:

Table 4.3	GWh
Statistical difference between gas available from upstream and gas input to downstream	-1,538
plus Downstream gas industry:	
Distribution losses and metering differences	2,741
Tables 4.1 and 4.2	
Statistical difference	1,201

Contact: Sally Mercer
  Energy Markets Information and Analysis
  sally.mercer@dti.gsi.gov.uk
  020 7215 2717

Tracy Halsey
Energy Information Systems
tracy.halsey@dti.gsi.gov.uk
020 7215 2684

The National gas transmission system, 2004

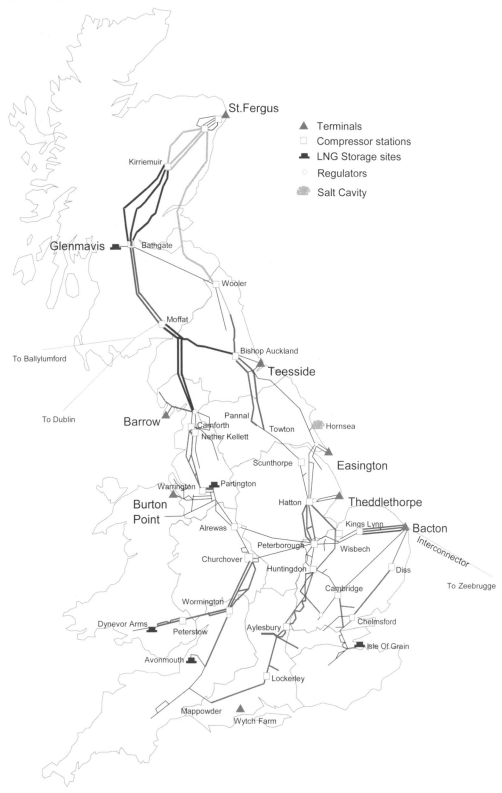

Terminals
Compressor stations
LNG Storage sites
Regulators
Salt Cavity

St.Fergus

Kirriemuir

Glenmavis   Bathgate

Wooler

Moffat

To Ballylumford

Bishop Auckland

Teesside

To Dublin

Barrow

Pannal

Camforth
Nether Kellett

Towton

Hornsea

Scunthorpe

Easington

Warrington   Partington

Burton
Point

Hatton

Theddlethorpe

Alrewas

Kings Lynn   Bacton

Peterborough   Wisbech

Interconnector

Churchover

Huntingdon

Diss

Cambridge

To Zeebrugge

Wormington

Dynevor Arms

Peterstow

Chelmsford

Aylesbury

Avonmouth

Isle Of Grain

Lockerley

Mappowder

Wytch Farm

Source: National Grid Transco

4.1 Commodity balances

Natural gas

GWh

	2002			2003			2004		
	Natural gas	Colliery methane	Total Natural gas	Natural gas	Colliery methane	Total Natural gas	Natural gas	Colliery methane	Total Natural gas
Supply									
Production	1,204,713	692	1,205,405	1,196,115r	915r	1,197,030r	1,115,744	810	1,116,554
Other sources	-	-	-	-	-	-	-	-	-
Imports	60,493	-	60,493	86,298	-	86,298	133,035	-	133,035
Exports	-150,731	-	-150,731	-177,039	-	-177,039	-114,111	-	-114,111
Marine bunkers	-	-	-	-	-	-	-	-	-
Stock change (1)	-7,356	-	-7,356	+3,532r	-	+3,532r	-6,235	-	-6,235
Transfers (3)	-99	-	-99	-82r	-	-82r	-39	-	-39
Total supply	1,107,020	692	1,107,712	1,108,824r	915r	1,109,739r	1,128,394	810	1,129,204
Statistical difference (2)	+1,779r	-	+1,779r	+1,167r	-	+1,167r	+1,201	-	+1,201
Total demand	1,105,241r	692	1,105,933r	1,107,657r	915r	1,108,572r	1,127,193	810	1,128,003
Transformation	351,450r	406	351,856r	343,756	653r	344,409r	370,002	595	370,597
Electricity generation	329,441r	406	329,847r	323,926r	653r	324,579r	338,153	595	338,748
Major power producers	291,264	-	291,264	284,662	-	284,662	304,495	-	304,495
Autogenerators	38,177r	406	38,583r	39,264r	653r	39,917r	33,658	595	34,253
Heat generation	22,009r	-	22,009r	19,830r	-	19,830r	31,849	-	31,849
Petroleum refineries	-	-	-	-	-	-	-	-	-
Coke manufacture	-	-	-	-	-	-	-	-	-
Blast furnaces	-	-	-	-	-	-	-	-	-
Patent fuel manufacture	-	-	-	-	-	-	-	-	-
Other	-	-	-	-	-	-	-	-	-
Energy industry use	91,064	196	91,260	88,720r	187	88,907r	87,313	150	87,463
Electricity generation	-	-	-	-	-	-	-	-	-
Oil and gas extraction	79,364	-	79,364	76,837r	-	76,837r	76,899	-	76,899
Petroleum refineries	3,350	-	3,350	2,773r	-	2,773r	2,204	-	2,204
Coal extraction	-	196	196	-	187	187	-	150	150
Coke manufacture	-	-	-	1r	-	1	-	-	-
Blast furnaces	222	-	222	539r	-	539r	728	-	728
Patent fuel manufacture	-	-	-	-	-	-	-	-	-
Pumped storage	-	-	-	-	-	-	-	-	-
Other	8,128	-	8,128	8,570r	-	8,570r	7,482	-	7,482
Losses (4)	9,666	-	9,666	6,215r	-	6,215r	8,174	-	8,174
Final consumption	653,061r	90	653,151r	668,966r	75	669,041r	661,704	65	661,769
Industry	165,076r	90	165,166r	166,142r	75	166,217r	145,166	65	145,231
Unclassified	-	90	90	-	75	75	-	65	65
Iron and steel	8,791r	-	8,791r	10,327r	-	10,327r	8,837	-	8,837
Non-ferrous metals	5,255r	-	5,255r	4,801r	-	4,801r	3,124	-	3,124
Mineral products	14,136r	-	14,136r	14,060r	-	14,060r	12,379	-	12,379
Chemicals	44,277r	-	44,277r	45,146r	-	45,146r	39,861	-	39,861
Mechanical Engineering, etc	9,273r	-	9,273r	9,130r	-	9,130r	8,069	-	8,069
Electrical engineering, etc	4,615r	-	4,615r	4,393r	-	4,393r	3,810	-	3,810
Vehicles	11,521r	-	11,521r	11,587r	-	11,587r	9,825	-	9,825
Food, beverages, etc	28,884r	-	28,884r	28,814r	-	28,814r	26,941	-	26,941
Textiles, leather, etc	7,837r	-	7,837r	7,855r	-	7,855r	6,637	-	6,637
Paper, printing, etc	15,452r	-	15,452r	15,905r	-	15,905r	14,850	-	14,850
Other industries	11,731r	-	11,731r	11,096r	-	11,096r	8,113	-	8,113
Construction	3,304r	-	3,304r	3,028r	-	3,028r	2,720	-	2,720
Transport	-	-	-	-	-	-	-	-	-
Air	-	-	-	-	-	-	-	-	-
Rail	-	-	-	-	-	-	-	-	-
Road (5)	-	-	-	-	-	-	-	-	-
National navigation	-	-	-	-	-	-	-	-	-
Pipelines	-	-	-	-	-	-	-	-	-
Other	477,205r	-	477,205r	492,803r	-	492,803r	506,517	-	506,517
Domestic	376,372	-	376,372	386,486r	-	386,486r	396,411	-	396,411
Public administration	42,998r	-	42,998r	44,362r	-	44,362r	45,825	-	45,825
Commercial	36,224r	-	36,224r	39,537r	-	39,537r	41,093	-	41,093
Agriculture	2,346	-	2,346	2,324r	-	2,324r	2,355	-	2,355
Miscellaneous	19,265r	-	19,265r	20,094r	-	20,094r	20,833	-	20,833
Non energy use	10,780r	-	10,780r	10,021r	-	10,021r	10,021	-	10,021

(1) Stock fall (+), stock rise (-).
(2) Total supply minus total demand.
(3) Natural gas used in the manufacture of synthetic coke oven gas.

(4) See paragraph 4.44 to 4.47.
(5) See footnote 5 to Table 4.2.

4.2 Supply and consumption of natural gas and colliery methane[1]

GWh

	2000	2001	2002	2003	2004
Supply					
Production	1,260,656	1,231,263	1,205,405	1,197,030r	1,116,554
Imports	26,032	30,464	60,493	86,298	133,035
Exports	-146,342	-138,330	-150,731	-177,039	-114,111
Stock change (2)	-11,068	-661	-7,356	3,532r	-6,235
Transfers	-442	-65	-99	-82r	-39
Total supply	**1,128,836**	**1,122,671**	**1,107,712**	**1,109,739r**	**1,129,204**
Statistical difference (3)	+2,818r	+2,079r	+1,779r	+1,167r	+1,201
Total demand	**1,126,018r**	**1,120,592r**	**1,105,933r**	**1,108,572r**	**1,128,003**
Transformation	**349,454**	**336,525r**	**351,856r**	**344,409**	**370,597**
Electricity generation	324,563	312,939r	329,847r	324,579	338,748
Major power producers	283,784	276,764	291,264	284,662	304,495
Autogenerators	40,779	36,175r	38,583r	39,917r	34,253
Heat generation	24,891	23,586	22,009r	19,830r	31,849
Other	-	-	-	-	-
Energy industry use	**77,941**	**91,451**	**91,260**	**88,907r**	**87,463**
Electricity generation	-	-	-	-	-
Oil and gas extraction	65,555	78,457	79,364	76,837r	76,899
Petroleum refineries	3,641	4,189	3,350	2,773r	2,204
Coal extraction	224	211	196	187	150
Coke manufacture	17	9	-	1	-
Blast furnaces	712	375	222	539r	728
Other	7,792	8,210	8,128	8,570r	7,482
Losses (4)	**20,481**	**8,863**	**9,666**	**6,215r**	**8,174**
Final consumption	**678,142r**	**683,753r**	**653,151r**	**669,041r**	**661,769**
Industry	**183,441**	**179,843**	**165,166r**	**166,217r**	**145,231**
Unclassified	120	105	90	75	65
Iron and steel	8,953r	8,502r	8,791r	10,327r	8,837
Non-ferrous metals	5,900r	5,663r	5,255r	4,801r	3,124
Mineral products	15,851r	15,565r	14,136r	14,060r	12,379
Chemicals	49,546r	50,064r	44,277r	45,146r	39,861
Mechanical engineering, etc	11,145r	9,656r	9,273r	9,130r	8,069
Electrical engineering, etc	5,281r	5,022r	4,615r	4,393r	3,810
Vehicles	11,760r	12,035r	11,521r	11,587r	9,825
Food, beverages, etc	29,835r	29,697r	28,884r	28,814r	26,941
Textiles, leather, etc	8,454r	7,966r	7,837r	7,855r	6,637
Paper, printing, etc	17,268r	16,569r	15,452r	15,905r	14,850
Other industries	16,261r	15,741r	11,731r	11,096r	8,113
Construction	3,067r	3,258r	3,304r	3,028r	2,720
Transport	-	-	-	-	-
Road (5)	-	-	-	-	-
Other	**480,365**	**492,537**	**477,205r**	**492,803r**	**506,517**
Domestic	369,909	379,426	376,372	386,486r	396,411
Public administration	44,552	46,232	42,998r	44,362r	45,825
Commercial	36,216	37,098	36,224r	39,537r	41,093
Agriculture	1,522	2,329	2,346	2,324r	2,355
Miscellaneous	28,166	27,452	19,265r	20,094r	20,833
Non energy use	**14,336r**	**11,373r**	**10,780r**	**10,021r**	**10,021**

(1) Colliery methane figures included within these totals are as follows:

	2000	2001	2002	2003	2004
Total production	**488**	**730**	**692**	**915r**	**810**
Electricity generation	150	418	406	653r	595
Coal extraction	218	207	196	187	150
Other industries	120	105	90	75	65
Total consumption	**488**	**730**	**692**	**915r**	**810**

(2) Stock fall (+), stock rise (-).
(3) Total supply minus total demand.
(4) For an explanation of what is included under losses, see paragraphs 4.44 to 4.47.

(5) A small amount of natural gas is consumed by road transport, but gas use in this sector is predominantly of petroleum gas, hence road use of gas is reported in the petroleum products balances in Chapter 3.

4.3 UK continental shelf and onshore natural gas production and supply[1]

GWh

	2000	2001	2002	2003	2004
Upstream gas industry:					
Gross production (2)	1,260,168	1,230,533	1,204,713	1,196,115r	1,115,744
Minus Producers' own use (3) (18)	65,555r	78,457	79,364	76,837r	76,899
Exports	146,342	138,330	150,731	177,039	114,111
Stock change (pipelines) (4) (18)	+161	-	-	-	-
Waste (5) (18)	-	-	-	-	-
Other losses and metering differences (6)(7)(18)	10,281	-	-	-	-
Plus Imports of gas	26,032	30,464	60,493r	86,298	133,035
Gas available at terminals (8)	1,063,858	1,044,210	1,035,111r	1,028,537	1,057,769
Minus Statistical difference (7)	+251	-690	-125r	-1,391r	-1,538
Downstream gas industry:					
Gas input into the national transmission system (9)	1,063,607	1,044,900	1,035,236r	1,029,928r	1,059,307
Minus Operators' own use (10)	6,701	6,549	7,017	7,475r	6,560
Stock change (storage sites) (11)	10,907	661	7,356	-3,532r	6,235
Metering differences (7)	2,088	1,798	1,821	-874r	137
Gas output from the national transmission system (12)	1,043,911	1,035,892	1,019,042r	1,026,859r	1,046,375
Minus Leakage assessment (13)	5,464	4,436r	5,283r	4,452	5,413
Own use gas (14)	442	438r	427	439	437
Theft (15)	2,206	2,190r	2,134	2,197	2,186
Transfers (16)	441	65	99	82	39
Statistical difference and metering differences (7)	2,562r	2,770r	1,884r	2,557r	2,741
Total UK consumption (17)	**1,032,795r**	**1,025,991r**	**1,009,213r**	**1,017,131r**	**1,035,560**
Stocks of gas (at end year)	26,080	26,741	34,097	30,565	36,800
Storage capacity (19)					41,770

(1) For details of where to find monthly updates of natural gas production and supply see paragraph 4.43.
(2) Includes waste and producers' own use, but excludes gas flared.
(3) Gas used for drilling, production and pumping operations.
(4) Gas held within the UKCS pipeline system. As sections are opened and closed between fields, gas moves in and out of the system, hence it is regarded as a change in stocks.
(5) Gas vented from oil and gas platforms as part of the production process. With effect from 1999 gas vented has been deducted from the Gross Production figure.
(6) Losses due to pipeline leakage.
(7) Measurement of gas flows, in volume and energy terms, occurs at several points along the supply chain. As such, differences are seen between the actual recorded flow through any one point and estimates calculated for the flow of gas at that point. More detail on the reasons for these differences is given in the technical notes and definitions section of this chapter, paragraphs 4.44 to 4.47.
(8) The volume of gas available at terminals for consumption in the UK as recorded by the terminal operators. The percentage of gas available for consumption in the UK from indigenous sources in 2004 was 87.4 per cent, compared with 91.6 per cent in 2003.
(9) Gas received as reported by the pipeline operators. The pipeline operators include Transco, who run the national pipeline network, and other pipelines that take North Sea gas supplies direct to consumers.
(10) Gas consumed by pipeline operators in pumping operations and on their own sites, office, etc.
(11) Stocks of gas held in specific storage sites, either as liquefied natural gas, pumped into salt cavities or stored by pumping the gas back into an offshore field. Stock rise (+), stock fall (-).
(12) Including public gas supply, direct supplies by North Sea producers, third party supplies and stock changes.
(13) This is a Tranco assessment of leakage through the local distribution system based on the National Leakage Reduction Monitoring Model.
(14) Equivalent to about 0.06 per cent of LDZ throughput this is an assessment of the energy used to counter the effects of gas cooling on pressure reduction.
(15) Calculated by Transco as 0.3 per cent of LDZ throughput, this is theft before the gas reaches customer meters.
(16) Transfers are the use within the iron and steel industry for use in the manufacture of synthetic coke oven gas.
(17) See paragraph 4.27 for an explanation of the relationship between these "Total UK consumption" figures and "Total demand" shown within the balance tables.
(18) A simplified PPRS reporting system was introduced in January 2001 requiring less data from respondents - see paragraph 4.30.
(19) Source:NGT Ten Year Statement, 2004. Converted from billion cubic metres to GWh assuming 10.992 kWh per cubic metre. See paragraph 4.31.

Chapter 5
Electricity

Introduction

5.1   This Chapter presents statistics on electricity from generation through to sales. In addition, statistics on generating capacity, on fuel used for generation and on load factors and efficiencies are included along with a map showing the transmission system in Great Britain and the location of the main power stations (page 121).

5.2   Commodity balances for electricity, for each of the last three years, form the introductory table (Table 5.1). The supply and consumption elements of the electricity balance are presented as 5-year time series in Table 5.2. Table 5.3 separates out the public distribution system for electricity from electricity generated and consumed by autogenerators and uses a commodity balance format. Fuels used to generate electricity in the United Kingdom in each of the last five years are covered in Table 5.4. Table 5.5 shows the relationship between the commodity balance definitions and traditional Digest definitions for electricity, so that the most recent data can be linked to the long term trends data, which can be found on the DTI energy statistics web site. Table 5.6 shows the relationship between fuels used, generation and supply in each of the latest five years. Tables on plant capacity (Tables 5.7, 5.8 and 5.9) and on plant loads and efficiency (Table 5.10) have been included and two of these contain data at a sub-national level. Table 5.11 lists individual power stations in operation and this year it is supplemented by a table showing large scale CHP schemes in the United Kingdom (new Table 5.12).   The long term trends commentary and tables on fuel use, generation, supply and consumption back to 1970 are to be found on DTI's energy statistics web site: www.dti.gov.uk/energy/inform/dukes/dukes2005/05longterm.pdf .

Structure of the industry

5.3   In the period covered by this Digest the electricity industries of Scotland, Northern Ireland and England and Wales operated independently although interconnectors joined all three grid systems together.   From April 2005 under the British Electricity Trading and Transmission Arrangements (BETTA), introduced in the Energy Act 2004, the electricity systems of England and Wales and Scotland have been integrated. The paragraphs below describe the position up to March 2005, but indicate the further changes that have been made under BETTA.

5.4   From the period immediately after privatisation of the industry in 1989, when there were 7 generating companies in England and Wales and 12 Regional Electricity companies distributing and supplying electricity to customers in their designated area, there were many structural and business changes. At the end of 2004 there were 37 major power producers operating in England and Wales[1]. Competition developed as follows:

(a)   From 1 April 1990, customers with peak loads of more than 1 MW (about 45 per cent of the non-domestic market) were able to choose their supplier.

(b)   From 1 April 1994, customers with peak loads of more than 100 kW were able to choose their supplier.

(c)   Between September 1998 and May 1999, the remaining part of the electricity market (ie below 100 kW peak load) was opened up to competition. Paragraph 5.9 and Table 5A give more details of the opening up of the domestic gas and electricity markets to competition.

5.5   At the same time, there have been moves to integrate vertically the electricity business with former generating companies acquiring electricity supply companies and supply companies purchasing generating stations or acquiring interests in companies building new power stations.

---

[1] Some of these producers are joint ventures and so the number of generating companies involved is less than 37.

Distribution businesses have been sold or acquired and merged. The National Grid Company, part of National Grid Transco, operates the high voltage transmission system linking generators to distributors and some large customers. The transmission system of Great Britain is linked to the transmission system of continental Europe via an interconnector to France under the English Channel. (See Table 5.11). Up to March 2005, the Scottish transmission system was linked to that in England and Wales by an interconnector. Under BETTA National Grid has taken on responsibility for operating the transmission system in Scotland as well as England and Wales, and a single Great Britain market has been created.

5.6   In Scotland, until the end of March 2005, the two main companies, Scottish Power and Scottish and Southern Energy, covered the full range of electricity provision. They operated generation, transmission, distribution and supply businesses. The entire output of the two nuclear power stations in Scotland, which are owned by British Energy plc, is sold to these two suppliers under long-term contracts. In addition, there are about 25 small independent hydro stations and some independent generators operating fossil-fuelled stations, which sell their output to Scottish Power and Scottish and Southern Energy.

5.7   The electricity supply industry in Northern Ireland is also privately owned. Northern Ireland Electricity plc (NIE) (part of the Viridian Group) is responsible for power procurement, transmission, distribution and supply in the Province. Generation is in the hands of three private sector companies who own the four major power stations. There is a link (re-established in 1996) between the Northern Ireland grid and that of the Irish Republic, along which electricity is both imported and exported. In December 2001, the link between Northern Ireland's grid and that of Scotland was inaugurated.

5.8   In March 2001, the means of trading electricity changed with the introduction in England and Wales of the New Electricity Trading Arrangements (NETA). These arrangements were based on bi-lateral trading between generators, suppliers, traders and customers and are designed to be more efficient and provide greater choice for market participants, whilst maintaining the operation of a

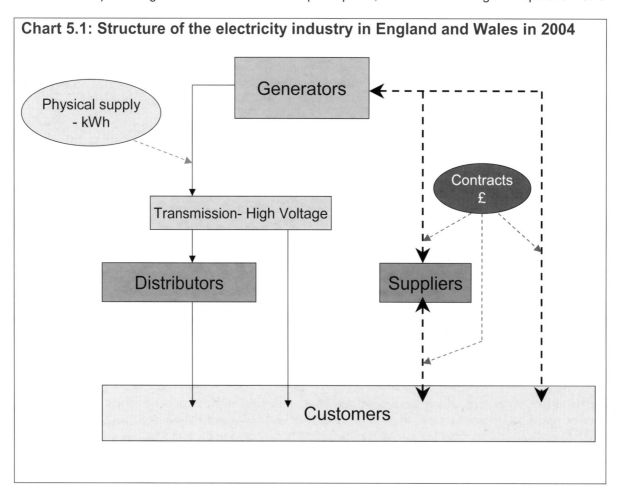

Chart 5.1: Structure of the electricity industry in England and Wales in 2004

secure and reliable electricity system. The system includes forwards and futures markets, a balancing mechanism to enable the National Grid Company, as system operator, to balance the system, and a settlement process. This system has been extended to Scotland under BETTA. The system is shown in simplified form in Chart 5.1.

5.9   By December 2004, nearly 11 million electricity consumers (42 per cent) were no longer with their home supplier. Table 5A gives market penetration in the fourth quarter of 2004. By the end of 2004, the former regional electricity companies had lost around 40 per cent of the credit, 50 per cent of the direct debit, and 40 per cent of the prepayment market.

Table 5A: Domestic electricity market penetration (in terms of percentage of customers supplied) by Public Electricity Supply area and payment type, fourth quarter of 2004

Region	Home Supplier			Non-Home Supplier		
	Credit	Direct Debit	Prepayment	Credit	Direct Debit	Prepayment
North West	45	43	49	55	57	51
West Midlands	51	50	58	49	50	42
Merseyside and North Wales	52	41	48	48	59	52
Northern	54	48	54	46	52	46
Yorkshire	56	45	54	44	55	46
East Midlands	58	55	51	42	45	49
Eastern	61	46	54	39	54	46
South Wales	64	52	60	36	48	40
South East	66	60	75	34	40	25
London	67	64	89	33	36	11
South Scotland	67	49	53	33	51	47
South	69	45	59	31	55	41
South West	70	50	71	30	50	29
North Scotland	86	69	77	14	31	23
Great Britain	60	50	60	40	50	40

Commodity balances for electricity (Table 5.1)

5.10   The first page of this balance table shows that 98 per cent of UK electricity supply in 2004 was home produced and 2 per cent was from imports net of exports. Just ½ per cent of home produced electricity was exported. Of the 393,000 GWh produced (excluding pumped storage production), 90½ per cent was from major power producers and 9½ per cent from other generators, 22 per cent was from primary sources and 78 per cent from secondary sources.

5.11   Electricity generated by each type of fuel is shown on the second page of the commodity balance table. The link between electricity generated and electricity supplied is made in Table 5.6 and electricity supplied by each type of fuel is illustrated in Chart 5.3. Paragraph 5.27 examines further the ways of presenting each fuel's contribution to electricity production.

5.12   Demand for electricity is predominantly from final consumers, who accounted for 84½ per cent in 2004. The remaining 15½ per cent is split 8 per cent to energy industries' use and 7½ per cent to losses. The electricity industry itself uses 55½ per cent of the energy industries' total use of electricity, with a further 11½ per cent used for pumping at pumped storage stations. Petroleum refineries are the next most significant consumer with 20 per cent of energy industry use. The losses item has three components. First, transmission losses from the high voltage transmission system represented about 19 per cent of the figure in 2004. Second, distribution losses, which occur between the gateways to the public supply system's network and the customers' meters, accounted for about 75 per cent of losses. Third, a small amount was lost through theft or meter fraud (6 per cent) (see also paragraph 5.65).

5.13   Industrial consumption was 34½ per cent of final consumption in 2004, slightly more than the consumption by households (34 per cent), with transport storage and communications and the services sector accounting for the remaining 31½ per cent.   Within the industrial sector the three largest consuming industries are chemicals, paper and food, which together account for 41½ per cent of industrial consumption.   The iron and steel sector is also a substantial user of electricity but part of its consumption is included against blast furnaces and coke ovens under energy industry uses.   This is because electricity is used by coke ovens and blast furnaces in the transformation of solid fuels into coke, coke oven gas and blast furnace gas.   Taken together, the engineering industries accounted for a further 18 per cent of final consumption of electricity.   A note on the estimates included within these figures is to be found at paragraph 5.66.   Chart 5.2 shows diagrammatically the demand for electricity in 2004.

5.14   The transport sector covers electricity consumed by companies involved in transport, storage and communications.   Within the overall total of 8,034 GWh, it is known that national railways consume about 2,700 GWh each year for traction purposes, and this figure has been shown separately in the balances.

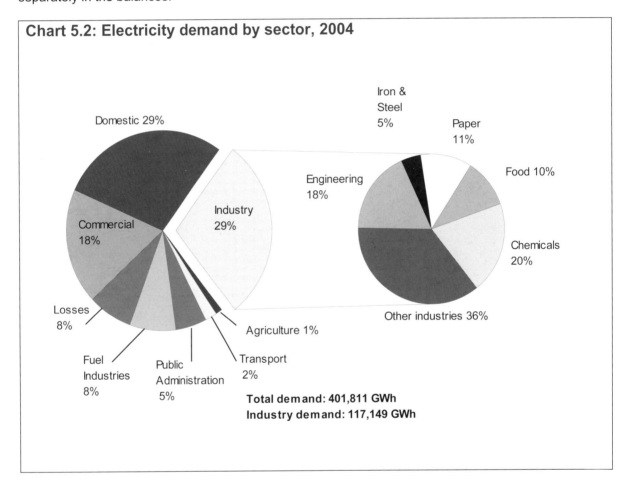

Chart 5.2: Electricity demand by sector, 2004

Domestic 29%

Commercial 18%

Losses 8%

Fuel Industries 8%

Public Administration 5%

Agriculture 1%

Transport 2%

Industry 29%

Iron & Steel 5%

Paper 11%

Food 10%

Engineering 18%

Chemicals 20%

Other industries 36%

Total demand: 401,811 GWh
Industry demand: 117,149 GWh

Supply and consumption of electricity (Table 5.2)

5.15   There was a ½ per cent increase in the supply of electricity in 2004.   Production (including pumped storage production) fell by ½ per cent, but import of electricity net of exports were 3½ times their level in 2003.   This was because in 2003 low UK prices made it less attractive to French exporters, while higher prices in continental Europe fostered a growth in exports, which were nearly four times their level in 2002.   In 2004 imports have returned to their former level but exports have only fallen back by a quarter.

5.16   Losses as a proportion of electricity demand in 2004 (7½ per cent) and energy industry use as a proportion of total demand, at 8 per cent, were both the same as in 2003.   Industrial consumption of electricity was 2½ per cent up on 2003's level, while consumption in the services sector fell by less than ½ per cent.   Consumption by transport, storage and communications fell by 3 per cent and domestic sector consumption fell but by less than ½ per cent. Temperatures influence the actual level of consumption in any one year in the winter months, as customers adjust heating levels in their homes. Temperatures in fourth quarter of 2003 were on average colder than in any of the 4 preceding years. In addition the hot summer of 2003 led to an increased use of electricity for air conditioning and cooling. 2004 did not have a hot summer, nor a cold fourth quarter but on average, temperatures were similar to those in 2003.

Regional electricity data

5.17 The restructuring of the electricity industry in 1990 and the privatisation of the electricity companies meant that it was no longer possible for this Digest to present regional data on the supply of electricity, as it would disclose information about individual businesses that were in competition with each other. Now that competition has been fully introduced, the Department of Trade and Industry has agreed with electricity suppliers and distributors the way in which electricity data can be collected at a regional (and sub-regional) level, in order to meet the requirements of users. The collection of data relating to regional and local consumption of electricity began in autumn 2004 and regional and local data on electricity consumption were published on an experimental basis in December 2004 in Energy Trends and undated in the March 2005 issue of the same publication. (See Annex C for more information about *Energy Trends*). Further information is available on the DTI Energy statistics web site www.dti.gov.uk/energy/inform/energy_stats/ . A summary of electricity consumption at regional level is given in Table 5B and relates to 2003.

5.18 The difference between total UK electricity sales, shown in Table 5B, and total UK electricity sales shown in Table 5.5 is a small statistical difference (136 GWh) that mainly arises from the fact that the regional data are not based exactly on a calendar year.

Table 5B: Electricity consumed, 2003

	Domestic sector sales (GWh)	Number of domestic customers (thousand) (1)	Industrial and commercial sector sales (GWh)	Number of I & C customers (thousand) (1)	All consumers sales (GWh)
Wales	5,196	1,212	9,961	99	15,158
Scotland	12,738	2,637	16,407	217	29,145
North East	4,538	1,158	7,684	83	12,222
North West	12,760	3,006	20,739	241	33,499
Yorkshire and the Humber	9,442	2,227	13,483	177	22,925
East Midlands	8,512	1,852	14,058	157	22,570
West Midlands	10,609	2,265	11,062	190	21,670
East of England	12,038	2,387	14,858	211	26,896
Greater London	13,786	3,206	25,651	421	39,437
South East	17,219	3,477	22,898	339	40,116
South West	11,413	2,265	13,183	232	24,597
Unallocated Consumption	503	122	19,540	66	20,042
Sales direct from high voltage lines (2)					9,210
Great Britain	118,754	25,814	189,523	2,433	317,487
Northern Ireland (3)					6,710
Total (4)					324,197

(1) Figures are the number of Meter Point Administration Numbers (MPANs); every metering point has this unique reference number.
(2) Based on estimate provided by Elexon Ltd.
(3) Northern Ireland data are based on data for electricity distributed provided by Northern Ireland Electricity.
(4) This is close to the figure for UK electricity sales in 2003 of 324,333 GWh shown in Table 5.5; see the article cited in paragraph 5.18 for the reasons for this small statistical difference.

Commodity balances for the public distribution system and for other generators (Table 5.3)

5.19 Table 5.3 expands on the commodity balance format to show consumption divided between electricity distributed over the public distribution system and electricity provided by other generators (largely autogeneration). Autogeneration is the generation of electricity wholly or partly for a company's own use as an activity which supplements the primary activity. However, most generators of electricity from renewable sources (apart from large scale hydro and some biofuels) are included as other generators because of their comparatively small size, even though their main activity is electricity generation. For a full list of companies included as major power producers see paragraph 5.50.

5.20 Table 5.3 also expands the domestic sector to show consumption by payment type and the commercial sector is expanded to show detailed data beyond that presented in Tables 5.1 and 5.2.

5.21 The proportion of electricity supplied by generators other than major power producers rose slightly in 2004 to just under 9½ per cent, the same as the peak level it reached in 2000 following steady yearly growth. The proportion of this electricity transferred to the public distribution system in 2004 was 24 per cent whereas in the previous 4 years this proportion has varied between 22 and 30 per cent according to market conditions. High gas prices and low electricity prices made it more difficult for electricity produced by other generators to compete in the electricity market in 2002 and 2004, but the position eased in 2003. Over the last 5 years there has also been greater generation from renewables and wastes (see Chapter 7).

5.22 In 2004, 6 per cent of final consumption of electricity was by other generators and did not pass over the public distribution system. This was slightly above the proportion in each of the previous two years. A substantial proportion of electricity used in the energy industries is self-generated with the proportion above 20 per cent in all three years shown in the table. At petroleum refineries the proportion is even higher and in 2004 over three quarters of electricity was self-generated.

5.23 In 2004, 16 per cent of the industrial demand for electricity was met by autogeneration. There was also a lesser proportion (about 2½ per cent) from autogeneration within the commercial and transport sectors. Transport autogeneration was sharply down in 2003 with the closure of one London Underground generating station. Table 1.9 in Chapter 1 shows the fuels used by autogenerators to generate this electricity within each major sector and also the quantities of electricity generated and consumed.

5.24 Within the domestic sector, about a third of the electricity consumed was purchased under some form of off-peak pricing structure (the same as in the previous two years). About 16 per cent of consumption was through prepayment systems, a proportion that has varied little over the three years shown.

Fuel used in generation (Table 5.4)

5.25 In this table fuel used by electricity generators is measured in both original units and for comparative purposes, in the common unit of million tonnes of oil equivalent. In Table 5.6 figures are quoted in a third unit, namely GWh, in order to show the link between fuel use and electricity generated.

5.26 The energy supplied basis defines the primary input (in million tonnes of oil equivalent) needed to produce 1 TWh of hydro, wind, or imported electricity as:

$$\text{Electricity generated (TWh)} \times 0.085985$$

The primary input needed to produce 1 TWh of nuclear electricity is similarly

$$\frac{\text{Electricity generated (TWh)} \times 0.085985}{\text{Thermal efficiency of nuclear stations}}$$

In the United Kingdom the thermal efficiency of nuclear stations has risen in stages from 32 per cent in 1982 to 38 per cent in 2004 (see Table 5.10 and paragraph 5.57 for the definition)[2]. The factor of 0.085985 is the energy content of one TWh divided by the energy content of one million tonnes of oil equivalent (see page 203 and inside back cover flap).

5.27   Figures on fuel use for electricity generation can be compared in two ways. Table 5.4 illustrates one way by using the volumes of **fuel input** to power stations (after conversion of inputs to an oil equivalent basis), but this takes no account of how efficiently that fuel is converted into electricity. The fuel input basis is the most appropriate to use for analysis of the quantities of particular fuels used in electricity generation (eg to determine the additional amount of gas or other fuels required as coal use declines under tighter emissions restrictions). A second way uses the amount of electricity generated and supplied by each fuel. This **output** basis is appropriate for comparing how much, and what percentage, of electricity generation comes from a particular fuel. It is the most appropriate method to use to examine the dominance of any fuel, and for diversity issues. Percentage shares based on fuel outputs reduce the contribution of coal and nuclear, and increase the contribution of gas (by about 6 percentage points in 2004) compared with the fuel input basis, because of the higher conversion efficiency of gas. This output basis is used in Chart 5.3, taking electricity supplied (gross) figures from Table 5.6. Trends in fuel used on this electricity supplied basis are described in the section on Table 5.6, in paragraphs 5.30 to 5.33, below.

5.28   A historical series of fuel used in generation on a consistent, energy supplied, fuel input basis is available at Table 5.1.1 on DTI's energy statistics web site.

Relating measurements of supply, consumption and availability (Table 5.5)

5.29   The balance methodology uses terms that cannot be readily employed for earlier years' data because statistics were not available in sufficient detail. Table 5.5 shows the relationship between these terms for the latest five years. For the full definitions of the terms used in the commodity balances see the Annex A, paragraphs A.7 to A.42.

Electricity generated, and supplied (Table 5.6)

5.30   The main data on generation and supply in Table 5.6 are presented by type of fuel. However, before 1996 data were presented by type of station and in order to maintain a link with this earlier data the final part of the table shows generation from conventional steam stations and from combined cycle gas turbine stations over the most recent five years.

5.31   Total electricity generated in the United Kingdom in 2004 was ½ per cent lower than generation in 2003. However, the average rate of growth over the last 5 years was 1½ per cent per year. Major power producers (as defined in paragraph 5.49) accounted for 91 per cent of electricity generation in 2004. Generation by other generators was 3 per cent up on a year earlier mainly because most (61 per cent in 2004) of the generation from renewables is included in the "other generators" category.

5.32   Generation from coal-fired stations was 4½ per cent lower in 2004 than in 2003, but still higher than in 2002 and 2001. Generation from gas in 2004 was 5 per cent higher than in 2003 and 2½ per cent above the previous record level in 2002. In 2004 gas fired generation was boosted by three new large stations that began generation or completed their first full year of generation. Generation from nuclear sources fell by 10 per cent because of a high level of outages for repairs and maintenance in 2004.

5.33   Table 5.6 also shows electricity supplied data. These data take into account the fact that some stations use relatively more electricity than others in the generation process itself. In total, electricity supplied (gross) was 5 per cent less than the volume generated in 2004, but for gas-fired stations it was 2 per cent less, and for nuclear stations it was 8 per cent less. Chart 5.3 shows how shares of the generation market in terms of electricity output have changed over the last five years. Gas' share of electricity supplied (net) plus imports in 2004 at 40 per cent equalled the previous highest share in 2002. Coal's share at 33 per cent was 5 percentage points higher than in 1999 but 1½ percentage

---

[2] *Note that the International Energy Agency uses 0.33 in its calculations, which is the European average thermal efficiency of nuclear stations in 1989, measured in net terms rather than the UK's gross terms.*

points lower than the high level in 2003. Nuclear's 19 per cent share was its lowest since 1987 having peaked at 26 per cent in 1998. Oil's share has halved to 1 per cent over the five years shown and imports' share has fallen from 4 per cent in 1999 to 2½ per cent in 2004.

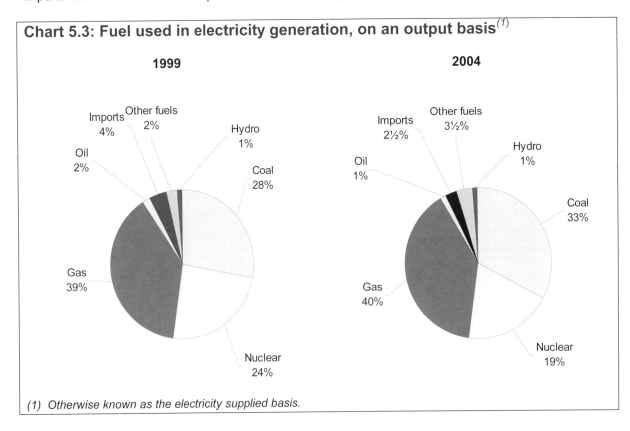

Chart 5.3: Fuel used in electricity generation, on an output basis[1]

1999

Imports 4%
Other fuels 2%
Oil 2%
Hydro 1%
Coal 28%
Nuclear 24%
Gas 39%

2004

Imports 2½%
Other fuels 3½%
Oil 1%
Hydro 1%
Coal 33%
Nuclear 19%
Gas 40%

(1) Otherwise known as the electricity supplied basis.

Plant capacity (Tables 5.7, 5.8 and 5.9)

5.34   Table 5.7 shows capacity, ie the maximum power available at any one time, for major power producers and other generators by type of plant.

5.35   In 2004, there was an increase of just over 1,800 MW (+2½ per cent) in the capacity of major power producers. This was due 1,600 MW of new gas fired plant coming on stream and 500 MW of gas and coal plant being re-instated. Chapelcross nuclear station closed and there were a number of other smaller re-ratings. In December 2004, major power producers accounted for 91 per cent of the total generating capacity, the same proportion as at the end of 2003. The capacity of other generators increased by 3½ per cent. Renewables capacity of other generators increased by 210 MW (see Chapter 7).

5.36   A breakdown of the capacity of the major power producers' plants at the end of March each year from 1993 to 1996 and at the end of December for 1996 to 2004 is shown in Chart 5.4.

5.37   Table 5.8 separates the capacities of major power producers geographically to show England and Wales, Scotland and Northern Ireland. So as not to disclose data for individual stations that have been provided in confidence, the breakdowns by type of station cannot be given in as much detail as in Table 5.7. In 2004, 84½ per cent of the generating capacity in the UK owned by major power producers was in England and Wales, 13 per cent was in Scotland and 2½ per cent in Northern Ireland. Out of the net increase in UK capacity of 1,808 MW in 2004, 1,809 MW was in England and Wales, 52 MW was in Scotland and there was a 53 MW reduction in Northern Ireland.

5.38   In Table 5.9, data for the generating capacity of industrial, commercial and transport undertakings are shown, according to the industrial classification of the generator. Nearly a fifth of the capacity is in the chemicals sector. Petroleum refineries have 14 per cent of capacity, paper, printing and publishing has a 11 per cent share, and engineering and other metal trades has a 9 per cent share.

Chart 5.4: Generating capacity of major power producers, 1993-2004

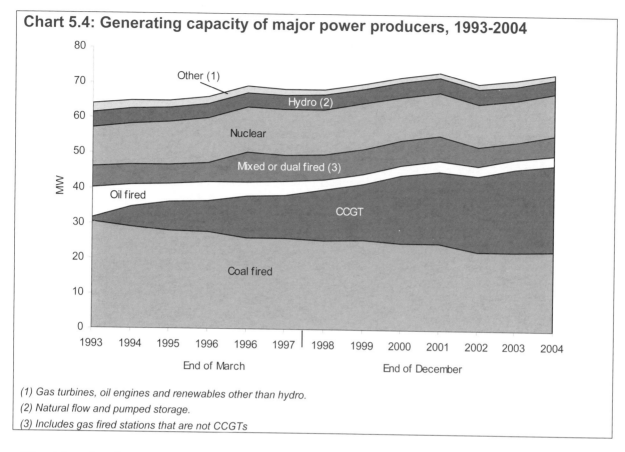

(1) Gas turbines, oil engines and renewables other than hydro.
(2) Natural flow and pumped storage.
(3) Includes gas fired stations that are not CCGTs

Plant loads, demand and efficiency (Table 5.10)

5.39   Table 5.10 shows the maximum load met each year, load factors (by type of plant and for the system in total) and indicators of thermal efficiency. Maximum demand figures cover the winter period ending the following March.   Maximum demand figures for England and Wales, Scotland, and Northern Ireland are shown separately as well as total UK maximum demand.

5.40   Maximum demand in the UK during the winter of 2004/2005 occurred in December 2004. This was 0.4 per cent lower than the previous year's maximum in December 2003. Maximum demand in 2004/2005 was 83.2 per cent of the UK capacity of major power producers (Table 5.7) as measured at the end of December 2004, compared with 84.6 per cent in 2003/04, and 87.7 per cent in 2002/03. The decrease in this percentage in 2004/5 is mainly because major power producers added 1,800 MW to capacity through new plant and re-instatements, see 5.35 above. In England and Wales maximum demand at the end of December 2004 was 86.9 per cent of the England and Wales capacity of major power producers (Table 5.8) compared with 88.2 per cent at the end of 2003. For Scotland the proportion was 58.2 per cent (62.0 per cent in 2003) and for Northern Ireland 88.0 per cent (85.0 per cent in 2003). These percentages do not include the capacities available via the interconnectors with neighbouring grid systems.

5.41   Plant load factors measure how intensively each type of plant has been used. The trend up to the end of the 1990s had been for conventional thermal plant to be used less intensively and CCGT stations more intensively. In 2000 increased maintenance and repair at nuclear stations and at CCGT stations, coupled with high gas prices at the end of the year, led to a departure from this trend. Nuclear stations recovered in 2001, suffered further outages in 2002, recovered again in 2003, but suffered further outages in 2004. Continuing high gas prices since the end of 2000 have brought about the lower CCGT load factors, which were particularly marked in 2003, but recovered slightly in 2004. The use of coal in competition with gas is reflected in the increased load factor for conventional thermal stations and coal fired stations, particularly in 2003.

5.42 2003 and 2001 were a particularly dry years, especially in the areas where hydro electricity is produced. As a result the load factors for natural flow hydro show substantial falls in those years. Pumped storage use was less affected by the dry weather in 2003 than in 2001. The low availability of hydro was another contributory factor to the high load factor for conventional thermal in 2003.

5.43 Thermal efficiency measures the efficiency with which the heat energy in fuel is converted into electrical energy. The efficiency of coal-fired stations had been on a downward trend as coal became the marginal fuel for generation, but coal's increased role since 2000 has halted the decline in the thermal efficiency of coal-fired generation. CCGT efficiency in each of the last seven years has been consistently within the band of 46.6 to 47.2 per cent. The efficiency of nuclear stations has been on a rising trends in recent years as older, less efficient stations have closed, but the outages in 2004 have reduced the efficiency slightly. The efficiencies presented in this table are calculated using **gross** calorific values to obtain the energy content of the fuel inputs. If **net** calorific values are used, efficiencies are higher, for example CCGT efficiencies rise by about 5 percentage points.

Power stations in the United Kingdom (Tables 5.11 and 5.12)

5.44 Table 5.11 lists the operational power stations in the United Kingdom as at the end of May 2005 along with their installed capacity and the year they began to generate electricity. Where a company operates several stations the stations are grouped together. In general the table aims to list all stations of 1 MW installed capacity or over. However, for CHP stations for which the information is publicly available, a new table has been included (Table 5.12) for stations of 1 MW and over, but it is the total power output of these stations that is given, not just that which is classed as good quality CHP under CHPQA (see Chapter 6), since CHPQA information for individual sites is not publicly available. In Table 5.11 generating stations using renewable sources are also listed in aggregate form in the "Other power stations" section apart from hydro stations and wind farms operated by the major power producers, which appear in the main table. For completeness CHP stations not appearing in the main table are also listed in aggregate in this section. Details of the interconnectors between England and Scotland, England and France, Scotland and Northern Ireland and Northern Ireland and the Irish Republic are also given in this table. The total installed capacity of all the power stations listed in Table 5.11 (including" other generators") is 76,972 MW.

Carbon dioxide emissions from power stations.

5.45 It is estimated that carbon dioxide emissions from power stations accounted for 30 per cent of the UK's total carbon dioxide emissions in 2004. Emissions vary by type of fuel used to generate the electricity, and the latest figures are shown in Table 5C below:

Table 5C: Carbon dioxide emissions from power stations

Fuel	Emissions (tonnes of carbon per GWh electricity supplied)
Coal	242.9
Oil	166.0
Gas	101.6
All fossil fuels	165.6
All fuels (including nuclear and renewables)	124.1

The Electricity Supply System in Great Britain in 2004

This map has been adapted from a map provided by Reed Business Publishing and National Grid Transco; it is available in colour on the DTI energy website

Technical notes and definitions

5.46 These notes and definitions are in addition to the technical notes and definitions covering all fuels and energy as a whole in Chapter 1, paragraphs 1.24 to 1.56. For notes on the commodity balances and definitions of the terms used in the row headings see Annex A, paragraphs A.7 to A.42. While the data in the printed and bound copy of this Digest cover only the most recent 5 years, these notes also cover data for earlier years that are available on the DTI web site.

Electricity generation from renewable sources
5.47 Figures on electricity generation from renewable energy sources are included in the tables in this section. Further detailed information on renewable energy sources is included in Chapter 7.

Combined heat and power
5.48 Electricity generated from combined heat and power (CHP) schemes, CHP generating capacities and fuel used for electricity generation are included in the tables in this chapter. However, more detailed analyses of CHP schemes are set out in Chapter 6.

Generating companies
5.49 Following the restructuring of the electricity supply industry in 1990, the term "Major generating companies" was introduced into the electricity tables to describe the activities of the former nationalised industries and distinguish them from those of autogenerators and new independent companies set up to generate electricity. The activities of the autogenerators and the independent companies were classified under the heading "Other generating companies". In the 1994 Digest, a new terminology was adopted to encompass the new independent producers, who were then beginning to make a significant contribution to electricity supply.   Under this terminology, all companies whose prime purpose is the generation of electricity are included under the heading "Major power producers" (or MPPs). The term "Other generators" ("Autogenerators" in the balance tables) is restricted to companies who produce electricity as part of their manufacturing or other commercial activities, but whose main business is not electricity generation.   "Other generators" also covers generation by energy services companies at power stations on an industrial or commercial site where the main purpose is the supply of electricity to that site, even if the energy service company is a subsidiary of a major power producer. Most generators of electricity from renewable sources (apart from large scale hydro and some biofuels) are also included as "Other generators" because of their comparatively small size, even though their main activity is electricity generation.

5.50 **Major power producers at the end of 2004 were:**
AES Electric Ltd., Anglian Power Generators Ltd, Baglan Generation Ltd., BNFL Magnox., British Energy plc., Centrica plc., Coolkeeragh Power Ltd., Corby Power Ltd., Coryton Energy Company Ltd., Deeside Power Ltd., Derwent Cogeneration Ltd., Drax Power Ltd., EDF Energy plc., Edison Mission Energy Ltd., Enfield Energy Centre Ltd., E.On UK plc., Fellside Heat and Power Ltd., Fibrogen Ltd., Fibropower Ltd., Fibrothetford Ltd., Great Yarmouth Power Ltd, Humber Power Ltd., Immingham CHP, International Power plc., National Grid Company (Keilder), NIGEN, Peterborough Power Ltd., Premier Power Ltd., Regional Power Generators Ltd., Rocksavage Power Company Ltd., RWE Innogy plc., Saltend Co-generation Company Ltd., Scottish Power plc., Scottish and Southern Energy plc., Seabank Power Ltd., SELCHP Ltd., Spalding Energy Company Ltd., Teesside Power Ltd., Thames Power Services Ltd, Western Power Generation Ltd. Since then E.On UK have acquired Enfield Energy Centre.

Types of station
5.51 The various types of station identified in the tables of this chapter are as follows:

Conventional steam stations are stations that generate electricity by burning fossil fuels to convert water into steam, which then powers steam turbines.

Nuclear stations are also steam stations but the heat needed to produce the steam comes from nuclear fission.

Gas turbines use pressurised combustion gases from fuel burned in one or more combustion chambers to turn a series of bladed fan wheels and rotate the shaft on which they are mounted. This then drives the generator. The fuel burnt is usually natural gas or gas oil.

Combined cycle gas turbine (CCGT) stations combine in the same plant gas turbines and steam turbines connected to one or more electrical generators. This enables electricity to be produced at higher efficiencies than is otherwise possible when either gas or steam turbines are used in isolation. The gas turbine (usually fuelled by natural gas or oil) produces mechanical power (to drive the generator) and waste heat. The hot exhaust gases (waste heat) are fed to a boiler, where steam is raised at pressure to drive a conventional steam turbine that is also connected to an electrical generator.

Natural flow hydro-electric stations use natural water flows to turn turbines.

Pumped storage hydro-electric stations use electricity to pump water into a high level reservoir. This water is then released to generate electricity at peak times. Where the reservoir is open, the stations also generate some natural flow electricity; this is included with natural flow generation. As electricity is used in the pumping process, pumped storage stations are net consumers of electricity.

Other stations include wind turbines and stations burning fuels such as landfill gas, sewage sludge, biomass and waste.

Public distribution system
5.52   This comprises the grids in England and Wales, Scotland and Northern Ireland.

Sectors used for sales/consumption
5.53   The various sectors used for sales and consumption analyses are standardised across all chapters of the 2004 Digest. For definitions of the sectors see Chapter 1 paragraphs 1.52 to 1.56 and Annex A paragraphs A.31 to A.42.

Declared net capability and declared net capacity
5.54   Declared net capability is the maximum power available for export from a power station on a continuous basis minus any power imported by the station from the network to run its own plant. It represents the nominal maximum capability of a generating set to supply electricity to consumers. The registered capacity of a generating set differs from declared net capability in that, for registered capacity, not all power consumed by the plant is subtracted from the normal full load capacity, only the MW consumed by the generating set through its transformer when generating at its normal full load capacity.

5.55   Declared net capacity is used to measure the maximum power available from generating stations that use renewable resources. For wind and tidal power a factor is applied to declared net capability to take account of the intermittent nature of the energy source (eg 0.43 for wind).

Load factors
5.56   The following definitions are used in Table 5.10:

Maximum load - Twice the largest number of units supplied in any consecutive thirty minutes commencing or terminating at the hour.

Simultaneous maximum load met - The maximum load on the grid at any one time. It is measured by the sum of the maximum load met in England and Wales and the loads met at the same time by companies in other parts of the United Kingdom. In 2004/05 the maximum load in England and Wales occurred on 13 December 2004 at 17.30 (53,795 MW). However, in Northern Ireland the maximum load occurred on 20 December 2004 at 17.30 (1,682 MW), which was the highest ever load met in the province and 2.8 per cent above the previous record on 7 January 2003. Maximum load in Scotland was also on 20 December 2004 with Scottish Power recording 4,145 MW and Scottish and Southern Energy 1,666 MW. Both were below the previous record levels of 16 January 2001 (4,382 MW), and

7 January 2003 (1,712 MW), respectively. In England and Wales the highest ever load met was 54,430 MW on 10 December 2002.

Plant load factor - The average hourly quantity of electricity supplied during the year, expressed as a percentage of the average output capability at the beginning and the end of year.

System load factor - The average hourly quantity of electricity available during the year expressed as a percentage of the maximum demand nearest the end of the year or early the following year.

Thermal efficiency

5.57   Thermal efficiency is the efficiency with which heat energy contained in fuel is converted into electrical energy. It is calculated for fossil fuel burning stations by expressing electricity generated as a percentage of the total energy content of the fuel consumed (based on average gross calorific values). For nuclear stations it is calculated using the quantity of heat released as a result of fission of the nuclear fuel inside the reactor. The efficiency of CHP systems is discussed separately in Chapter 6, paragraph 6.21and 6.22 and Table 6D. Efficiencies based on gross calorific value of the fuel (sometimes referred to as higher heating values or HHV) are lower than the efficiencies based on net calorific value (or lower heating value LHV). The difference between HHV and LHV is due to the energy associated with the latent heat of the evaporation of water products from the steam cycle which cannot be recovered and put to economic use.

Period covered

5.58   Until 2004 figures for the major power producers relate to periods of 52 weeks as listed below (although some data provided by electricity supply companies related to calendar months and were adjusted to the statistical calendar). In 2004 a change was made to a calendar year basis:

Year	52 weeks ended
1999	2 January 2000
2000	31 December 2000
2001	30 December 2001
2002	29 December 2002
2003	28 December 2003
2004	12 months ended 31 December 2004

5.59   Figures for industrial, commercial and transport undertakings relate to calendar years ending on 31 December, except for the iron and steel industry where figures relate to the following 52 or 53 week periods:

Year	52 weeks ended
1999	1 January 2000
2000	30 December 2000
2001	29 December 2001
2002	28 December 2002
	53 weeks ended
2003	3 January 2004
	52 weeks ended
2004	1 January 2005

Monthly and quarterly data

5.60   Monthly and quarterly data on fuel use, electricity generation and supply and electricity availability and consumption are available on DTI's Energy Statistics web site www.dti.gov.uk/energy/inform/energy stats/. Monthly data on fuel used in electricity generation by major power producers are given in Monthly Table 5.3 and monthly data on supplies by type of plant and type of fuel are given in Monthly Table 5.4, while monthly data on availability and consumption of electricity by the main sectors of the economy are given in Monthly Table 5.5. A quarterly commodity balance for electricity is published in DTI's quarterly statistical bulletin *Energy Trends* (Quarterly Table 5.2) along with a quarterly table of fuel use for generation by all generators and electricity supplied by major power producers (Quarterly Table 5.1). Both these quarterly tables are also available from DTI's Energy Statistics web site. See Annex C for more information about *Energy Trends*.

Data collection

5.61   For Major Power Producers, as defined in paragraph 5.49, the data for the tables in this Digest are obtained from the results of an annual DTI inquiry, sent to each company, covering generating capacity, fuel use, generation, sales and distribution of electricity.

5.62   Another annual inquiry is sent to electricity distributors to establish electricity distributed by these companies. Similarly an annual inquiry is sent to licensed suppliers of electricity to establish electricity sales by these companies. For 2000 and subsequent years, electricity consumption for the iron and steel sector is based on data provided by the Iron and Steel Statistics Bureau (ISSB) rather than electricity suppliers since electricity suppliers were over estimating their sales to this sector. The difference between the ISSB and electricity suppliers' figures has been re-allocated to other sectors using the results of the Office for National Statistics' Purchases Inquiry.

5.63   Companies that generate electricity mainly for their own use (known as autogenerators or autoproducers - see paragraph 5.49, above) are covered by an annual inquiry commissioned by DTI but carried out by the Office for National Statistics (ONS) from their Newport offices. Where autogenerators operate a combined heat and power (CHP) plant, this survey is now supplemented by information from the CHP Quality Assessment scheme (for autogenerators who have registered under the scheme - see Chapter 6 on CHP). The ONS inquiry only covers generators with capacities greater than 100 kWe and DTI estimates fuel use and electricity generation for smaller companies or includes estimates made by FES for CHP electricity, described in Chapter 6. There are two areas of autogeneration that are covered by direct data collection by DTI, mainly because the return contains additional energy information needed by the Department. These are the Iron and Steel industry, and generation on behalf of London Underground.

Losses and statistical differences

5.64   Statistical differences are included in Tables 5.1, 5.2 and 5.3. These arise because data collected on production and supply do not match exactly with data collected on sales or consumption. One of the reasons for this is that some of the data are based on different calendars as described in paragraphs 5.58 and 5.59, above. Sales data based on calendar years will always include more electricity consumption than the slightly shorter statistical year of exactly 52 weeks.

5.65   Of the losses shown in the commodity balance for electricity of almost 31,000 GWh in 2004, it is estimated that about 5,700 GWh (1½ per cent of electricity available) were lost from the high voltage transmission system of the National Grid and 23,000 GWh (6 per cent) between the grid supply points (the gateways to the public supply system's distribution network) and customers' meters. The balance (about ½ per cent of electricity available) is accounted for by theft and meter fraud, accounting differences and calendar differences (as described in paragraph 5.64, above).

5.66   Care should be exercised in interpreting the figures for individual industries in the commodity balance tables. As new suppliers have entered the market and companies have moved between suppliers, it has not been possible to ensure consistent classification between and within industry sectors and across years. The breakdown of final consumption includes some estimated data. For about 11 per cent of consumption of electricity supplied by the public distribution system, the sector figures are partially estimated.

Contact: *Mike Janes (Statistician)*   *Joe Ewins*
            Energy Markets Information and Analysis   *Energy Information Systems*
            mike.janes@dti.gsi.gov.uk   *joe.ewins@dti.gsi.gov.uk*
            020-7215 5186   *020-7215 5190*

5.1 Commodity balances

Electricity

GWh

	2002	2003	2004
Total electricity			
Supply			
Production	384,594r	395,732r	392,979
Other sources (1)	2,652	2,734	2,649
Imports	9,182	5,119	9,784
Exports	-768	-2,959	-2,294
Marine bunkers	-	-	-
Stock change (2)	-	-	-
Transfers	-	-	-
Total supply	**395,661r**	**400,626r**	**403,118**
Statistical difference (3)	+983r	+1,072r	+1,307
Total demand	**394,678r**	**399,554r**	**401,811**
Transformation			
Electricity generation	-	-	-
Major power producers	-	-	-
Other generators	-	-	-
Heat generation	-	-	-
Petroleum refineries	-	-	-
Coke manufacture	-	-	-
Blast furnaces	-	-	-
Patent fuel manufacture	-	-	-
Other	-	-	-
Energy industry use	**31,297r**	**32,273r**	**31,040**
Electricity generation	17,126r	18,185r	17,186
Oil and gas extraction	540	551	558
Petroleum refineries	6,553r	5,932r	6,177
Coal extraction	-	-	-
Coke manufacture	1,163r	1,190r	1,118
Blast furnaces	502r	492r	468
Patent fuel manufacture	-	-	-
Pumped storage	3,463	3,546	3,497
Other	1,950	2,376r	2,037
Losses	**29,980**	**29,862**	**30,728**
Final consumption	**333,401r**	**337,419r**	**340,043**
Industry	**112,648r**	**114,299r**	**117,149**
Unclassified	-	-	-
Iron and steel	5,092r	5,434r	5,412
Non-ferrous metals	6,365r	6,636r	7,277
Mineral products	7,115r	7,651r	7,849
Chemicals	22,861r	22,653r	23,170
Mechanical engineering, etc	8,794r	8,839r	8,513
Electrical engineering, etc	5,880r	6,019r	6,818
Vehicles	5,625r	5,660r	5,686
Food, beverages, etc	12,166r	11,949r	12,324
Textiles, leather, etc	3,463r	3,443r	3,396
Paper, printing, etc	11,988r	12,749r	13,253
Other industries	21,599r	21,562r	21,653
Construction	1,700r	1,701r	1,799
Transport	**8,454r**	**8,280r**	**8,034**
Air	-	-	-
Rail (4)	2,700	2,700	2,700
Road	-	-	-
National navigation	-	-	-
Pipelines	-	-	-
Other	**212,299r**	**214,840r**	**214,860**
Domestic	114,534r	115,761	115,526
Public administration	20,657r	20,816r	20,924
Commercial	72,963	74,238	74,215
Agriculture	4,145	4,025	4,194
Miscellaneous	-	-	-
Non energy use	-	-	-

5.1 Commodity balances (continued)

Electricity

			GWh
	2002	2003	2004
Electricity production			
Total production (5)	**384,594r**	**395,732r**	**392,979**
Primary electricity			
Major power producers	**91,776**	**91,254**	**84,252**
Nuclear	87,848	88,686	79,999
Large scale hydro (5)	3,927	2,568	3,982
Small scale hydro (6)	-	-	271
Wind	-	-	-
Other generators	**2,119**	**1,948**	**2,616**
Nuclear	-	-	-
Large scale hydro	657	545	666
Small scale hydro (6)	204	115	11
Wind	1,259	1,288	1,939
Secondary electricity			
Major power producers	**259,566**	**268,612**	**271,758**
Coal	120,958	134,023	127,827
Oil	2,011	2,197	1,883
Gas	135,741	131,238	140,577
Renewables	856	1,154	1,471
Other	-	-	-
Other generators	**31,133r**	**33,918r**	**34,353**
Coal	3,321r	4,282r	4,184
Oil	2,788r	2,397r	3,032
Gas	16,536r	17,633r	15,526
Renewables	4,769	5,547r	6,407
Other	3,719r	4,059r	5,204
Primary and secondary production (7)			
Nuclear	87,848	88,686	79,999
Hydro	4,788	3,228	4,930
Wind	1,259	1,288	1,939
Coal	124,279r	138,305r	132,011
Oil	4,799r	4,595r	4,915
Gas	152,277r	148,871r	156,103
Other renewables	5,625	6,701r	7,878
Other	3,719r	4,059r	5,204
Total production	**384,594r**	**395,732r**	**392,979**

(1) Pumped storage production.
(2) Stock fall (+), stock rise (-).
(3) Total supply minus total demand.
(4) See paragraph 5.14.
(5) Excludes pumped storage production.
(6) A re-assessment in 2004 showed that some small scale hydro output previously classified to Other Genera should be classified to Major Power Producers. Work is continuing to see if the re-classification can be extended back to earlier years.
(7) These figures are the same as the electricity generated figures in Table 5.6 except that they exclude pumped storage production. Table 5.6 shows that electricity used on works is deducted to obtain electricity supplied. It is electricity supplied that is used to produce Chart 5.3 showing each fuel's share of electricity output (see paragraph 5.27).

5.2 Electricity supply and consumption

GWh

	2000	2001	2002	2003	2004
Supply					
Production	374,374r	382,364r	384,594r	395,732r	392,979
Other sources (1)	2,694	2,422	2,652	2,734	2,649
Imports	14,308	10,663	9,182	5,119	9,784
Exports	-134	-264	-768	-2,959	-2,294
Total supply	**391,243**	**395,185r**	**395,661r**	**400,626r**	**403,118**
Statistical difference (2)	+1,497r	+1,175r	+983r	+1,072r	+1,307
Total demand	**389,746r**	**394,010**	**394,678r**	**399,554r**	**401,811**
Transformation	-	-	-	-	-
Energy industry use	**30,680r**	**30,387**	**31,297r**	**32,273r**	**31,040**
Electricity generation	16,304	17,394	17,126r	18,185r	17,186
Oil and gas extraction	527	675	540	551	558
Petroleum refineries	6,362	5,231	6,553r	5,932r	6,177
Coal and coke	1,283	1,223	1,163r	1,190r	1,118
Blast furnaces	877	885	502r	492r	468
Pumped storage	3,499	3,210	3,463	3,546	3,497
Other	1,828	1,769	1,950	2,376r	2,037
Losses	**29,649**	**30,902**	**29,980**	**29,862**	**30,728**
Final consumption	**329,420r**	**332,721**	**333,401r**	**337,419r**	**340,043**
Industry	**114,112**	**111,337**	**112,648r**	**114,299r**	**117,149**
Unclassified	-	-	-	-	-
Iron and steel	6,349r	5,303r	5,092r	5,434r	5,412
Non-ferrous metals	6,152r	7,324r	6,365r	6,636r	7,277
Mineral products	8,109r	7,247r	7,115r	7,651r	7,849
Chemicals	23,732r	21,079r	22,861r	22,653r	23,170
Mechanical engineering. etc	9,420r	8,569r	8,794r	8,839r	8,513
Electrical engineering, etc	6,196r	5,697r	5,880r	6,019r	6,818
Vehicles	6,316r	5,824r	5,625r	5,660r	5,686
Food, beverages, etc	11,724r	11,570r	12,166r	11,949r	12,324
Textiles, leather, etc	3,599r	3,303r	3,463r	3,443r	3,396
Paper, printing, etc	11,416r	11,511r	11,988r	12,749r	13,253
Other industries	19,514r	22,213r	21,599r	21,562r	21,653
Construction	1,586	1,698r	1,700r	1,701r	1,799
Transport	**8,623**	**8,828**	**8,454r**	**8,280r**	**8,034**
Other	**206,685r**	**212,557**	**212,299r**	**214,840r**	**214,860**
Domestic	111,842	115,337	114,534	115,761	115,526
Public administration	20,913	21,105	20,657r	20,816r	20,924
Commercial	69,571	72,014	72,963	74,238	74,215
Agriculture	4,358	4,100	4,145	4,025	4,194
Miscellaneous	-	-	-	-	-
Non energy use	-	-	-	-	-

(1) Pumped storage production.
(2) Total supply minus total demand.

5.3 Commodity balances

Public distribution system and other generators

GWh

	2002			2003			2004		
	Public distribution system	Other generators	Total	Public distribution system	Other generators	Total	Public distribution system	Other generators	Total
Supply									
Major power producers	351,342	-	351,342	359,866	-	359,866	356,010	-	356,010
Other generators	-	33,252r	33,252r	-	35,866r	35,866r	-	36,969	36,969
Other sources (1)	2,652	-	2,652	2,734	-	2,734	2,649	-	2,649
Imports	9,182	-	9,182	5,119	-	5,119	9,784	-	9,784
Exports	-768	-	-768	-2,959	-	-2,959	-2,294	-	-2,294
Transfers	+7,553r	-7,553r	-	+10,773r	-10,773r	-	+8,927	-8,927	-
Total supply	**369,962r**	**25,699r**	**395,661r**	**375,533r**	**25,093r**	**400,626r**	**375,076**	**28,042**	**403,118**
Statistical difference (2)	+983r	-	+983r	+1,064r	+8r	+1,072r	+1,577	-270	+1,307
Total demand	**368,979r**	**25,699r**	**394,678r**	**374,469r**	**25,085r**	**399,554r**	**373,499**	**28,312**	**401,811**
Transformation	-	-	-	-	-	-	-	-	-
Energy industry use	**23,959**	**7,337r**	**31,297r**	**25,133**	**7,140r**	**32,273r**	**23,736**	**7,305**	**31,040**
Electricity generation	15,746	1,380r	17,126r	16,747	1,439r	18,185r	15,590	1,595	17,186
Oil and gas extraction	540	-	540	551	-	551	558	-	558
Petroleum refineries	1,598	4,955r	6,553r	1,550	4,382r	5,932r	1,478	4,698	6,177
Coal and coke	1,064	98r	1,163r	1,091	99r	1,190r	1,027	91	1,118
Blast furnaces	-	502r	502r	-	492r	492r	-	468	468
Pumped storage	3,463	-	3,463	3,546	-	3,546	3,497	-	3,497
Other fuel industries	1,548	403r	1,950	1,649	727r	2,376r	1,585	452	2,037
Losses	**29,970r**	**10r**	**29,980**	**29,845r**	**17r**	**29,862**	**30,701**	**27**	**30,728**
Final consumption	**315,050**	**18,352r**	**333,401r**	**319,492r**	**17,927r**	**337,419r**	**319,063**	**20,980**	**340,043**
Industry	**96,843**	**15,805r**	**112,648r**	**98,507r**	**15,792r**	**114,299r**	**98,592**	**18,558**	**117,149**
Iron and steel	4,144r	948r	5,092r	4,489r	945r	5,434r	4,480	932	5,412
Non-ferrous metals	4,252r	2,113r	6,365r	4,403r	2,233r	6,636r	4,183	3,095	7,277
Mineral products	7,115r	-	7,115r	7,443r	208r	7,651r	7,635	215	7,849
Chemicals	15,231r	7,630	22,861r	15,481r	7,172r	22,653r	14,612	8,558	23,170
Mechanical engineering, etc	8,528r	265	8,794r	8,501r	338r	8,839r	8,294	218	8,513
Electrical engineering, etc	5,869r	11	5,880r	6,008r	11	6,019r	6,807	11	6,818
Vehicles	5,480r	145	5,625r	5,534r	127r	5,660r	5,554	132	5,686
Food, beverages, etc	10,728r	1,438	12,166r	10,837r	1,112r	11,949r	10,665	1,658	12,324
Textiles, leather, etc	3,348r	114	3,463r	3,330r	113r	3,443r	3,285	110	3,396
Paper, printing, etc	9,550r	2,437r	11,988r	9,590r	3,159r	12,749r	10,023	3,229	13,253
Other industries	20,911r	688	21,599r	21,203r	359r	21,562r	21,268	384	21,653
Construction	1,685r	15	1,700r	1,686r	15	1,701r	1,784	15	1,799
Transport	**7,051**	**1,404r**	**8,454r**	**7,534r**	**746r**	**8,280r**	**7,320**	**715**	**8,034**
Of which National Rail (3)	2,700	-	2,700	2,700	-	2,700	2,700	-	2,700
Other	**211,156**	**1,143r**	**212,299r**	**213,451**	**1,389r**	**214,840r**	**213,152**	**1,708**	**214,860**
Domestic	114,534	-	114,534r	115,761	-	115,761	115,526	-	115,526
Standard	63,225	-	63,225	64,381	-	64,381	64,441	-	64,441
Economy 7 and other off-peak	32,207	-	32,207	32,109	-	32,109	31,968	-	31,968
Prepayment (standard)	12,608	-	12,608	12,643	-	12,643	12,527	-	12,527
Prepayment (off-peak)	6,055	-	6,055	6,191	-	6,191	6,179	-	6,179
Sales under any other arrangement	440	-	440	437	-	437	411	-	411
Public administration	19,514	1,143r	20,657r	19,427	1,389r	20,816r	19,216	1,708	20,924
Public lighting (4)	1,923	-	1,923	2,050	-	2,050	1,991	-	1,991
Other public sector	17,591	1,143r	18,734r	17,377	1,389r	18,766r	17,225	1,708	18,933
Commercial	72,963	-	72,963	74,238	-	74,238	74,215	-	74,215
Shops	33,769	-	33,769	34,180	-	34,180	34,029	-	34,029
Offices	21,928	-	21,928	22,105	-	22,105	22,252	-	22,252
Hotels	8,253	-	8,253	8,611	-	8,611	8,645	-	8,645
Combined domestic/ commercial premises	1,767	-	1,767	1,896	-	1,896	1,831	-	1,831
Post and telecommunications	5,597	-	5,597	5,746	-	5,746	5,709	-	5,709
Unclassified	1,650	-	1,650	1,700	-	1,700	1,750	-	1,750
Agriculture	4,145	-	4,145	4,025	-	4,025	4,194	-	4,194

(1) Pumped storage production.
(2) Total supply minus total demand.
(3) See paragraph 5.14
(4) Sales for public lighting purposes are increasingly covered by wider contracts that cannot distinguish the public lighting element.

5.4 Fuel used in generation[1]

	Unit	2000	2001	2002	2003	2004
						Original units of measurement
Major power producers (2)						
Coal	M tonnes	44.76	49.29	46.14	50.90r	48.97
Oil (3)	"	0.75	0.79	0.67	0.63	0.55
Gas	GWh	283,784	276,764	291,264	284,662	304,495
Other generators (2)						
Transport undertakings:						
Gas	GWh	2,194	2,238	1,793	93	27
Undertakings in industrial and commercial sectors:						
Coal (4)	M tonnes	1.47	1.65	1.61	1.57r	1.54
Oil (5)	"	0.71	0.55	0.54	0.48r	0.51
Gas (6)	GWh	38,585	33,937r	36,790r	39,824r	34,226
						Million tonnes of oil equivalent
Major power producers (2)						
Coal		27.765	30.575	28.623	31.570r	30.375
Oil (3)		0.772	0.818	0.689	0.654	0.572
Gas		24.401	23.797	25.044	24.476	26.182
Nuclear		19.635	20.768	20.100	20.041	18.164
Hydro (natural flow) (7)		0.372	0.276	0.338	0.221	0.366
Other renewables (7)		0.237	0.253	0.274	0.381	0.540
Net imports		1.219	0.894	0.724	0.186	0.644
Total major power producers (2)		**74.401**	**77.381**	**75.792**	**77.529r**	**76.842**
Of which: conventional thermal and other stations (9)		31.400r	32.629	30.574	33.288r	32.045
combined cycle gas turbine stations		21.775	22.814	24.056	23.793	25.623
Other generators (2)						
Transport undertakings:						
Gas		0.189	0.192	0.154	0.008	0.002
Undertakings in industrial and commercial sectors:						
Coal (4)		0.905	1.031	1.003	0.972r	0.962
Oil (5)		0.777	0.605	0.599	0.539r	0.564
Gas (6)		3.318	2.918r	3.163r	3.424r	2.943
Hydro (natural flow) (7)		0.065	0.072	0.074	0.057	0.058
Other renewables (7)		1.416	1.704	1.907	2.178	2.446
Other fuels (8)		1.354	1.036	1.061	1.890r	1.550
Total other generators (2)		**8.024**	**7.559r**	**7.962r**	**9.067r**	**8.525**
All generating companies						
Coal (4)		28.670	31.606	29.626	32.542r	31.336
Oil (3)(5)		1.549	1.423	1.288	1.193r	1.136
Gas (6)		27.908	26.908r	28.362r	27.909r	29.127
Nuclear		19.635	20.768	20.100	20.041	18.164
Hydro (natural flow) (7)		0.437	0.348	0.412	0.278	0.423
Other renewables (7)		1.653	1.957	2.181	2.559	2.986
Other fuels (8)		1.354	1.036r	1.061	1.890r	1.550
Net imports		1.219	0.894	0.724	0.186	0.644
Total all generating companies		**82.425**	**84.941r**	**83.754r**	**86.597r**	**85.367**

(1) For details of where to find monthly updates of fuel used in electricity generation by major power producers and quarterly updates of fuel used in electricity generation by all generating companies see paragraph 5.60.

(2) See paragraphs 5.49 and 5.50 for information on companies covered

(3) Includes Orimulsion, oil used in gas turbine and diesel plants, and oil used for lighting up coal fired boilers

(4) Includes coke oven coke

(5) Includes refinery gas.

(6) Includes colliery methane.

(7) Renewable sources, which are included under hydro and other renewables in this table, are shown separately in Table 7.7 o Chapter 7.

(8) Main fuels included are coke oven gas, blast furnace gas, and waste products from chemical processes

(9) Includes gas turbines, oil engines and plants producing electricity from renewable sources other than hydro

5.5 Electricity supply, electricity supplied (net), electricity available, electricity consumption and electricity sales

GWh

	2000	2001	2002	2003	2004
Total supply					
(as given in Tables 5.1 and 5.2)	391,243	395,185r	395,661r	400,626r	403,118
less imports of electricity	-14,308	-10,663	-9,182	-5,119	-9,784
plus exports of electricity	+134	+264	+768	+2,959	+2,294
less electricity used in pumped storage	-3,499	-3,210	-3,463	-3,546	-3,497
less electricity used on works	-16,304	-17,394	-17,126r	-18,185r	-17,171
equals					
Electricity supplied (net)	357,266	364,182r	366,657r	376,735r	374,959
(as given in Tables, 5.6, 5.1.2 and 5.1.3)					
Total supply					
(as given in Tables 5.1 and 5.2)	391,243	395,185r	395,661r	400,626r	403,118
less electricity used in pumped storage	-3,499	-3,210	-3,463	-3,546	-3,497
less electricity used on works	-16,304	-17,394	-17,126r	-18,185r	-17,171
equals					
Electricity available	371,440	374,581r	375,072r	378,895r	382,449
(as given in Table 5.1.2)					
Final consumption					
(as given in Tables 5.2 and 5.3)	329,420r	332,721	333,401r	337,419r	340,043
plus Iron and steel consumption counted as energy industry use	+1,174	+1,158	+648r	+648r	+625
equals					
Final users	330,594r	333,879	334,049r	338,067r	340,668
(as given in Table 5.1.2)					
Final consumption					
Public distribution system					
(as given in Table 5.3)	309,957	315,862	315,050	319,492r	319,063
plus Oil and gas extraction use	+527	+675	+540	+551	+558
plus Petroleum refineries use	+1,665	+1,912	+1,598	+1,550	+1,478
plus Coal and coke use	+1,097	+1,047	+1,064	+1,091	+1,027
plus Other fuel industries use	+1,419r	+1,571	+1,548	+1,649	+1,585
equals					
UK Electricity sales (1)	314,665r	321,067	319,800	324,333r	323,711

(1) The renewables obligation percentage is calculated using total renewables generation on an obligation basis from Table 7.4 (x 100) as the numerator, and this figure as the denominator. Separate electricity sales data for public electricity suppliers are given for England and Wales, Scotland and Northern Ireland in Table 5.5 of Energy Trends on the DTI web site at www.dti.gov.uk/energy/inform/energy_stats/electricity/5_5elecconsumption-ettab23.xls

5.6 Electricity fuel use, generation and supply

GWh

	Thermal sources							Non-thermal sources			
	Coal	Oil	Gas	Nuclear	Renew-ables (1)	Other (3)	Total	Hydro-natural flow	Hydro-pumped storage	Other (4)	Total All sources
2000											
Major power producers (2)											
Fuel used	322,907	8,981	283,781	228,358	2,921	-	846,949	4,331	2,694	-	853,974
Generation	117,025	2,415	129,558	85,063	698	-	334,758	4,331	2,694	-	341,783
Used on works	5,175	292	2,592	6,729	58	-	14,846	15	91	-	14,952
Supplied (gross)	111,850	2,123	126,965	78,334	640	-	319,912	4,316	2,603	-	326,831
Used in pumping	-	-	-	-	-	-	-	-	-	-	3,499
Supplied (net)	-	-	-	-	-	-	-	-	-	-	323,332
Other generators	-	-	-	-	-	-	-	-	-	-	-
Fuel used	10,522	9,042	40,779	-	15,517	15,743	91,603	755	-	947	93,304
Generation	2,925	4,109	18,519	-	3,630	4,401	33,584	755	-	947	35,285
Used on works	39	304	592	-	203	202	1,340	12	-	-	1,352
Supplied	2,887	3,805	17,927	-	3,427	4,198	32,244	743	-	947	33,933
All generating companies											
Fuel used	333,429	18,023	324,560	228,358	18,439	15,743	938,551	5,085	2,694	947	947,278
Generation	119,950	6,524	148,077	85,063	4,328	4,401	368,342	5,085	2,694	947	377,069
Used on works	5,214	596	3,184	6,729	261	202	16,186	27	91	-	16,304
Supplied (gross)	114,736	5,928	144,892	78,334	4,067	4,198	352,156	5,058	2,603	947	360,764
Used in pumping	-	-	-	-	-	-	-	-	-	-	3,499
Supplied (net)	-	-	-	-	-	-	-	-	-	-	357,266
2001											
Major power producers (2)											
Fuel used	355,582	9,510	276,761	241,537	3,102	-	886,492	3,215	2,422	-	892,129
Generation	127,128	2,472	126,999	90,093	738r	-	347,429r	3,215	2,422	-	353,066r
Used on works	5,830	281	2,709	7,108	46	-	15,973	11	82	-	16,066
Supplied (gross)	121,298	2,192	124,289	82,985	692r	-	331,456r	3,203	2,340	-	336,999r
Used in pumping											3,210
Supplied (net)											333,789r
Other generators (2)											
Fuel used	11,987	7,035	35,757	-	18,849r	12,053	85,682r	840	-	967r	87,489
Generation	4,333	2,781	14,906	-	4,316r	3,577	29,913r	840	-	967r	31,721
Used on works	230	196	480	-	246	165	1,316	12	-	-	1,328
Supplied	4,104	2,585	14,426	-	4,070r	3,412	28,597r	829	-	967r	30,393
All generating companies											
Fuel used	367,569	16,545	312,518	241,537	21,951r	12,053	972,174r	4,055	2,422	967r	979,618
Generation	131,461r	5,253	141,905	90,093	5,054r	3,577	377,342r	4,055	2,422	967r	384,786r
Used on works	6,059	476	3,189	7,108	292	165	17,289	23	82	-	17,394
Supplied (gross)	125,402	4,777	138,716	82,985	4,762r	3,412	360,053r	4,032	2,340	967r	367,392r
Used in pumping											3,210
Supplied (net)											364,182r
2002											
Major power producers (2)											
Fuel used	332,889	8,011	291,264	233,765	3,186	-	869,115	3,927	2,652	-	875,694
Generation	120,958	2,011	135,741	87,848	856	-	347,414	3,927	2,652	-	353,994
Used on works	5,574	378	2,877	6,758	55	-	15,643	14	90	-	15,746
Supplied (gross)	115,383	1,633	132,864	81,090	802	-	331,772	3,914	2,562	-	338,248
Used in pumping											3,463
Supplied (net)											334,785
Other generators (2)											
Fuel used	11,663	6,966r	38,177r	-	20,922r	12,343r	90,071r	860	-	1,259	92,190r
Generation	3,321r	2,788r	16,536r	-	4,769	3,719r	31,133r	860	-	1,259	33,252r
Used on works	230	204r	530r	-	264	141r	1,369r	11	-	-	1,380r
Supplied	3,092r	2,584r	16,006r	-	4,505	3,578r	29,765r	849	-	1,259	31,873r
All generating companies											
Fuel used	344,552	14,977r	329,442r	233,765	24,107r	12,343r	959,186r	4,788	2,652	1,259	967,884r
Generation	124,279r	4,799r	152,277r	87,848	5,625	3,719r	378,548r	4,788	2,652	1,259	387,246r
Used on works	5,804r	582r	3,407r	6,758	318	141r	17,011r	25	90	-	17,126r
Supplied (gross)	118,475r	4,217r	148,870r	81,090	5,307r	3,578r	361,537r	4,763	2,562	1,259	370,120r
Used in pumping											3,463
Supplied (net)											366,657r

5.6 Electricity fuel use, generation and supply (cont'd)

GWh

| | Thermal sources | | | | | | | Non-thermal sources | | | |
	Coal	Oil	Gas	Nuclear	Renew-ables (1)	Other (3)	Total	Hydro-natural flow	Hydro-pumped storage	Other (4)	Total All sources
2003											
Major power producers (2)											
Fuel used	367,162r	7,604	284,662	233,080	4,434r	-	896,941r	2,568	2,734	-	902,243r
Generation	134,023	2,197	131,238	88,686	1,154	-	357,299	2,568	2,734	-	362,600
Used on works	6,325	249	3,201	6,775	95	-	16,645	9	92	-	16,747
Supplied (gross)	127,698	1,948	128,037	81,911	1,059	-	340,654	2,559	2,641	-	345,854
Used in pumping											3,546
Supplied (net)											342,308
Other generators (2)											
Fuel used	11,301r	6,263r	39,264r	-	24,043r	21,981r	102,852r	660	-	1,288	104,801r
Generation	4,282r	2,397r	17,633r	-	5,547r	4,059r	33,918r	660	-	1,288	35,866r
Used on works	220r	174r	546r	-	335	157r	1,432r	7	-	-	1,439r
Supplied	4,062r	2,223r	17,087r	-	5,212r	3,902r	32,486r	653	-	1,288	34,427r
All generating companies											
Fuel used	378,463r	13,867r	323,926r	233,080	28,477r	21,981r	999,793r	3,228	2,734	1,288	1,007,043r
Generation	138,305r	4,595r	148,871r	88,686r	6,701r	4,059r	391,217r	3,228	2,734	1,288	398,467r
Used on works	6,545r	424r	3,747r	6,775	430r	157r	18,077r	16	92	-	18,185r
Supplied (gross)	131,760r	4,171r	145,124r	81,911	6,271r	3,902r	373,140r	3,212	2,641	1,288	380,281r
Used in pumping											3,546
Supplied (net)											376,735r
2004											
Major power producers (2)											
Fuel used	353,256	6,685	304,495	212,248	6,480	-	882,163	4,253	2,649	-	889,065
Generation	127,827	1,883	140,577	79,999	1,471	-	351,757	4,253	2,649	-	358,659
Used on works	5,890	354	2,820	6,317	104	-	15,486	15	90	-	15,590
Supplied (gross)	121,937	1,528	137,758	73,682	1,367	-	336,271	4,238	2,559	-	343,068
Used in pumping											3,497
Supplied (net)											339,571
Other generators (2)											
Fuel used	11,186	6,559	33,658	-	26,508	18,025	95,936	677	-	1,939	98,552
Generation	4,184	3,032	15,526	-	6,407	5,204	34,353	677	-	1,939	36,969
Used on works	219	216	481	-	453	211	1,580	1	-	-	1,581
Supplied	3,965	2,816	15,045	-	5,954	4,993	32,773	676	-	1,939	35,388
All generating companies											
Fuel used	364,442	13,245	338,152	212,248	32,988	18,025	978,099	4,930	2,649	1,939	987,617
Generation	132,011	4,915	156,103	79,999	7,878	5,204	386,110	4,930	2,649	1,939	395,628
Used on works	6,109	571	3,301	6,317	557	211	17,066	16	90	-	17,171
Supplied (gross)	125,902	4,344	152,803	73,682	7,321	4,993	369,044	4,914	2,559	1,939	378,456
Used in pumping											3,497
Supplied (net)											374,959

| | 2000 | | 2001 | | 2002 | | 2003 | | 2004 | |
	Conv-entional thermal (5)	CCGT	Conv-entional thermal (5)	CCGT	Conv-entional thermal (5)	CCGT	Conv-entional thermal (5)	CCGT	Conv-entional thermal (5)	CCGT
Major power producers (2)										
Generated	131,760	117,935	133,482	123,846	127,550	132,016	147,536	121,076	142,497	129,261
Supplied (gross)	125,468	116,110	127,126r	121,344	121,297	129,384	140,196	118,546	135,400	127,189
Other generators										
Generated	22,724	10,859	20,937	8,979	20,557r	10,577	22,850r	11,068r	23,240	11,113
Supplied (gross)	21,926	10,318	20,066r	8,531	19,716r	10,049	21,970r	10,516r	22,214	10,559
All generating companies										
Generated	154,485	128,794	154,418	132,825	148,107r	142,593	170,386r	132,144r	165,737	140,374
Supplied (gross)	147,394	126,428	147,192r	129,875	141,013r	139,433	162,166r	129,062r	157,614	137,748

(1) Thermal renewable sources are those included under biofuels and non-biodegradable wastes in Chapter 7.
(2) See paragraphs 5.49 and 5.50 on companies covered.
(3) Other thermal sources include coke oven gas, blast furnace gas and waste products from chemical processes.
(4) Other non-thermal sources include wind, wave and solar photovoltaics.
(5) Includes gas turbines, oil engines and plants producing electricity from renewable sources other than hydro.

5.7 Plant capacity - United Kingdom

MW

	2000	2001	2002	2003	end December 2004
Major power producers *(1)*					
Total declared net capability	**72,193**	**73,382**	**70,369r**	**71,500r**	**73,308**
Of which:					
Conventional steam stations:	34,835	34,835	30,687	30,327r	31,182
Coal fired	24,810	24,810	22,427	22,524	22,639
Oil fired	2,933	2,933	2,708	2,930	2,930
Mixed or dual fired *(2)*	7,092	7,092	5,552	4,873r	5,613
Combined cycle gas turbine stations	19,349	20,517	21,800	23,577r	24,591
Nuclear stations	12,486	12,486	12,240r	11,852r	11,852
Gas turbines and oil engines	1,291	1,291	1,433r	1,537r	1,477
Hydro-electric stations:					
Natural flow	1,327	1,348	1,304	1,302	1,301
Pumped storage	2,788	2,788	2,788	2,788	2,788
Renewables other than hydro	117	117	117	117	117
Other generators *(1)*					
Total capacity of own generating plant	**6,258**	**6,296**	**6,336r**	**6,829r**	**7,062**
Of which:					
Conventional steam stations *(3)*	3,544	3,464	3,325r	3,451r	3,450
Combined cycle gas turbine stations	1,709	1,777	1,854	1,956r	1,980
Hydro-electric stations (natural flow)	158	160	162	166	159
Renewables other than hydro	847	895	995r	1,256r	1,473
All generating companies					
Total capacity	**78,451**	**79,678**	**76,705r**	**78,329r**	**80,370**
Of which:					
Conventional steam stations *(3)*	38,379	38,299	34,012r	33,778r	34,632
Combined cycle gas turbine stations	21,058	22,294	23,654	25,533r	26,571
Nuclear stations	12,486	12,486	12,240r	11,852r	11,852
Gas turbines and oil engines	1,291	1,291	1,433r	1,537r	1,477
Hydro-electric stations:					
Natural flow	1,485	1,508	1,466	1,468	1,460
Pumped storage	2,788	2,788	2,788	2,788	2,788
Renewables other than hydro	964	1,012	1,112r	1,373r	1,590

(1) See paragraphs 5.49 and 5.50 for information on companies covered.
(2) Includes gas fired stations that are not Combined Cycle Gas Turbines.
(3) For other generators, conventional steam stations include combined heat and power plants (electrical capacity only), but
exclude combined cycle gas turbine plants, hydro-electric stations and plants using renewable sources.

5.8 Plant capacity - England and Wales, Scotland, and Northern Ireland

MW

					end December
	2000	2001	2002	2003	2004
Major power producers in England and Wales *(1)*					
Total declared net capability	**60,585**	**61,850**	**59,087r**	**60,053r**	**61,863**
Of which:					
Conventional steam stations:	28,128	28,128	25,634	26,171r	27,026
Coal fired	21,240	21,240	18,971	19,068	19,183
Oil fired	2,753	2,753	2,528	2,750	2,750
Mixed or dual fired *(2)*	4,135	4,135	4,135	4,353r	5,093
Combined cycle gas turbine stations	19,275	20,443	20,186	20,967	21,932
Nuclear stations	10,046	10,046	9,800r	9,412r	9,412
Gas turbines and oil engines	807	897	1,131	1,168r	1,159
Hydro-electric stations:					
Natural flow	124	131	131	131	129
Pumped storage	2,088	2,088	2,088	2,088	2,088
Renewables other than hydro	117	117	117	117	117
Major power producers in Scotland *(1)*					
Total declared net capability	**9,677**	**9,601**	**9,465**	**9,531**	**9,583**
Of which:					
Conventional steam and combined cycle gas turbine stations	5,070	5,070	5,069	5,070	5,119
Nuclear stations	2,440	2,440	2,440	2,440	2,440
Gas turbines and oil engines	264	174	83	150	152
Hydro-electric stations:					
Natural flow	1,203	1,217	1,173	1,171	1,172
Pumped storage	700	700	700	700	700
Major power producers in Northern Ireland *(1)*					
Total declared net capability	**1,930**	**1,930**	**1,816**	**1,915**	**1,862**

(1) See paragraphs 5.49 and 5.50 for information on companies covered.
(2) Includes gas fired stations that are not Combined Cycle Gas Turbines.

5.9 Capacity of other generators

MW

					end-December
	2000	2001	2002	2003	2004
Capacity of own generating plant [1]					
Undertakings in industrial and commercial sector:					
Petroleum refineries	1,003	1,000r	954	955r	955
Iron and steel	373	379	309r	312r	314
Chemicals	1,314r	1,340r	1,390r	1,324r	1,360
Engineering and other metal trades	615	617	621	647r	670
Food, drink and tobacco	412r	394	404	379	379
Paper, printing and publishing	577r	548r	598	804	789
Other *(2)*	1,682r	1,735r	1,958r	2,304r	2,491
Total industrial and commercial sector	5,975	6,013	6,233r	6,726r	6,959
Undertakings in transport sector	283	283	103	103	103
Total other generators	**6,258**	**6,296**	**6,336r**	**6,829r**	**7,062**

(1) For combined heat and power plants the electrical capacity only is included. Further CHP capacity is included under major
  power producers in Table 5.7. A detailed analysis of CHP capacity is given in the tables of Chapter 6.
(2) Includes companies in the commercial sector.

5.10 Plant loads, demand and efficiency

Major power producers [1]

	Unit	2000	2001	2002	2003	2004
Simultaneous maximum load met [2][3]	MW	58,452	58,589	61,717	60,501	61,013
of which England and Wales	MW	51,020	51,548	54,430	52,965	53,795
Scotland	MW	5,861	5,504	5,688	5,909	5,579
Northern Ireland	MW	1,571	1,537	1,599	1,627	1,639
Maximum demand as a percentage of UK capacity	Per cent	81.1	80.0	87.7r	84.6r	83.2
Plant load factor						
Combined cycle gas turbine stations	Per cent	75.0	69.7	70.0r	59.8	60.3
Nuclear stations	"	70.5	76.1	75.1r	77.8r	71.0
Hydro-electric stations:						
Natural flow	"	37.2	27.4	33.8	22.5	37.2
Pumped storage	"	10.7	9.6	10.5	10.8	10.5
Conventional thermal and other stations [4]	"	39.2r	40.2r	40.6r	50.0	47.7
of which coal-fired stations	"	50.8	56.0	55.9	65.0	62.0
All plant	"	**52.5r**	**53.0r**	**53.9**	**55.8r**	**54.1**
System load factor	"	**67.4**	**68.7**	**64.8**	**67.0**	**66.3**
Thermal efficiency						
(gross calorific value basis)						
Combined cycle gas turbine stations	"	46.6	46.7	47.2	46.4	46.8
Coal fired stations	"	36.2	35.8	36.3r	36.5r	36.2
Nuclear stations	"	37.3	37.3	37.6	38.1	37.9

(1) See paragraphs 5.49 and 5.50 for information on companies covered.
(2) Data cover the 12 months ending March of the following year eg 2004 data are for the year ending March 2005
(3) The demands shown are those that occurred in Scotland and Northern Ireland at the same time as England and Wales had their maximum demand. See paragraph 5.56 for further details.
(4) Conventional steam plants, gas turbines and oil engines and plants producing electricity from renewable sources other than hydro.

5.11 Power Stations in the United Kingdom
(operational at the end of May 2005)[1]

Company Name	Station Name	Fuel	Installed Capacity (MW)	Year of commission or year generation began
AES	Kilroot	coal/oil	520	1981
	Indian Queens	gas oil/kerosene	140	1996
Airtricity	Ardrossan	wind	24	2004
	Tappaghan	wind	20	2005
Alcan	Lynemouth	coal	420	1995
	Fort William	hydro	62	1929
	Kinlochleven	hydro	30	1907
Baglan Generation Ltd	Baglan Bay	gas turbine	575	2002
Barking Power	Barking	CCGT	1,000	1994
Beaufort Wind Ltd	Kirkby Moor	wind	5	1993
	Taff Ely	wind	9	1993
	Bryn Titli	wind	10	1994
	Trysglwyn	wind	6	1996
	Carno	wind	34	1996
	Novar	wind	17	1997
	Llyn Alaw	wind	20	1997
	Mynydd Gorddu	wind	10	1996
	Bein Ghlas	wind	8	1999
	Lambrigg	wind	7	2000
	Tow Law	wind	2	2001
British Energy	Dungeness B	nuclear	1,110	1985
	Hartlepool	nuclear	1,210	1989
	Heysham1	nuclear	1,150	1989
	Heysham 2	nuclear	1,250	1989
	Hinkley Point B	nuclear	1,220	1976
	Sizewell B	nuclear	1,188	1995
	Hunterston B	nuclear	1,190	1976
	Torness	nuclear	1,250	1988
	Eggborough	coal	1,960	1967
	Bridgewater District Energy	gas	10	2000
	Solutia District Energy	gas	10	2000
	Sevington District Energy	gas	10	2000
	Aberdare District Energy	gas	10	2002
BNFL British Nuclear Group	Dungeness A	nuclear	450	1965
	Oldbury	nuclear	434	1967
	Sizewell A	nuclear	420	1966
	Wylfa	nuclear	980	1971
	Maentwrog	hydro	28	1928
Calpine Corporation	Saltend (2)	CCGT	1,200	2000
Cemmaes Windfarm Ltd	Cemmaes	wind	15	2002 (3)
Centrica	Barry	CCGT	250	1998
	Glanford Brigg	CCGT	240	1993
	Killingholme	CCGT	650	1994
	Kings Lynn	CCGT	340	1996
	Peterborough	CCGT	380	1993
	Roosecote	CCGT	229	1991
Cold Northcott Windfarm Ltd	Cold Northcott	wind	7	1993

5.11 Power Stations in the United Kingdom
(operational at the end of May 2005)[1] (continued)

Company Name	Station Name	Fuel	Installed Capacity (MW)	Year of commission or year generation began
Citigen (London) UK Ltd	Charterhouse St, London	gas/gas oil	31	1995
Coolkeeragh ESB Ltd	Coolkeeragh	CCGT	420	2005
Corby Power Ltd	Corby	CCGT	401	1993
Coryton Energy Company Ltd	Coryton	CCGT	753	2001
Derwent Cogeneration	Derwent	gas CHP	236	1994
Drax Power Ltd	Drax	coal	3,870	1974
	Drax GT	gas oil	75	1971
EDF Energy	Sutton Bridge	CCGT	800	1999
	Cottam	coal	2,008	1969
	West Burton	coal	1,972	1967
	West Burton GT	gas oil	40	1967
EPR Ely Limited	Elean	straw/gas	38	2001
E.On UK	Kingsnorth	coal/oil	1,940	1970
	Ironbridge	coal	970	1970
	Ratcliffe	coal	2,000	1968
	Grain (4)	oil	650	1979
	Grain GT	gas oil	55	1978
	Kingsnorth GT	gas oil	34	1967
	Ratcliffe GT	gas oil	34	1966
	Taylor's Lane GT	gas oil	132	1979
	Connahs Quay	CCGT	1,380	1996
	Cottam Development Centre	CCGT	395	1999
	Brimsdown	CCGT	392	1999
	Killingholme	CCGT	900	1993
	Rheidol	hydro	49	1961
	Askam	wind	5	1999
	Bessy Bell	wind	5	1995
	Blood Hill	wind	2	1992
	Bowbeat	wind	31	2002
	Deucheran Hill	wind	16	2001
	Great Eppleton	wind	3	1997
	Hare Hill	wind	5	2004
	High Volts	wind	8	2004
	Holmside	wind	5	2004
	Lowca	wind	5	2000
	Oldside	wind	5	1996
	Out Newton	wind	9	2002
	Rheidol	wind	2	1997
	Scroby Sands	wind (offshore)	60	2004
	Siddick	wind	4	1996
	St Breock	wind	5	1994
Fellside Heat and Power	Fellside	gas CHP	168	1993
Fibrogen	Glanford	meat & bone meal	13	1993
Fibropower Ltd	Eye, Suffolk	poultry litter	13	1992
Fibrothetford	Thetford	poultry litter	39	1998
Gaz de France	Shotton	gas CHP	180	2001
Great Orton Windfarm Ltd	Great Orton	wind	4	1999 (3)
Great Yarmouth Power Ltd	Great Yarmouth	CCGT	420	2001

5.11 Power Stations in the United Kingdom
(operational at the end of May 2005)[1] (continued)

Company Name	Station Name	Fuel	Installed Capacity (MW)	Year of commission or year generation began
Humber Power	South Humber Bank 1	CCGT	785	1996
	South Humber Bank 2	CCGT	527	1998
Immingham CHP LLP	Immingham CHP	gas CHP	734	2004
International Power	Deeside	CCGT	500	1994
	Rugeley	coal	1,006	1972
	Rugeley GT	gas oil	50	1972
IPM Energy Ltd	Dinorwig	pumped storage	1,728	1983
	Ffestiniog	pumped storage	360	1961
Llangwyryfon Windfarm Ltd	Llangwyryfon	wind	9	2003 (3)
Npower Renewables	North Hoyle	wind (offshore)	60	2003
	Windy Standard	wind	22	1996
	Bears Down	wind	10	2001
	Causeymire	wind	48	2004
Premier Power Ltd	Ballylumford	CCGT	996	2002
Rocksavage Power Co. Ltd	Rocksavage	CCGT	750	1997
RWE Npower Plc	Aberthaw B	coal	1,455	1971
	Tilbury B (5)	coal/oil	1,029	1968
	Didcot A	coal/gas	1,940	1972
	Aberthaw GT	gas oil	51	1971
	Cowes	gas oil	70	1982
	Didcot GT	gas oil	100	1972
	Fawley GT	gas oil	34	1969
	Littlebrook GT	gas oil	105	1982
	Tilbury GT	gas oil	34	1968
	Fawley (5)	oil	484	1969
	Littlebrook D	oil	2,055	1982
	Didcot B	CCGT	1,370	1998
	Little Barford	CCGT	665	1995
	Cwm Dyli	hydro	10	2002 (3)
	Dolgarrog High Head	hydro	18	2002 (3)
	Dolgarrog Low Head	hydro	15	1926/2002
Scottish & Southern Energy plc **Hydro Schemes:** Affric/Beauly	Mullardoch Tunnel	hydro	2.4	1955
	Fasnakyle	hydro	69	1951
	Deanie	hydro	38	1963
	Culligran	hydro	19	1962
	Aigas	hydro	20	1962
	Kilmorack	hydro	20	1962
Breadalbane	Lubreoch	hydro	4	1958
	Cashlie	hydro	11	1959
	Lochay	hydro	47	1958
	Finlarig	hydro	17	1955
	Lednock	hydro	3	1961
	St. Fillans	hydro	17	1957
	Dalchonzie	hydro	4	1958
Conon	Achanalt	hydro	3	1956
	Grudie Bridge	hydro	19	1950
	Mossford	hydro	19	1957
	Luichart	hydro	34	1954
	Orrin	hydro	18	1959
	Torr Achilty	hydro	15	1954

5.11 Power Stations in the United Kingdom
(operational at the end of May 2005)[1] (continued)

Company Name	Station Name	Fuel	Installed Capacity (MW)	Year of commission or year generation began
Scottish & Southern Energy plc				
Hydro Schemes (continued)				
Foyers	Foyers	hydro/pumped storage	300	1974
Great Glen	Foyers Falls	hydro	5	1968
	Mucomir	hydro	2	1962
	Ceannacroc	hydro	20	1956
	Livishie	hydro	15	1962
	Glenmoriston	hydro	37	1957
	Quoich	hydro	19	1955
	Ivergarry	hydro	20	1956
	Kingairloch	hydro	4	2005
Shin	Cassley	hydro	10	1959
	Lairg	hydro	4	1959
	Shin	hydro	19	1958
Sloy/Awe	Sloy	hydro	153	1950
	Sron Mor	hydro	5	1957
	Clachan	hydro	40	1955
	Alt-na-Lairgie	hydro	6	1956
	Nant	hydro	15	1963
	Inverawe	hydro	25	1963
	Kilmelfort	hydro	2	1956
	Loch Gair	hydro	6	1961
	Lussa	hydro	2	1952
	Striven	hydro	8	1951
Tummel	Gaur	hydro	8	1953
	Cuaich	hydro	3	1959
	Loch Ericht	hydro	2	1962
	Rannoch	hydro	44	1930
	Tummel	hydro	34	1933
	Errochty	hydro	75	1955
	Clunie	hydro	61	1950
	Pitlochry	hydro	15	1950
Wind	Spurness	wind	8	2004
	Tangy	wind	13	2002
Small Hydros:	Chliostair	hydro	1	1960
	Kerry Falls	hydro	1	1951
	Loch Dubh	hydro	1	1954
	Nostie Bridge	hydro	1	1950
	Storr Lochs	hydro	2	1952
	Cuileag	hydro	3	2002
Thermal:	Peterhead (6)	CCGT oil/gas	1,540	1980
	Medway	CCGT	688	1995
	Fife Power Station	CCGT	120	2000
	Keadby	CCGT	745	1994
	Ferrybridge C	coal/biomass co-fired	1,955	1966
	Fiddler's Ferry	coal/biomass co-fired	1,961	1971
	Ferrybridge GT	gas oil	34	1966
	Fiddler's Ferry GT	gas oil	34	1969
	Chickerell	gas	45	1998
	Burghfield	gas	45	1998
	Thatcham	diesel	9	1994
	Five Oaks	diesel	9	1995
	Chippenham	gas	10	2002
	Wheldale	gas	10	2002

5.11 Power Stations in the United Kingdom
(operational at the end of May 2005)[1] (continued)

Company Name	Station Name	Fuel	Installed Capacity (MW)	Year of commission or year generation began
Scottish Power				
Island Generation	Stornoway	diesel	24	1950
	Lerwick	diesel	67	1953
	Arnish	diesel	3	2001
	Kirkwall	diesel	16	1953
	Loch Carnan, South Uist	diesel	12	1971
	Bowmore	diesel	6	1946
	Tiree	diesel	3	1945
	Barra	diesel	2	1990
Galloway	Carsfad	hydro	12	1936
	Drumjohn	hydro	2	1985
	Earlstoun	hydro	14	1936
	Glenlee	hydro	24	1935
	Kendoon	hydro	24	1936
	Tongland	hydro	33	1935
Lanark	Bonnington	hydro	11	1927
	Stonebyres	hydro	5	1927
Cruachan	Cruachan	pumped storage	399	1966
Thermal:	Cockenzie	coal	1,152	1967
	Longannet	coal	2,304	1970
	Knapton	gas	40	1994
	Rye House	CCGT	715	1993
	Damhead Creek	CCGT	792	2000
	Shoreham	CCGT	400	2000
Wind	Beinn an Tuirc	wind	30	2002
	Dun Law	wind	17	2000
	Hare Hill	wind	13	2000
	Hagshaw Hill	wind	16	1995
	Cruach Mhor	wind	30	2004
	Coal Clough	wind	10	1992
	Carland Cross	wind	6	1992
	Rigged Hill	wind	5	1994
	Corkey	wind	5	1994
	Elliots Hill	wind	5	1995
	Penryddian & Llidiartywaun	wind	31	1992
Seabank Power Limited	Seabank 1	CCGT	812	1998
	Seabank 2	CCGT	410	2000
Sita Tyre Recycling Ltd	Wolverhampton(7)	waste	20	1994
South East London Combined Heat & Power Ltd	Landmann Way, London	waste	32	1994
Spalding Energy Company Ltd	Spalding	CCGT	903	2004
Teesside Power Ltd	Teesside Power Station	CCGT	1,875	1992
Uskmouth Power Company Ltd	Uskmouth (2)	coal	393	2000
Western Power Generation	St Marys	gas oil	6	1958
	Princetown	kerosene	3	1959
	Lynton	gas oil	2	1961
	Roseland	kerosene	5	1963
Total			**76,972**	

For footnotes see next page

5.11 Power Stations in the United Kingdom
(operational at the end of May 2005)[1] (continued)

Other power stations[9]

Station type	Fuel	Capacity (MW)
Renewable sources	wind	227
and combustible wastes	landfill gas	722
	sewage gas	119
	hydro	207
	waste	275
	other	90
CHP schemes listed in Table 5.12	various fuels	2,731
CHP schemes other than major power producers and renewables and those listed in Table 5.12	mainly gas	1,295
Other autogenerators	various fuels	926

Interconnectors

	Capacity (MW)
England - Scotland (10)	2,200
England - France	2,000
Scotland - Northern Ireland	500
Northern Ireland - Irish Republic	600

Footnotes
(1) This list covers stations of more than 1 MW capacity, but excludes some renewables stations of over 1 MW which are included in the sub table on page 142.
(2) This station was in the process of being sold to International Power in Summer 2005
(3) Recommissioning date.
(4) 650 MW remain mothballed and may be re-instated in 2005
(5) Excludes mothballed capacity.
(6) Total capacity is 2,319 MW but because of transmission constraints only 1,540 MW can be used at any one time.
(7) There has been no generation from this site for several years.
(8) Formerly Fifoots Point; resumed generation under new ownership in 2004
(9) As at end December 2004.
(10) From April 2005 this became part of the Great Britain wide electricity network

5.12 Large scale CHP schemes in the United Kingdom
(operational at the end of December 2004)[1]

Company Name	Scheme Location	Installed Capacity (MWe) [2]
Acordis UK Ltd	Grimsby, South Humberside	48.4
Addenbrookes NHS Trust	Addenbrookes Hospital, Cambridge	4.2
Alta Estate Services Limited	The University of Birmingham	6.0
Amylum UK Ltd (Tunnel Refineries)	Greenwich	17.6
Archer Daniels Midland Ltd (ADM Ltd)	Erith	14.0
Arjo Wiggins Appleton plc	Chartham, Kent	10.9
	Dartford	10.0
	Aberdeen	10.0
	Fort William	6.0
Arreton Valley Nursery Ltd	Isle of Wight	33.3
Astra-Zeneca UK Ltd	Macclesfield	22.8
Bayer Cropscience	Norwich	4.4
BBC	Shepherds Bush, London	4.9
BMW UK Manufacturing Ltd	Cowley, Oxfordshire	3.2
Boots Company plc	Beeston, Nottingham	13.8
BP PLC	BP Oil Grangemouth	289.9
	Sullom Voe Terminal	98.4
BP Energy Ltd	Nestle Rowntree, York	9.6
BPB PLC	Aberdeen	8.0
British Salt Ltd	Middlewich, Cheshire	10.0
British Sugar plc	Wissington, Norfolk	88.5
	Bury St Edmunds, Suffolk	85.6
	Cantley, Norfolk	14.8
	Newark, Nottinghamshire	10.0
	York	10.0
	Allscott, Shropshire	7.5
Brunner Mond (UK) Ltd	Winnington, Cheshire	26.5
	Lostock, Cheshire	12.5
Cargill plc	Tilbury, Essex	4.5
Carlesberg Tetley Brewing Ltd	Leeds	1.0
Cerestar UK Ltd	Manchester	12.0
Cogenco Ltd	Tangmere Nurseries, Chichester, West Sussex	3.0
CIBA Speciality Chemicals plc	Low Moor, Bradford	7.5
City Hospital NHS Trust	Dudley Road Hospital, Birmingham	3.4
City Hospitals Sunderland NHS Trust	Sunderland General Hospital, Tyne and Wear	1.1
Coventry and Solihull Waste Disposal	Coventry	13.0
Crisp Maltings Ltd	Fakenham, Norfolk	1.2
Dalkia Utility Services	Leeds General Infirmary	18.1
	Queen Elizabeth Hospital, Edgbaston, Warwickshire	3.6
	Royal Liverpool University Hospital	2.8
	Freeman Hospital, Newcastle-upon-Tyne	2.6
De La Rue International Ltd	Basingstoke, Hampshire	6.2
De Mulder and Sons Ltd	Hartshill	2.9
Diageo Distillers Ltd	Glasgow	6.3
DSM Nutritional Products UK Ltd	Dalry, Ayrshire	45.8
Dupont (UK) Ltd	Maydown works, Londonderry	11.7
Dwr Cymru	Pen-y-Bont, Glamorgan	6.0
EE Realisation Ltd	Nottingham District Heating Scheme	18.3
E.On UK (CHP) Ltd	Grovehurst Energy Ltd, Sittingbourne, Kent	80.6
	Hickson and Welch, Castleford, West Yorkshire	56.0
	Iggesund, Workington, Cumbria	42.0
	Conoco Humber refinery, South Killingholme, Humberside	34.0
	Queens Medical Centre, Nottingham	4.9
	A H Marks, Bradford	4.5
	St James University Hospital, Leeds	4.5
Flexsys plc	Cefn Mawr, Wrexham	3.7
Georgia-Pacific GB Ltd	Oughtibridge, Sheffield	5.0

5.12 Large scale CHP schemes in the United Kingdom
(operational at the end of December 2004)[1] (continued)

Company Name	Scheme Location	Installed Capacity (MWe) [2]
GlaxoSmithKline Ltd	Wellcome Foundation, Dartford	13.5
	Ulverston	6.1
Grampian Country Pork Ltd	Malton, Yorkshire	1.0
Harrods Ltd	London	5.2
Ineos Chlor	Runcorn, Cheshire	38.4
Elyo Industrial UK Ltd	Thornton Cleveleys, Lancashire	41.0
Imerys Minerals	Par Harbour, Cornwall	7.5
	Plympton, Devon	3.8
	Bugle, Cornwall	3.8
Imperial Tobacco	Nottingham	4.0
International Paper UK Ltd	Federal Tait, Inverurie, Aberdeenshire	22.7
James Cropper Ltd	Kendal, Cumbria	7.0
Kappa SSK Ltd	Nechells, Birmingham	3.5
Kodak Ltd	Harrow, Middlesex	17.3
Kraft Jacobs Suchard Ltd	Banbury, Oxon	7.2
Kronospan Ltd	Chirk, Wrexham	12.4
Land Rover Ltd	Solihull, West Midlands	11.2
Leicester Royal Infirmary NHS Trust	Leicester	2.1
Manchester Airport plc	Manchester	9.4
NEL Power Ltd	Mill Nurseries, Keyingham, Hull	15.0
Newcastle City Council	Byker Reclamation Plant	1.0
North Hampshire NHS Trust	Basingstoke Hospital	1.0
North Tees and Hartlepool NHS Trust	North Tees Hospital, Stockton	1.0
Northumbrian Healthcare NHS Trust	North Tyneside General Hospital, Whitley Bay	1.5
North West Water Ltd	Davyhulme Waste Water Treatment Works, Manchester	5.7
	Bolton Waste Water Treatment Works	1.1
Novartis	Grimsby, South Humberside	7.6
RWE Npower Cogen Ltd	Esso Oil Refinery, Fawley	135.0
	Aylesford Newsprint Ltd, Kent	98.0
	BASF PLC, Seal Sands, Middlesbrough	75.0
	Bridgewater Paper, Ellesmere Port	58.0
	Philips Petroleum, Teesside	58.0
	Lindsey Oil Refinery Ltd, South Humberside	38.0
	Dow Corning, Barry	20.5
	Huntsman Tioxide, Grimsby, South Humberside	20.5
	Millenium Inorganic Chemicals, Stallingborough	15.0
	Huntsman Surface Science, Whitehaven	9.0
	Georgia Pacific, Bridgend	9.0
	SCA Hygene Products, Skelmersdale, Lancashire	7.0
	Rhodia Consumer Specialities, Oldbury	3.7
	Lancaster University	1.6
Petroplus Tank Storage Ltd	Milford Haven	19.8
Pfizer Ltd	Sandwich, Kent	16.0
Rigid Paper Ltd	Selby, North Yorkshire	4.6
Rolls Royce Power Ventures Ltd	Derby Cogeneration Ltd, Derby	62.0
	Bristol Energy Project	49.9
Roquette UK Ltd	Corby	14.5
Sembcorp Utilities	Wilton, Redcar, Cleveland	220.0
Scottish and Southern Energy plc	Townsend Hook, Kent	52.0
	Salt Union, Cheshire	47.0
	Hedon Salads, Burstwick	10.0
	Hazelwood VHB, Runcton	4.0
	Hedon Salads, Newport	3.9
	Eli Lilly, Speke	3.6
	Tayside Universities NHS Trust	2.6
	Dundee University Hospitals NHS Trust	2.6

5.12 Large scale CHP schemes in the United Kingdom
(operational at the end of December 2004)[1] *(continued)*

Company Name	Scheme Location	Installed Capacity (MWe) [2]
Scottish and Southern Energy plc (continued)	Hazelwood VHB, Angmering, West Sussex	2.0
	Koopers UK Ltd, Port Clarence, Teesside	2.0
	Hedon Salads, Slough	1.9
	Buckland Nurseries, Reigate, Surrey	1.9
	University of North Staffordshire NHS Trust	1.4
	Red Roofs, Cottingham, Yorks	1.4
	Bromley Hospitals Healthcare Trust	1.0
	Western General Hospital, Edinburgh	1.0
Sevalco Ltd	Avonmouth, Bristol	6.6
Severn Trent Water Ltd	Minworth Water Reclamation Works, Sutton Coldfield, West	4.2
	Stoke Bardolph Sewage Treatment Works, Nottingham	2.4
	Loughborough Sewage Treatment Works, Leicestershire	1.0
	Netheridge Sewage Treatment Works	1.0
Slough Heat and Power Ltd	Slough	90.0
Solutia UK plc	Newport	1.2
South Durham Healthcare NHS Trust	Darlington Hospital, Co Durham	1.0
Stanlow Manufacturing Complex	Stanlow, Cheshire	108.4
St Georges's Healthcare NHS Trust	St George's Hospital, Tooting, London	4.4
Stiell Faciliies Management	Airbus Aerostructures, Broughton, Cheshire	3.1
Surface Specialities plc	Wigton, Cumbria	5.3
Syngenta Ltd	Grangemouth, Stirilingshire	7.5
	Huddersfield	16.3
Tate and Lyle plc	Silvertown, London	10.0
	Selby, North Yorkshire	5.4
Thames Valley Power Ltd	Heathrow Airport	15.0
Thames Water Utilities	Crossness Sewage Treatment Works, Abbey Wood, London	96.0
	Beckton Sewage Treatment Works, Barking, Essex	10.0
	Mogden Sewage Treatment Works, Isleworth, Middlesex	9.6
	Maple Lodge Sewage Treatment Works, Rickmansworth, Herts	3.2
	Beddington Sewage Treatment Works, Croydon, Surrey	3.1
	Deephams Sewage Treatment Works, Edmonton, London	3.0
	Riverside Sewage Treatment Works, Rainham, Essex	2.2
	Rye Meads Sewage Treatment Works, Ware, Herts	1.5
Thameswey Energy	Woking, Surrey	1.4
Tullis Russell and Company Ltd	Glenrothes, Fife	25.0
UK Coal plc	Harworth Colliery, Burcoates, Doncaster	18.0
United Biscuits UK Ltd	Manchester	2.0
University of Liverpool	Liverpool	3.7
University of Nottingham	Nottingham	3.6
Wessex Water Services Ltd	Bristol Waste Water Treatment Works, Avonmouth	5.8
Wimpey Mainsprint Joint Venture	West Quarry, Appley Bridge	1.1
W S Atkins Power	Fen Drayton	4.5
	Britannia Salads, Villa Nursery, Roydon, Essex	3.0
	Glen Avon Growers, Cottingham, North Humberside	3.0
	Anchor Nurseries Ltd, Beverley	3.0
	Abbey View Nurseries, Waltham Abbey, Essex	3.0
	UK Salads, Roydon, Essex	3.0
Total [2]		3,102.9
Electrical capacity of good quality CHP for these sites in total		2,730.9

(1) These are sites of 1 MW installed electrical capacity or more that either have agreed to be listed in the Ofgem register of CHP plants or whose details are publicly available elsewhere, or who have provided the information directly to DTI. It excludes CHP sites that have been listed as major power producers in Table 5.11.

(2) This is the total power output from these sites and includes all the capacity at that site, not just that classed as good quality CHP under CHPQA.

Chapter 6
Combined heat and power

Introduction

6.1   This chapter sets out the contribution made by Combined Heat and Power (CHP) to the United Kingdom's energy requirements. The data presented in this Chapter have been derived from information submitted to the CHP Quality Assurance programme (CHPQA). This programme was introduced by Government to provide the methods and procedures to assess and certify the quality of the full range of CHP schemes. It is a rigorous system for the Government to ensure that the incentives on offer are targeted fairly and benefit schemes in relation to their environmental performance. The data presented in this chapter have been derived from information submitted to CHPQA or by following the same procedures where no information has been provided directly.

6.2   CHP is the simultaneous generation of usable heat and power (usually electricity) in a single process. The term CHP is synonymous with cogeneration and total energy, which are terms often used in other Member States of the European Community and the United States. CHP uses a variety of fuels and technologies across a wide range of sites and scheme sizes. The basic elements of a CHP plant comprise one or more prime movers (a reciprocating engine, gas turbine, or steam turbine) driving electrical generators, where the steam or hot water generated in the process is utilised via suitable heat recovery equipment for use either in industrial processes, or in community heating and space heating.

6.3   A CHP plant provides primary energy savings compared to separate generation of heat and power. In addition, CHP is typically sized to make use of the available heat, and connected to the lower voltage distribution system (ie embedded). This provides efficiency gains compared to electricity-only plant, which is larger, and connected at very high voltage to the grid transmission system, by avoiding significant transmission and distribution losses. CHP can also provide important network services such as black start, improvements to power quality, and the ability to operate in island mode if the grid goes down.

6.4   There are four principal types of CHP systems: steam turbine, gas turbine, combined cycle systems and reciprocating engines. Each of these is defined in paragraph 6.33 below.

Government policy towards CHP

6.5   To reduce carbon emissions and help deliver the UK's Climate Change Programme, the Government has a target of achieving at least 10,000 MWe of Good Quality CHP capacity by 2010. At the end of the year 2003, installed Good Quality CHP capacity was 4,777 MWe. This figure is based on all submissions to the CHPQA programme and is lower than the end of year 2003 figure reported in the 2004 DUKES. The decrease is due to a number of schemes that closed during the period, but notification of closure was not received until after the previous data were published. During 2004, there was an increase in the total number of CHP schemes from 1,534 at the beginning of the year to 1,552 at the end, and an increase in capacity to 5,606 MWe.

6.6   In 2004 the Levy Exemption Certificates (LECs) system, which extends CCL exemption to electricity from Good Quality CHP electricity, was used by schemes for the first time. This system allows CHP station operators to sell or transfer their LECs with the amount of electricity supplied indirectly from the station. The scheme allows commercial freedom to maximise the benefit. It enables supplies of "Good Quality" electricity to be identified as such, as part of an auditable process.

International context

6.7   The EU Emissions Trading Scheme (EU-ETS) commenced on 1st January 2005 and involves the trading of emissions allowances. The purpose of the EU-ETS is to reduce emissions by a fixed amount at least cost to the regulated sources. Each year participants in the scheme are allocated a set number of allowances and the number of allowances equal to the reported emissions must be given up. If participants reduce emissions below their allocations, they will have allowances to trade or keep for use in future years. If emissions rise above their allocations allowances must be purchased. Although the EU-ETS is expected to encourage lower carbon technologies such as CHP, the exact impact on will depend on:

- the effect of the EU-ETS on electricity prices. If electricity prices were to rise due to EU-ETS, this would be beneficial to the economics for CHP.

- the need to account for carbon emissions from fuel use in CHP. The net effect will depend on the allocation, in developing the National Allocation Plan, the UK Government sought to ensure that CHP was not disadvantaged by the allocation. There are ring-fenced allowances for new entrant CHP (CHP schemes coming on line during the first phase of the EU-ETS).

UK Energy markets, and their effect on CHP

6.8   Two major factors affecting the economics of CHP are the relative cost of fuel (principally natural gas) and the value that can be realised for electricity. Energy price trends that are applicable to CHP schemes differ depending upon the size and sector of the scheme. Generally, however, electricity prices declined in real terms up until 2003, after which they started to rise again. Gas prices were on a downward trend until 2000, but in 2001 structural changes in the gas market caused prices to peak. Although gas prices reduced slightly in 2002, they have risen again in 2003 and 2004.

Use of CHPQA in producing CHP statistics

6.9   The CHPQA programme is now the major source for CHP statistics. The following factors need to be kept in mind when using the statistics produced:

- Scheme operators have previously determined the boundary of a CHP scheme (what is regarded as part of the CHP installation and what is not). Now, through CHPQA, scheme operators have been given guidance on how to determine scheme boundaries. A scheme can include multiple CHP prime movers, along with supplementary boilers and generating plant, subject to appropriate metering installed to support the CHP scheme boundaries proposed, and subject to appropriate metering and threshold criteria (see CHPQA Guidance Note 11 available at www.chpqa.com).
- The output of a scheme is based on gross power output, ignoring parasitic loads (ie ignoring power used in pumps, fans, etc within the scheme itself).

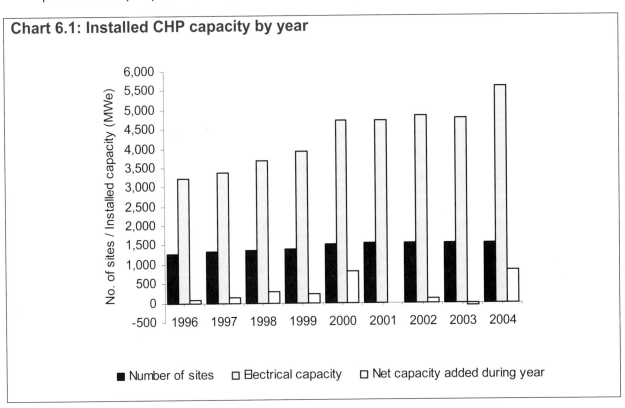

Chart 6.1: Installed CHP capacity by year

■ Number of sites   □ Electrical capacity   □ Net capacity added during year

- The main purpose of a number of CHP schemes is the generation of electricity including export to others. Such schemes may not be sized to use all of the available heat. The total capacity and output of these schemes have been scaled back using the methodologies outlined in CHPQA.

Only the portion of the capacity and output that qualifies as Good Quality is counted in this chapter and the remaining capacity and output are regarded as power only and reported in Chapter 5. The fuel allocated to the power-only portion of the output is calculated from the power efficiency of the prime mover.

- The load factor presented in Table 6A is based on the Good Quality Power Output and Good Quality Power Capacity reported in this Chapter. For schemes that are scaled back, this load factor is likely to be smaller than the actual load factor (hours run) for the prime mover in these schemes. In 2004 the average load factor has shown a decrease due to a number of new schemes coming on line part of the way through the year. This is because, relative to the installed good quality capacity, the output for 2004 is relatively low. When these new schemes are excluded the average load factor in 2004 is 60 per cent.

Progress towards the Government's targets

6.10   Chart 6.1 shows the change in installed CHP capacity over the last eight years. Installed capacity at the end of 2004 stood at 5,606 MWe. A number of schemes ceased to operate in 2003 and whilst new schemes also came on line during this period, the net effect was an overall reduction in capacity in 2003 of 71 MWe. In 2004 the capacity has increased to 5,606 MWe. Table 6A summarises recent developments in CHP.

Capacity in 2004

6.11   In 2004, 24 new schemes came into operation and 6 ceased to operate.

6.12   In the current market conditions, a number of operators have chosen to mothball their CHP schemes rather than continue to operate. As these schemes are still able to operate they have been included in the total capacity. At the end of 2004, there were 57 mothballed schemes with a total capacity of 28 MWe.

6.13   59 per cent of capacity is now gas turbine based, with about 78 per cent of this in combined cycle mode. Capacity in all technologies has increased in 2004, except for back pressure steam turbines, which dropped by approximately 3 per cent, and gas turbines, which remained unchanged (see Tables 6A and 6.5). Heat generation fell slightly between 2000 and 2002 but has shown a recent up turn such that 2004 levels are back at those seen in 2000. There was a dip in electricity generation in 2001. This reflected the difficulties encountered by smaller generators faced with rising gas prices, and falling electricity prices under NETA. As a result CHP plants were used less and the average load factor fell from 64 per cent in 2000 to 54 per cent in 2001. Since 2001 electrical generation has slowly been increasing and in 2004 electrical generation exceeded 2000 levels.

Table 6A: A summary of the recent development of CHP

	Unit	2000	2001	2002	2003	2004
Number of schemes		1,522	1,552	1,534	1,534	1,552
Net number of schemes added during		*139*	*30*	*-18*	*-*	*18*
Electrical capacity (CHP$_{QPC}$)	MWe	4,730	4,732	4,848	4,777	5,606
Net capacity added during year		*818*	*2*	*116*	*-71*	*869*
Capacity added in percentage terms	Per cent	*21*	*-*	*2.5*	*-1.4*	*18*
Heat capacity	MWth	11,888	11,898	11,559	11,221	11,398
Heat to power ratio *(1)*		2.51	2.69	2.45	2.41	2.27
Fuel input *(3)*	GWh	11,745	119,735	123,064	122,199	125,051
Electricity generation (CHP$_{QPO}$)	GWh	26,539	22,444	24,420	24,916	27,354
Heat generation (CHP$_{QHO}$)	GWh	62,121	60,584	59,721	60,052	62,065
Overall efficiency *(2)*	Per cent	75.5	69.3	69.56	69.64	71.43
Load factor *(4)*	Per cent	64.1	54.1	57.5	59.5	55.3

(1)   Heat to power ratios are calculated from the qualifying heat output (QHO) and the qualifying power output (QPO).
(2)   These are calculated using gross calorific values; overall net efficiencies are some 5 percentage points higher.
(3)   The fuel figures for 2000 are based on the previous methodology for assigning fuel to partial CHP schemes (see paragraph 6.9)
(4)   The load factor reported in this table is based on the qualifying power generation and capacity and does not correspond exactly to the number of hours run by the prime movers in a year (see paragraph 6.21). See paragraph 6.9 (final bullet) for an explanation of the low load factor in 2004.

Installed capacity and output in 2004

6.14   Table 6A gives a summary of the overall CHP market. The electricity generated by CHP schemes in 2004 was 27,354 GWh. This represents nearly 7 per cent of the total electricity generated in the UK in 2004. Across the commercial and industrial sectors (including the fuel industries other than electricity generation) electrical output from CHP accounted for 11½ per cent of electricity consumption. CHP schemes in total supplied 62,065 GWh of heat.

6.15   In terms of electrical capacity, schemes larger than 10 MWe represent 83 per cent of the total electrical capacity of CHP schemes as shown in Table 6B. However, in terms of number of schemes, the largest share (>80 per cent) is in schemes less than 1 MWe. Schemes of 1 MWe or larger make up 17 per cent of the total number of schemes. Table 6.5 provides data on electrical capacity for each type of CHP installation.

Table 6B: CHP schemes by capacity size ranges in 2004

Electrical capacity size range	Number of schemes	Share of total (per cent)	Total electricity capacity (MWe)	Share of total (per cent)
Less than 100 kWe	618	39.8	38	0.7
100 kWe - 999 kWe	665	42.9	162	2.9
1 MWe - 9.9 MWe	194	12.5	756	13.4
Greater than 10 MWe	75	4.8	4,650	83.0
Total	**1,552**	**100.0**	**5,606**	**100.0**

6.16   In terms of electrical and heat capacity by type of scheme, combined cycle gas turbines now make up the largest proportion for both capacities, (46 per cent and 44 per cent respectively), with steam turbines providing the next largest proportion, (29 per cent and 33 per cent respectively). Table 6.7 provides data on heat capacity for each type of CHP installation.

Fuel used by types of CHP installation

6.17   Table 6.1 shows the fuel used to generate electricity and heat in CHP schemes, (see paragraphs 6.34 to 6.36, below for an explanation of the convention for dividing fuel between electricity and heat production). Table 6.3 gives the overall fuel used by types of CHP installation (which are explained in paragraph 6.33). Total fuel use is summarised in Chart 6.2. In 2004, 65 per cent of the total fuel use was natural gas, a slight increase on the proportion in 2003 (64 per cent). CHP schemes accounted for 8 per cent of UK gas consumption in 2004 (see Table 4.3).

6.18   Non-conventional fuels (liquids, solids or gases which are by-products or waste products from industrial processes, or are renewable fuels) account for a quarter of fuel used in CHP. These are fuels that are not commonly used by the mainstream electricity generating industry, and some would otherwise be flared or disposed of by some means. These fuels (with the exception of some waste gases) will always be burnt in external combustion engines, such as boilers feeding steam turbines. In almost all cases, the technical nature of the combustion process (lower calorific value of the fuel, high moisture content of the fuel, the need to maintain certain combustion conditions to ensure complete disposal etc) will always imply a lower efficiency. However, given that the use of such fuels avoids the use of fossil fuels, and since they need to be disposed of in some way, the use of these fuels in CHP provides environmental benefits.

CHP capacity, output and fuel use by sector

6.19   Table 6.8 gives data on all operational schemes by economic sector. A definition of the sectors used in this table can be found in Chapter 1, paragraph 1.52 to 1.56

and Table 1F:

- 401 schemes (94 per cent of electrical capacity) are in the industrial sector and 1,151 schemes (6 per cent of capacity) are in the agricultural, commercial, public administration, residential and transport sectors.

- Four industrial sectors account for three quarters of the CHP electrical capacity - chemicals (27½ per cent of capacity), oil refineries (31½ per cent), paper, publishing and printing (12 per cent) and food, beverages and tobacco (6½ per cent). Capacity by sector is shown in Chart 6.3.

Chart 6.2: Types of fuel used by CHP schemes in 2004

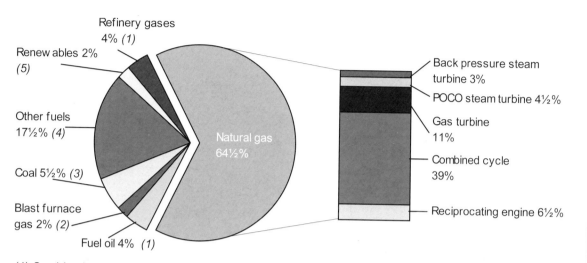

Refinery gases 4% *(1)*

Renewables 2% *(5)*

Other fuels 17½% *(4)*

Coal 5½% *(3)*

Blast furnace gas 2% *(2)*

Fuel oil 4% *(1)*

Natural gas 64½%

Back pressure steam turbine 3%

POCO steam turbine 4½%

Gas turbine 11%

Combined cycle 39%

Reciprocating engine 6½%

(1) Combined cycle accounts for over 80 per cent of fuel oil use and around two thirds of refinery gas use.
(2) POCO steam turbines account for all blast furnace gas use.
(3) Coal use is about one quarter in back pressure steam turbines and two thirds in POCO steam turbines.
(4) Other fuels include coke oven gas, gas oil and process by-products.
(5) Reciprocating engines account for around 50 per cent of renewable fuel use.

6.20   Table 6C gives a summary of the 1,121 schemes installed in the commercial, public sector and residential buildings. These schemes form a major part of the "Transport, commerce and administration" and "Other" sectors in Tables 6.8 and 6.9. The vast majority of these schemes (over 95 per cent) are based on spark ignition reciprocating engines fuelled with natural gas, though the larger schemes use compression ignition reciprocating engines or gas turbines. The largest proportion of the capacity is in the health sector, mainly hospitals. Leisure and hotels account for more than half the total number of schemes. Table 6.9 gives details of the quantities of fuels used in each sector.

Table 6C: Number and capacity of CHP schemes installed in buildings by sector in 2004

	Number of schemes	Electrical capacity (MWe)	Heat capacity (MWth)
Leisure	430	46.8	67.3
Hotels	311	39.2	58.3
Health	2016	114.9	207.4
Residential Group Heating	48	44.2	99.3
Universities	33	35.3	85.7
Offices	26	19.9	22.3
Education	23	10.3	18.1
Government Estate	16	12.3	17.9
Retail	13	6.8	5.9
Other *(1)*	5	17.6	22.7
Total	**1,121**	**347.3**	**604.9**

(1) Other includes: agriculture, airports, and domestic buildings

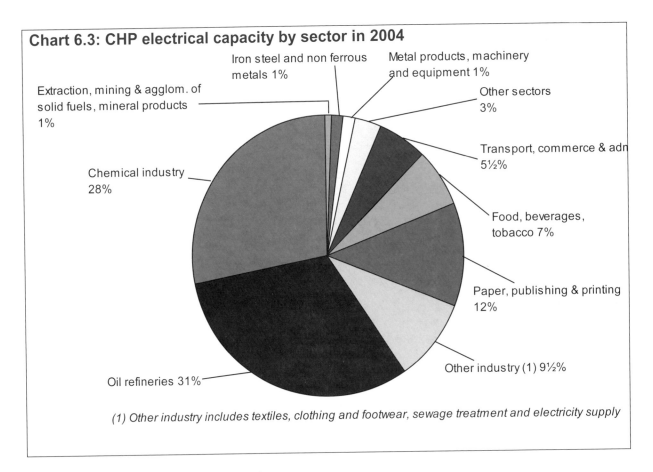

Chart 6.3: CHP electrical capacity by sector in 2004

Iron steel and non ferrous metals 1%

Metal products, machinery and equipment 1%

Extraction, mining & agglom. of solid fuels, mineral products 1%

Other sectors 3%

Chemical industry 28%

Transport, commerce & adn 5½%

Food, beverages, tobacco 7%

Paper, publishing & printing 12%

Oil refineries 31%

Other industry (1) 9½%

(1) Other industry includes textiles, clothing and footwear, sewage treatment and electricity supply

CHP performance by main prime mover

6.21 Table 6D gives a summary of the performance of schemes in 2004 by main prime mover type. Combined cycle gas turbines have the highest average operating hours at 6,008 hours. The average for all schemes of 4,856 hours is slightly lower than in 2003 (4,969 hours).

6.22 The average electrical efficiency is 22 per cent and heat efficiency 50 per cent, giving an overall average of 71 per cent. (All percentages are on a gross calorific value basis).

Table 6D: A summary of scheme performance in 2004

	Typical operating hours per annum (Full load equivalent)	Average electrical efficiency (% GCV)	Average heat efficiency (% GCV)	Average overall efficiency (% GCV)	Average heat to power ratio
Main prime mover in CHP plant					
Back pressure steam turbine	4,236	12	65	77	5.6
Pass out condensing steam turbine	3,189	16	48	64	3.1
Gas turbine	4,989	23	51	74	2.2
Combined cycle	6,008	26	48	73	1.9
Reciprocating engine	3,833	25	44	69	1.8
All schemes	**4,856**	**22**	**50**	**71**	**2.3**

CHP schemes which export and schemes with mechanical power output

6.23 Table 6E shows the electrical exports from CHP schemes between 2002 and 2004. Where a scheme that exports is Good Quality for only a portion of its capacity and output, the exports have been scaled back in the same way as power output has been scaled back (see paragraph 6.9, above). Exports accounted for about 35 per cent of power generation from CHP in 2004.

6.24   Table 6E also shows revised figures for electrical exports for 2003 (2002 figures remain unchanged). In 2003, the exemption from the climate change levy was extended to exports via licensed suppliers and it can be seen that the exports to this area have generally increased across the period 2002 to 2004, showing a peak in 2003.

Table 6E: Electrical exports from CHP

GWh

	2002	2003	2004
To part of same qualifying group *(1)*	820	616	477
To a firm NOT part of same qualifying group	3,527	2,980	3,505
To an electricity supplier	3,584	6,938	5,526
Customer not specified	27	0	0
Total	**7,958**	**10,534**	**9,508**

(1) A qualifying group is a group of two or more corporate consumers that are connected or related to each other, for example, as a subsidiary, or via a parent or holding company, or in terms of share capital.

6.25   Around 35 large schemes also export heat, some larger schemes to more than one customer. Together they supplied 9,024 GWh of heat in 2004, an increase of around 3 per cent compared to 2003 (8,772 GWh).

6.26   There are an estimated 13 schemes with mechanical power output. For those schemes, mechanical power accounts for around 12 per cent of their capacity (Table 6F). These schemes are predominantly on petro-chemicals or steel sites, using by-product fuels in boilers to drive steam turbines. The steam turbine is used to provide mechanical rather than electrical power, driving compressors, blowers or fans, rather than an alternator.

Table 6F: CHP schemes with mechanical power output in 2004

	Unit	
Number of schemes		13
Total Power Capacity of these schemes (CHP_{TPC})	MWe	1,871
Mechanical power capacity of these schemes	MWe	219

Emissions savings

6.27   The calculation of carbon emissions savings from CHP is important, given the substantial contribution that CHP can make to the Climate Change Programme. However the derivation of the savings is complex because CHP displaces a variety of fuels, technologies and sizes of plant. The methodology and assumptions used for calculating carbon emission savings were outlined in Energy Trends, June 2003 www.dti.gov.uk/energy/inform/energy_stats/ and the figures compare CHP with the UK fossil fuel basket carbon intensity and the UK total basket carbon intensity which includes nuclear and renewable generation. The carbon emission savings from CHP in 2004 as compared to the fossil fuel basket was 4.5 MtC, which equates to 0.8 MtC per 1,000 MWe installed capacity. Against the total basket, in 2004 CHP saved 3.4 MtC, or 0.6 MtC per 1,000 MWe installed capacity.

List of large scale CHP schemes in the United Kingdom

6.28   Table 5.11 in Chapter 5 (Electricity) lists major power stations in operation in the United Kingdom. This year it has been supplemented by a table showing large scale CHP schemes in the UK (Table 5.12 on page 143). However, this new table lists only large scale (over 1 MWe) CHP stations for which the information is already in the public domain, and it is the total power output of these stations that is given, not just that which is classed as Good Quality CHP under CHPQA. This is because CHPQA information for individual sites is not publicly available.

Technical notes and definitions

6.29   These notes and definitions are in addition to the technical notes and definitions covering all fuels and energy as a whole in Chapter 1, paragraphs 1.24 to 1.53.

Data for 2004

6.30   The data are summarised from the results of a long-term project being undertaken by Future Energy Solutions on behalf of the Department of Trade and Industry (DTI), the Department for Environment, Food and Rural Affairs (Defra), and the Statistical Office of the European Communities (Eurostat). Data are included for CHP schemes installed in all sectors of the UK economy.

6.31   The project continues to be overseen by a Steering Group that comprises officials from the DTI, Defra, the Office of Gas and Electricity Markets (OFGEM) and the Combined Heat and Power Association (CHPA), all of whom have an interest in either the collection of information on CHP schemes or the promotion of the wider use of CHP in the UK.

6.32   Data for 2004 were based largely on data supplied to the CHPQA programme, supplemented by a survey carried out by the Office for National Statistics (ONS) between December 2004 and March 2005 of companies (other than major power producers) who generate their own electricity, either in CHP schemes or in electricity-only schemes. Information on the CHP plant included in the major power producers category comes from surveys conducted by DTI as part of the electricity statistics system. For 2003, the Iron and Steel Statistics Bureau agreed with the industry a method for calculating CHP fuel inputs and electricity and heat outputs at integrated steel works. This method has also been used for 2004, but data on CHP in iron and steel for 2002 and earlier years is largely based on statistics collected in previous years and there is therefore a break of series. Over half of CHP schemes and around 85 per cent of capacity are based on returns under CHPQA, while around 3 per cent of schemes and 5 per cent of CHP capacity are based on data from ONS. Data for schemes not applying for CHPQA and not included in the ONS survey (eg because they were below the cut off capacity for the survey) were interpolated from historical data.

Definitions of schemes

6.33   There are four principal types of CHP systems:

- **Steam turbine,** where steam at high pressure is generated in a boiler. In **back pressure steam turbine systems**, the steam is wholly or partly used in a turbine before being exhausted from the turbine at the required pressure for the site. In **pass-out condensing steam turbine systems**, a proportion of the steam used by the turbine is extracted at an intermediate pressure from the turbine with the remainder being fully condensed before it is exhausted at the exit. (Condensing steam turbines without passout and which do not utilise steam are not included in these statistics as they are not CHP). The boilers used in such schemes can burn a wide variety of fuels including coal, gas, oil, and waste-derived fuels. With the exception of waste-fired schemes, steam turbine plant has often been in service for several decades. Steam turbine schemes capable of supplying useful steam have electrical efficiencies of between 10 and 20 per cent, depending on size, and thus between 70 per cent and 30 per cent of the fuel input is available as useful heat. Steam turbines used in CHP applications typically range in size from a few MWe to over 100 MWe.

- **Gas turbine systems**, often aero-engine derivatives, where fuel (gas, or gas-oil) is combusted in the gas turbine and the exhaust gases are normally used in a waste heat boiler to produce usable steam, though the exhaust gases may be used directly in some process applications. Gas turbines range from 30kWe upwards, achieving electrical efficiency of 23 to 30 per cent (depending on size) and with the potential to recover up to 50 per cent of the fuel input as useful heat. They have been common in CHP since the mid 1980s. The waste heat boiler can include supplementary or auxiliary firing using a wide range of fuels, and thus the heat to power ratio of the scheme can vary.

- **Combined cycle systems**, where the plant comprises more than one prime mover. These are usually gas turbines where the exhaust gases are utilised in a steam generator, the steam from which is passed wholly or in part into one or more steam turbines. In rare cases reciprocating engines may be linked with steam turbines. Combined cycle is suited to larger installations of 7 MWe and over. They achieve higher electrical efficiency and a lower heat to power ratio than steam turbines or gas turbines. Recently installed combined cycle gas turbine (CCGT) schemes have achieved an electrical efficiency approaching 50 per cent, with 20 per cent heat recovery, and a heat to power ratio of less than 1:1.

- **Reciprocating engine systems** range from less than 100 kWe up to around 5 MWe, and are found in applications where production of hot water (rather than steam) is the main requirement, for example, on smaller industrial sites as well as in buildings. They are based on auto engine or marine engine derivatives converted to run on gas. Both compression ignition and spark ignition firing is used. Reciprocating engines operate at around 28 to 33 per cent electrical efficiency with around 50 per cent to 33 per cent of the fuel input available as useful heat. Reciprocating engines produce two grades of waste heat: high grade heat from the engine exhaust and low grade heat from the engine cooling circuits.

Determining fuel consumption for heat and electricity

6.34   In order to provide a comprehensive picture of electricity generation in the United Kingdom and the fuels used to generate that electricity, the energy input to CHP schemes has to be allocated between heat and electricity production. This allocation is notional and is not determinate.

6.35   The convention used to allocate the fuels to heat and electricity relates the split of fuels to the relative efficiency of heat and electricity supply. The efficiency of utility plant varies widely: electricity generation from as little as 25 per cent to more than 50 per cent and boilers from as little as 50 per cent to more than 90 per cent. Thus it is around twice as hard to generate a unit of electricity as it is to generate a unit of heat. Accordingly a simple convention can be implemented whereby twice as many units of fuel are allocated to each unit of electricity generated, as to each unit of heat supplied. This approach is consistent with the Defra Guidelines for Company Reporting on greenhouse gas emissions and for Negotiated Agreements on energy efficiency agreed between Government and industry as part of the Climate Change Levy (CCL) package. It recognises that in developing a CHP scheme, both the heat customer(s) and the electricity generator share in the savings, reflecting the fact that more than three-quarters of CHP build in the last few years has been supplied under an energy services arrangement.

6.36   The assumption in this convention that it is twice as hard to generate a unit of electricity as heat, is appropriate for the majority of CHP schemes. However, for some types of scheme (for example in the iron and steel sector) this allocation is less appropriate and can result in very high apparent heat efficiencies. These however are only notional efficiencies.

The effects on the statistics of using CHPQA

6.37   Paragraph 6.9 described how schemes were scaled back so that only CHP_{QPC} and CHP_{QPO} were included in the CHP statistics. This is illustrated in Table 6G. In 2004, 61 schemes have been scaled back. The power output from these schemes was scaled back from a total of 29,708 GWh to 6,421 GWh. The total fuel input to these schemes is 81,667 GWh of which 56,882 GWh is regarded as power only.

Table 6G: CHP capacity, output and fuel use which has been scaled back in 2004

	Units	
Number of schemes requiring scaling back		61
Total Power Capacity of these schemes (CHP_{TPC})	MWe	7,122
Qualifying Power Capacity of these schemes (CHP_{QPC})	MWe	1,257
Total power output of these schemes (CHP_{TPO})	GWh	29,708*
Qualifying Power Output of these schemes (CHP_{QPO})	GWh	6,421
Electricity regarded as "Power only" not from CHP ($CHP_{TPO} - CHP_{QPO}$)	GWh	23,287
Total Fuel Input of these schemes (CHP_{TFI})	GWh	81,667
Fuel input regarded as being for "Power only" use ie not for CHP	GWh	56,882

*This figure includes generation from major power producers

Contacts:
Adrian Crispin, Future Energy Solutions
adrian.crispin@aeat.co.uk
0870 1906085

Mike Janes (Statistician), DTI
mike.janes@dti.gsi.gov.uk
020-7215 5186

6.1 CHP installations by capacity and size range

	2000	2001	2002	2003	2004
Number of schemes (1)	**1,522**	**1,552**	**1,534r**	**1,534r**	**1,552**
Less than 100 kWe	667	664	641r	622r	618
100 kWe to 999 kWe	593	631	637r	648r	665
1 MWe to 9.9 MWe	192	185	184	190r	194
10.0 MWe and above	70	72	72	74r	75
					MWe
Total capacity	**4,730**	**4,732**	**4,848r**	**4,777r**	**5,606**
Less than 100 kWe	41	40	39	38	38
100 kWe to 999 kWe	145	155	154r	158r	162
1 MWe to 9.9 MWe	803	747	750	756r	756
10.0 MWe and above	3,741	3,790	3,905r	3,826r	4,650

(1) A site may contain more than one CHP scheme.

6.2 Fuel used to generate electricity and heat in CHP installations

					GWh
	2000	2001	2002	2003	2004
Fuel used to generate electricity (1)					
Coal (2)	1,524	2,412	2,303r	2,372r	2,356
Fuel oil	3,071	2,817	2,237	2,053r	1,888
Natural gas	37,842	35,422	39,857r	40,780r	41,805
Renewable fuels (3)	943	1,076	1,083	1,204r	1,261
Other fuels (4)	10,530	9,379	9,648r	8,586r	10,772
Total all fuels	**53,908**	**51,106**	**55,128r**	**54,995r**	**58,083**
Fuel used to generate heat					
Coal (2)	3,845	4,825	4,762r	4,676r	4,694
Fuel oil	3,342	5,244	3,210	2,901r	2,780
Natural gas	37,618	38,501	41,273r	40,155r	39,283
Renewable fuels (3)	1,024	1,090	1,183	1,419r	1,483
Other fuels (4)	17,714	18,968	17,508r	18,052r	18,729
Total all fuels	**63,542**	**68,629**	**67,936r**	**67,203r**	**66,969**
Overall fuel use					
Coal (2)	5,369	7,237	7,065r	7,049r	7,050
Fuel oil	6,412	8,061	5,447	4,954r	4,668
Natural gas	75,459	73,923	81,129r	80,935r	81,088
Renewable fuels (3)	1,967	2,166	2,267	2,623r	2,744
Other fuels (4)	28,243	28,348	27,156r	26,638r	29,501
Total all fuels	**117,450**	**119,735**	**123,064r**	**122,199r**	**125,051**

(1) The allocation of fuel use between heat generation and electricity generation has been changed to match that used in CHPQA. See paragraphs 6.34 to 6.36 for an explanation of the method used.
(2) Includes coke and semi-coke.
(3) Renewable fuels include: sewage gas; other biogases; municipal waste and refuse derived fuels.
(4) Other fuels include: process by-products, coke oven gas, blast furnace gas, gas oil and uranium.

6.3 Fuel used by types of CHP installation

GWh

	2000	2001	2002	2003	2004
Coal					
Back pressure steam turbine	2,333	2,103	1,923	1,853	1,740
Gas turbine	30	34	46	42	50
Combined cycle	347	466	257r	172r	118
Reciprocating engine	-	-	-	-	-
Pass out condensing steam turbine	2,659	4,810	4,839	4,983r	5,142
Total coal	**5,369**	**7,414**	**7,065r**	**7,049r**	**7,049**
Fuel oil					
Back pressure steam turbine	555	551	452	487	476
Gas turbine	651	403	288	506r	25
Combined cycle	4,361	5,995	4,077	3,607r	3,776
Reciprocating engine	226	175	221	197r	201
Pass out condensing steam turbine	619	937	409	156r	210
Total fuel oil	**6,412**	**8,061**	**5,447**	**4,954r**	**4,689**
Natural gas					
Back pressure steam turbine	6,116	5,267	5,212	4,617r	4,218
Gas turbine	16,050	13,025	12,998r	14,370r	13,880
Combined cycle	39,256	43,878	51,147	52,606r	49,137
Reciprocating engine	7,455	7,436	8,539r	7,938r	8,325
Pass out condensing steam turbine	6,583	4,317	3,233	1,405r	5,528
Total natural gas	**75,459**	**73,923**	**81,129r**	**80,935r**	**81,088**
Renewable fuels *(1)*					
Back pressure steam turbine	8	10	14	13	12
Gas turbine	-	19	21	21	21
Combined cycle	20	40	28	263r	411
Reciprocating engine	1,417	1,573	1,564	1,434r	1,434
Pass out condensing steam turbine	522	524	640	892r	866
Total renewable fuels	**1,966**	**2,166**	**2,267**	**2,623r**	**2,744**
Other fuels *(2)*					
Back pressure steam turbine	4,847	5,811	5,310	5,343r	4,987
Gas turbine	3,185	1,481	1,577	1,435r	1,790
Combined cycle	6,863	7,409	8,062r	6,842r	7,628
Reciprocating engine	107	89	58	59r	85
Pass out condensing steam turbine	13,241	13,381	12,149	12,959r	15,013
Total other fuels	**28,243**	**28,171**	**27,156r**	**26,638r**	**29,501**
Total - all fuels					
Back pressure steam turbine	13,859	13,743	12,911	12,313r	11,432
Gas turbine	19,916	14,961r	14,929r	16,373r	15,766
Combined cycle	50,847	57,787r	63,571r	63,490r	61,069
Reciprocating engine	9,205	9,274r	10,382r	9,627r	10,032
Pass out condensing steam turbine	23,623	23,970r	21,271	20,395r	26,752
Total all fuels	**117,450**	**119,735**	**123,064r**	**122,199r**	**125,051**

(1) Renewable fuels include: sewage gas; other biogases; municipal waste and refuse derived fuels.
(2) Other fuels include: process by-products, coke oven gas, blast furnace gas, gas oil and uranium.

6.4 CHP - electricity generated by fuel and type of installation

GWh

	2000	2001	2002	2003	2004
Coal					
Back pressure steam turbine	192	151	151	140	131
Gas turbine	6	6	7	7	8
Combined cycle	45	56r	29r	25r	15
Reciprocating engine	-	-	-	-	-
Pass out condensing steam turbine	396	771	732	795r	801
Total coal	**639**	**984**	**920r**	**967r**	**956**
Fuel oil					
Back pressure steam turbine	54	51	51	54	53
Gas turbine	116	84	60	89r	5
Combined cycle	1,245	902	765	732r	785
Reciprocating engine	69	54	67	60r	60
Pass out condensing steam turbine	109	145	46	23r	29
Total fuel oil	**1,593**	**1,236**	**989**	**957r**	**932**
Natural gas					
Back pressure steam turbine	515	437	508	540r	528
Gas turbine	4,022	2,936	2,817r	3,262r	3,153
Combined cycle	11,362	10,134	12,330	13,018r	12,480
Reciprocating engine	2,237	1,991	2,129r	1,948r	2,080
Pass out condensing steam turbine	987	432	264r	112r	1,373
Total natural gas	**19,124**	**15,930**	**18,049r**	**18,881r**	**19,613**
Renewable fuels *(1)*					
Back pressure steam turbine	1	1	1	1	1
Gas turbine	-	3	4	4	4
Combined cycle	5	6	2	16r	25
Reciprocating engine	370	365	368	333r	333
Pass out condensing steam turbine	46	57	60	89r	84
Total renewable fuels	**422**	**432**	**435r**	**443r**	**447**
Other fuels *(2)*					
Back pressure steam turbine	624	661	678	640r	629
Gas turbine	536	293	314	267r	461
Combined cycle	1,800	1,174	1,526r	1,403r	2,287
Reciprocating engine	35	28	17	15r	22
Pass out condensing steam turbine	1,767	1,705	1,492	1,342r	2,008
Total other fuels	**4,761**	**3,862**	**4,026r**	**3,668r**	**5,406**
Total - all fuels					
Back pressure steam turbine	1,385	1,301r	1,389	1,375r	1,342
Gas turbine	4,680	3,323r	3,202r	3,630r	3,631
Combined cycle	14,457	12,272	14,653r	15,194r	15,591
Reciprocating engine	2,711	2,437r	2,581r	2,356r	2,495
Pass out condensing steam turbine	3,306	3,110r	2,595r	2,361r	4,295
Total all fuels	**26,539**	**22,444r**	**24,420r**	**24,916r**	**27,354**

(1) Renewable fuels include: sewage gas; other biogases; municipal waste and refuse derived fuels.
(2) Other fuels include: process by-products, coke oven gas, blast furnace gas, gas oil and uranium.

6.5 CHP - electrical capacity by fuel and type of installation

	2000	2001	2002	2003	MWe 2004
Coal					
Back pressure steam turbine	63	55	48	40	39
Gas turbine	1	1	1	1	1
Combined cycle	8	11	5r	6r	3
Reciprocating engine	-	-	-	-	-
Pass out condensing steam turbine	93	195	208	227r	230
Total coal	**165**	**261**	**262r**	**274r**	**274**
Fuel oil					
Back pressure steam turbine	16	17	14	14	15
Gas turbine	31	27	23	39r	2
Combined cycle	201	251	144	130r	136
Reciprocating engine	20	16	20	21r	21
Pass out condensing steam turbine	24	33	13	6r	7
Total fuel oil	**291**	**344**	**213**	**211r**	**182**
Natural gas					
Back pressure steam turbine	145	143	177	159r	149
Gas turbine	594	521	533	601r	584
Combined cycle	1,785	1,834	2,040	2,151r	2,017
Reciprocating engine	437	473	513r	537r	548
Pass out condensing steam turbine	214	97	79	40r	569
Total natural gas	**3,175**	**3,068**	**3,341r**	**3,488r**	**3,908**
Renewable fuels *(1)*					
Back pressure steam turbine	-	-	-	-	-
Gas turbine	-	-	-	1	1
Combined cycle	1	1	-	3	6
Reciprocating engine	86	85	84	81r	81
Pass out condensing steam turbine	18	16	18	23	22
Total renewable fuels	**105**	**103**	**104**	**107**	**110**
Other fuels *(2)*					
Back pressure steam turbine	111	109	109	109	109
Gas turbine	129	97	99	89r	143
Combined cycle	288	292	275r	263r	402
Reciprocating engine	11	9	4	5	6
Pass out condensing steam turbine	456	448	441	232r	513
Total other fuels	**993**	**955**	**928r**	**697r**	**1,173**
Total - all fuels					
Back pressure steam turbine	336	323	348r	322r	313
Gas turbine	754	646	656r	731	731
Combined cycle	2,282	2,389	2,464	2,552	2,606
Reciprocating engine	552	584	621	643	655
Pass out condensing steam turbine	804	790	759	529	1,341
Total all fuels	**4,729**	**4,732**	**4,848r**	**4,777**	**5,606**

(1) Renewable fuels include: sewage gas; other biogases; municipal waste and refuse derived fuels.
(2) Other fuels include: process by-products and uranium.

6.6 CHP - heat generated by fuel and type of installation

GWh

	2000	2001	2002	2003	2004
Coal					
Back pressure steam turbine	1,493	1,342	1,226	1,180	1,110
Gas turbine	17	18	27	31	28
Combined cycle	179	219	109r	89r	58
Reciprocating engine	-	-	-	-	-
Pass out condensing steam turbine	1,546	2,370	2,451	2,543r	2,643
Total coal	**3,235**	**3,949**	**3,813**	**3,843r**	**3,839**
Fuel oil					
Back pressure steam turbine	399	394	329	352	350
Gas turbine	274	231	168r	245r	14
Combined cycle	2,460	3,419	2,110	1,954r	2,190
Reciprocating engine	55	60	71	61r	61
Pass out condensing steam turbine	376	518	180	83r	111
Total fuel oil	**3,564**	**4,622**	**2,858**	**2,695r**	**2,726**
Natural gas					
Back pressure steam turbine	4,125	3,867	3,637	3,263r	2,969
Gas turbine	7,154	6,389	6,076r	6,874r	6,788
Combined cycle	19,097	18,904	22,442	22,772r	21,570
Reciprocating engine	3,072	3,314	3,601r	3,642r	3,717
Pass out condensing steam turbine	4,380	3,032	1,770r	1,060r	2,121
Total natural gas	**37,828**	**35,507**	**37,526r**	**37,611r**	**37,164**
Renewable fuels *(1)*					
Back pressure steam turbine	4	5	6	5	5
Gas turbine	-	9	11	11	11
Combined cycle	16	16	7	61	83
Reciprocating engine	514	577	580	531r	531
Pass out condensing steam turbine	253	223	267	324	307
Total renewable fuels	**787**	**830**	**870**	**931r**	**936**
Other fuels *(2)*					
Back pressure steam turbine	2,562	3,145	2,943	3,361r	3,038
Gas turbine	1,446	838	871	690r	1,185
Combined cycle	4,358	3,877	3,888r	3,669r	5,358
Reciprocating engine	41	35	27	29	37
Pass out condensing steam turbine	8,300	7,781	6,924	7,223r	7,781
Total other fuels	**16,707**	**15,676**	**14,653r**	**14,971r**	**17,399**
Total - all fuels					
Back pressure steam turbine	8,582	8,753	8,142	8,162r	7,472
Gas turbine	8,890	7,487	7,153r	7,851r	8,026
Combined cycle	26,111	26,435	28,556	28,545r	29,258
Reciprocating engine	3,682	3,986	4,278r	4,262r	4,346
Pass out condensing steam turbine	14,856	13,924	11,592r	11,232r	12,963
Total all fuels	**62,121**	**60,584**	**59,721r**	**60,052r**	**62,065**

(1) Renewable fuels include: sewage gas; other biogases; municipal waste and refuse derived fuels.
(2) Other fuels include: process by-products and uranium.

6.7 CHP - heat capacity by fuel and type of installation

MWth

	2000	2001	2002	2003	2004
Coal					
Back pressure steam turbine	446	405	305	246	246
Gas turbine	3	3	4	3	4
Combined cycle	25	34	18r	19r	10
Reciprocating engine	-	-	-	-	-
Pass out condensing steam turbine	314	573	606	646r	659
Total coal	**787**	**1,014**	**934r**	**915r**	**919**
Fuel oil					
Back pressure steam turbine	124	128	90	94	96
Gas turbine	103	95	87	162r	9
Combined cycle	474	572	357	337r	334
Reciprocating engine	21	20	21	25r	25
Pass out condensing steam turbine	70	104	51	19r	24
Total fuel oil	**791**	**920**	**605**	**637r**	**489**
Natural gas					
Back pressure steam turbine	830	761	685	588r	587
Gas turbine	1,286	1,146	1,121	1,130r	1,080
Combined cycle	3,315	3,417	3,774	3,911r	3,590
Reciprocating engine	774	918	930r	840r	839
Pass out condensing steam turbine	820	573	400	208r	332
Total natural gas	**7,025**	**6,815**	**6,910r**	**6,678r**	**6,427**
Renewable fuels (1)					
Back pressure steam turbine	1	1	5	5	5
Gas turbine	-	2	2	2	2
Combined cycle	2	2	1	9	13
Reciprocating engine	138	139	136	131r	131
Pass out condensing steam turbine	57	46	62	86r	85
Total renewable fuels	**199**	**190**	**206**	**233r**	**236**
Other fuels (2)					
Back pressure steam turbine	358	357	357	381r	381
Gas turbine	466	384	388	314r	517
Combined cycle	777	787	803r	786r	1,077
Reciprocating engine	11	9	6	6	8
Pass out condensing steam turbine	1,475	1,421	1,350	1,271r	1,344
Total other fuels	**3,086**	**2,959**	**2,904r**	**2,757r**	**3,327**
Total - all fuels					
Back pressure steam turbine	1,758	1,652	1,442	1,315r	1,315
Gas turbine	1,858	1,630	1,602	1,612r	1,612
Combined cycle	4,593	4,812	4,953	5,062r	5,024
Reciprocating engine	944	1,087	1,094	1,003r	1,003
Pass out condensing steam turbine	2,736	2,717	2,469	2,230r	2,445
Total all fuels	**11,888**	**11,898**	**11,559r**	**11,221r**	**11,398**

(1) Renewable fuels include: sewage gas; other biogases; municipal waste and refuse derived fuels.
(2) Other fuels include: process by-products and uranium.

6.8 CHP capacity, output and total fuel use[1] by sector

	Unit	2000	2001	2002	2003	2004
Iron and steel and non ferrous metals						
Number of sites		6	7	5	6r	7
Electrical capacity	MWe	74	80	63	66r	68
Heat capacity	MWth	491	497	285	285	285
Electrical output	GWh	486	493	365r	253r	269
Heat output	GWh	2,377	2,197	1,321r	1,707r	1,721
Fuel use	GWh	2,751	3,251	1,914	3,085r	3,066
of which : for electricity	GWh	818	984	693	654r	680
for heat	GWh	1,933	2,267	1,221	2,431r	2,386
Chemicals						
Number of sites		55	49	50	50r	50
Electrical capacity	MWe	1,524	1,517	1,475	1,517r	1,541
Heat capacity	MWth	4,022	3,940	3,763	3,605r	3,605
Electrical output	GWh	9,675	8,344	8,016	8,402r	8,939
Heat output	GWh	22,959	21,645	21,087	20,580r	21,002
Fuel use	GWh	45,838	43,839	43,786r	42,407r	40,056
of which : for electricity	GWh	20,390	19,048	18,601r	18,884r	18,001
for heat	GWh	25,448	24,792	25,185r	23,523r	22,055
Oil refineries						
Number of sites		10	10	9	9r	10
Electrical capacity	MWe	986	984	954	955r	1,767
Heat capacity	MWth	2,995	3,098	3,066	3,088r	3,303
Electrical output	GWh	5,710	4,214	5,198r	5,181r	7,182
Heat output	GWh	14,667	14,823	14,630	15,216r	17,096
Fuel use	GWh	25,249	27,472	28,396	27,479r	33,273
of which : for electricity	GWh	11,676	10,119	11,993	11,069r	15,294
for heat	GWh	13,574	17,352	16,403	16,410r	17,979
Paper, publishing and printing						
Number of sites		36	35	37	36	35
Electrical capacity	MWe	559	529	596	691r	676
Heat capacity	MWth	1,331	1,316	1,390	1,453r	1,415
Electrical output	GWh	3,827	3,413	3,660r	3,943r	3,988
Heat output	GWh	9,065	8,852	8,508r	8,394r	8,427
Fuel use	GWh	16,718	16,611	16,710	16,844r	16,815
of which : for electricity	GWh	7,526	7,145	7,603	8,075r	8,070
for heat	GWh	9,192	9,466	9,107	8,770r	8,746
Food, beverages and tobacco						
Number of sites		47	45	45	42	43
Electrical capacity	MWe	405	393	404	379	379
Heat capacity	MWth	1,166	1,121	1,108	982r	982
Electrical output	GWh	2,113	1,674	1,953	1,957r	1,877
Heat output	GWh	5,536	5,101	5,767r	5,620r	5,287
Fuel use	GWh	10,089	8,706	9,990	9,734r	9,291
of which : for electricity	GWh	4,316	3,402	3,984	3,937r	3,805
for heat	GWh	5,772	5,304	6,005	5,797r	5,485
Metal products, machinery and equipment						
Number of sites		15	16	14	15r	15
Electrical capacity	MWe	86	82	78	101r	101
Heat capacity	MWth	90	91	66	79r	79
Electrical output	GWh	523	182	202	317r	212
Heat output	GWh	302	388	344	403r	336
Fuel use	GWh	1,446	821	800	1,105r	784
of which : for electricity	GWh	1,132	391	430	674r	432
for heat	GWh	313	430	370	431r	352

For footnotes see page 164

6.8 CHP capacity, output and total fuel use[1] by sector (continued)

	Unit	2000	2001	2002	2003	2004
Mineral products, extraction, mining and agglomeration of solid fuels						
Number of sites		10	10	10	10	10
Electrical capacity	MWe	56	56	54	53r	53
Heat capacity	MWth	180	180	180	180	180
Electrical output	GWh	313	242	225	227r	220
Heat output	GWh	913	848	819	800r	778
Fuel use	GWh	1,592	1,474	1,443	1,321r	1,286
of which : for electricity	GWh	666	536	514	490r	472
for heat	GWh	927	938r	929	831r	813
Sewage treatment						
Number of sites		113	113	113	112r	112
Electrical capacity	MWe	102	102	101	101r	101
Heat capacity	MWth	160	162	159	158	158
Electrical output	GWh	428	424	429	395r	395
Heat output	GWh	586	654	659	611r	611
Fuel use	GWh	1,624	1,782	1,776	1,652r	1,652
of which : for electricity	GWh	931	997	991r	921r	921
for heat	GWh	692	786	784	731r	731
Electricity supply						
Number of sites		6	6	7r	6	6
Electrical capacity	MWe	437	470	555r	340r	329
Heat capacity	MWth	370	370	462r	387r	387
Electrical output	GWh	874	1,157	2,025r	1,984r	1,903
Heat output	GWh	1,500	1,837	2,408r	2,259r	2,250
Fuel use	GWh	2,624	6,173	7,969	8,386r	8,143
of which : for electricity	GWh	1,397	3,577	4,995	5,325r	5,111
for heat	GWh	1,228	2,596	2,974	3,062r	3,032
Other industrial branches (2)						
Number of sites		17	16	14r	14r	15
Electrical capacity	MWe	58	57	55r	51r	52
Heat capacity	MWth	206	181	161	96r	96
Electrical output	GWh	348	333	333	306r	324
Heat output	GWh	528	699	648r	529r	555
Fuel use	GWh	1,135	1,419	1,303r	1,135r	1,208
of which : for electricity	GWh	600	680	653r	609r	651
for heat	GWh	534	739	651r	526r	557
Total industry						
Number of sites		315	307	304r	300r	303
Electrical capacity	MWe	4,288	4,269	4,335r	4,254r	5,066
Heat capacity	MWth	11,011	10,954	10,639r	10,313r	10,490
Electrical output	GWh	24,295	20,474	22,405r	22,966r	25,307
Heat output	GWh	58,432	57,042	56,192r	56,118r	58,063
Fuel use	GWh	109,065	111,548	114,087r	113,148r	115,574
of which : for electricity	GWh	49,452	46,877	50,457r	50,637r	53,437
for heat	GWh	59,612	64,671	63,630r	62,512r	62,136

For footnotes see page 164

6.8 CHP capacity, output and total fuel use[1] by sector (continued)

	Unit	2000	2001	2002	2003	2004
Transport, commerce and administration						
Number of sites		1,110	1,148	1,134r	1,138r	1,151
Electrical capacity	MWe	268	293	294	308r	319
Heat capacity	MWth	586	657	555r	526r	526
Electrical output	GWh	1,347	1,337	1,271r	1,256r	1,311
Heat output	GWh	2,219	2,388	2,310r	2,377r	2,438
Fuel use	GWh	4,870	5,289	5,279r	5,074r	5,343
of which : for electricity	GWh	2,645	2,798	2,765r	2,603r	2,754
for heat	GWh	2,225	2,491	2,514r	2,472r	2,589
Other (3)						
Number of sites		97	97	95r	96r	98
Electrical capacity	MWe	174	170	219r	215r	220
Heat capacity	MWth	292	287	364r	382r	382
Electrical output	GWh	897	633	743r	694r	736
Heat output	GWh	1,470	1,156	1,220r	1,557r	1,563
Fuel use	GWh	3,515	2,898	3,698r	3,976r	4,135
of which : for electricity	GWh	1,811	1,431	1,906r	1,755r	1,891
for heat	GWh	1,705	1,467	1,792r	2,220r	2,244
Total CHP usage by all sectors						
Number of sites		1,522	1,552	1,533r	1,534r	1,552
Electrical capacity	MWe	4,730	4,732	4,848r	4,777r	5,606
Heat capacity	MWth	11,888	11,898	11,558r	11,221r	11,398
Electrical output	GWh	26,539	22,445	24,419r	24,916r	27,354
Heat output	GWh	62,121	60,586	59,721r	60,052r	62,065
Fuel use	GWh	117,450	119,735	123,064r	122,199r	125,051
of which : for electricity	GWh	53,908	51,106	55,128r	54,995r	58,083
for heat	GWh	63,542	68,629	67,936r	67,203r	66,969

(1) *The allocation of fuel use between electricity and heat is largely notional and the methodology is outlined in paragraphs 6.34 to 6.36.*

(2) *Other industry includes Textiles, clothing and footwear sector.*

(3) *Sectors included under Other are agriculture, community heating, leisure, landfill and incineration*

6.9 CHP - use of fuels by sector

GWh

	2000	2001	2002	2003	2004
Iron and steel and non ferrous metals					
Coal	97	97	-	-	-
Fuel oil	160	179	49	45	94
Natural gas	422	513	247	217r	262
Blast furnace gas	1,643	1,971	1,256	2,401	2,346
Coke oven gas	405	445	363	422	364
Other fuels (2)	24	46	-	-	-
Total iron and steel and non ferrous metals	**2,751**	**3,251**	**1,914**	**3,085r**	**3,066**
Chemicals					
Coal	2,416	4,479	4,473	4,818r	4,712
Fuel oil	868	1,182	526	148r	173
Gas oil	80	98	74	32r	31
Natural gas	31,116	27,584	28,213r	26,823r	24,895
Refinery gas	393	66	28	-	-
Renewable fuels (1)	-	19	21	21	21
Other fuels (2)	10,965	10,412	10,451	10,565r	10,224
Total chemical industry	**45,838**	**43,839**	**43,786r**	**42,407r**	**40,056**
Oil refineries					
Fuel oil	4,596	5,946	4,136	4,079r	3,758
Gas oil	266	134	134	134	44
Natural gas	7,050	7,794	10,248	10,884r	14,472
Refinery gas	7,961	7,526	8,152	5,612r	5,060
Other fuels (2)	5,377	6,072	5,727	6,771r	9,939
Total oil refineries	**25,249**	**27,472**	**28,396**	**27,479r**	**33,273**
Paper, publishing and printing					
Coal	731	797	713	450r	635
Fuel oil	366	361	313	268	266
Gas oil	21	43	43	22	29
Natural gas	15,441	15,217	15,450	15,958r	15,754
Renewable fuels (1)	2	4	3	2	1
Other fuels (2)	157	188	188	145	130
Total paper, publishing and printing	**16,718**	**16,611**	**16,710**	**16,844r**	**16,815**
Food, beverages and tobacco					
Coal	1,521	1,292	1,241	1,179	1,066
Fuel oil	194	184	188	214	191
Gas oil	56	66	11	20r	771
Natural gas	8,316	7,164	8,550	8,313r	7,240
Renewable fuels (1)	2	-	-	-	-
Other fuels (2)	-	-	-	8	23
Total food, beverages and tobacco	**10,088**	**8,706**	**9,990**	**9,734r**	**9,291**
Metal products, machinery and equipment					
Coal	32	32	-	-	-
Fuel oil	107	51	92	91	89
Gas oil	-	-	-	-	-
Natural gas	1,306	737	708	1,014r	695
Total metal products, machinery and equipment	**1,446**	**821**	**800**	**1,105r**	**784**
Mineral products, extraction, mining and agglomeration of solid fuels					
Coal	69	176	-	-	-
Fuel oil	-	-	-	2	-
Natural gas	1,373	1,148	1,048	1,091r	1,057
Coke oven gas	150	150	395r	228r	228
Total mineral products, extraction, mining and agglomeration of solid fuels	**1,592**	**1,474**	**1,443**	**1,321r**	**1,286**

For footnotes see page 166

6.9 CHP - use of fuels by sector (continued)

GWh

	2000	2001	2002	2003	2004
Sewage treatment					
Fuel oil	71	71	71	61r	61
Gas oil	30	30	30	30	30
Natural gas	114	114	114	129r	129
Renewable fuels (1)	1,408	1,567	1,561	1,432r	1,432
Total sewage treatment	**1,624**	**1,782**	**1,776**	**1,652r**	**1,652**
Electricity supply					
Coal	178	178	216	288	288
Fuel oil	-	3	3	3	4
Gas oil	-	-	-	-	2
Natural gas	1,857	5,213	7,576	7,930r	7,685
Renewable fuels (1)	-	-	-	-	-
Other fuels (2)	590	780	174	164r	164
Total electricity supply	**2,625**	**6,173**	**7,969**	**8,386r**	**8,143**
Other industrial branches (3)					
Fuel oil	2	2	-	-	-
Gas oil	3	1	-	-	-
Natural gas	1,125	1,411	1,298r	1,130r	1,203
Renewable fuels (1)	6	5	5	5	5
Total other industrial branches	**1,135**	**1,419**	**1,304r**	**1,135r**	**1,208**
Transport, commerce and administration					
Coal	30	34	46	42	50
Fuel oil	32	67	64	42r	33
Gas oil	74	65	18	17r	22
Natural gas	4,727	5,116	5,148r	4,971r	5,236
Refinery gas	1	1	1	-	-
Renewable fuels (1)	5	5	2	2	2
Other fuels (2)	1	1	1	1	1
Total transport, commerce and administration	**4,870**	**5,289**	**5,279r**	**5,074r**	**5,343**
Other (4)					
Coal	294	329	377	272r	299
Fuel oil	18	14	6	-	-
Gas oil	44	22	17	15	42
Natural gas	2,613	1,913	2,531	2,476r	2,460
Renewable fuels (1)	543	566	675	1,161r	1,283
Other fuels (2)	3	54	92	51r	51
Total other	**3,515**	**2,898**	**3,698**	**3,976r**	**4,135**
Total - all sectors					
Coal	5,369	7,414	7,065r	7,049r	7,050
Fuel oil	6,412	8,061	5,447	4,954r	4,668
Gas oil	573	458	327	271r	971
Natural gas	75,459	73,923	81,129r	80,935r	81,088
Blast furnace gas	1,643	1,971	1,256r	2,401r	2,346
Coke oven gas	555	595	758r	650r	592
Refinery gas	8,355	7,594	8,182	5,612r	5,060
Renewable fuels (1)	1,967	2,166	2,267r	2,623r	2,744
Other fuels (2)	17,117	17,553	16,633r	17,704r	20,533
Total CHP fuel use	**117,450**	**119,735**	**123,064r**	**122,199r**	**125,051**

(1) Renewable fuels include: sewage gas; other biogases; clinical waste; municipal waste.
(2) Other fuels include: process by-products and uranium.
(3) Other industry now includes textiles, clothing and footwear which was shown as a separate sector in previous Digests.
(4) Sectors included under Other are agriculture, community heating, leisure, landfill and incineration.

Chapter 7
Renewable sources of energy

Introduction

7.1   This chapter provides information on the contribution of renewable energy sources to the United Kingdom's energy requirements. It includes sources that under international definitions are not counted as renewable sources or are counted only in part. This is to ensure that this Digest covers all sources of energy available in the United Kingdom. However, within this chapter the international definition of total renewables is used and this excludes non-biodegradable wastes. The energy uses of wastes are still shown in the tables of this chapter but as "below the line" items. This chapter covers both the use of renewables to generate electricity and the burning of renewable fuels to produce heat either in boilers (or cookers) or in combined heat and power plants.

7.2   The data summarise the results of an ongoing study undertaken by the Future Energy Solutions (FES - part of AEA Technology (AEAT) Environment), on behalf of the Department of Trade and Industry, to update a database containing information on all relevant renewable energy sources in the United Kingdom. This database is called RESTATS, the Renewable Energy STATisticS database.

7.3   The study started in 1989, when all relevant renewable energy sources were identified and, where possible, information was collected on the amounts of energy derived from each source. The renewable energy sources identified were the following: active solar heating; photovoltaics; onshore and offshore wind power; wave power; large and small scale hydro; biofuels; geothermal aquifers. The technical notes at the end of this chapter define each of these renewable energy sources. The database now contains 16 years of data from 1989 to 2004.

7.4   The information contained in the database is collected by a number of methods. For larger projects, an annual survey is carried out in which questionnaires are sent to project managers. For technologies in which there are large numbers of small projects, the values given in this chapter are estimates based on information collected from a sub-sample of the projects. Further details about the data collection methodologies used in RESTATS, including the quality and completeness of the information, are given in the technical notes at the end of this chapter.

7.5   Commodity balances for renewable energy sources covering each of the last three years form the first three tables (Tables 7.1 to 7.3). These are followed by the 5-year table showing capacity of, and electricity generation from, renewable sources (Table 7.4). A new table has been included this year to show generation from sources eligible for the Renewables Obligation and sources qualifying under the Renewables Directive (Table 7.5), and this is followed by a table summarising all the renewable orders (Table 7.6). Table 7.7 shows renewable sources used to generate electricity and heat in each of the last five years. A long-term trends commentary and table (Table 7.1.1) covering the use of renewables to generate electricity and heat is available on DTI's energy statistics web site: www.dti.gov.uk/energy/inform/dukes/dukes2005/07longterm.pdf .

7.6   Unlike in the commodity balance tables in other chapters of the Digest, Tables 7.1 to 7.3 have zero statistical differences. This is because the data for each category of fuel are, in the main, taken from a single source where there is less likelihood of differences due to timing or measurement.

Renewables Obligation and Renewables Directive

7.7   In April 2002 the Renewables Obligation (RO) (and the analogous Renewables (Scotland) Obligation) came into effect[1]. It is an obligation on all electricity suppliers to supply a specific proportion of electricity from eligible renewable sources. Eligible sources include all those covered by this chapter but with specific exclusions. These are: existing hydro plant of over 20 MW; all plant using renewable sources built before 1990 (unless re-furbished and less than 20 MW); and energy from mixed waste combustion unless the waste is first converted to fuel using advanced conversion technology. Only the biodegradable fraction of any waste is eligible (in line with the EU Directive, see

---

[1] Parliamentary approval of the Renewables Obligation Orders under The Utilities Act 2000 was given in March 2002.

paragraph 7.8, below). All stations outside the United Kingdom (the UK includes its territorial waters and the continental shelf) are also excluded. The upper part of table 7.5 shows all the components of total electricity generation on an RO basis. Strictly speaking until 2005, the RO covers only Great Britain, but in these UK based statistics Northern Ireland renewable sources have been treated as if they were also part of the RO.

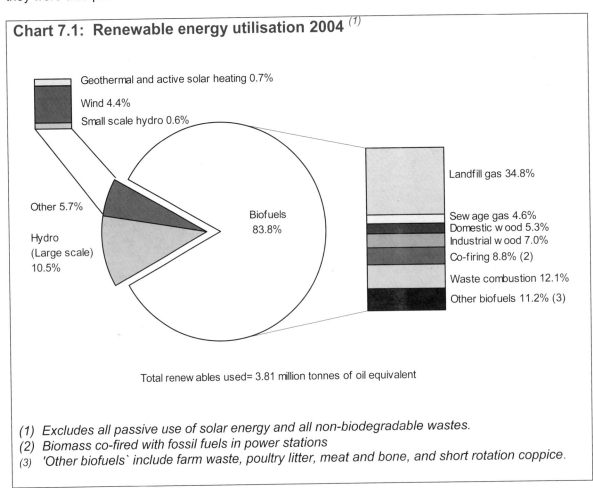

Chart 7.1: Renewable energy utilisation 2004 [1]

Geothermal and active solar heating 0.7%

Wind 4.4%

Small scale hydro 0.6%

Other 5.7%

Hydro (Large scale) 10.5%

Biofuels 83.8%

Landfill gas 34.8%

Sew age gas 4.6%
Domestic w ood 5.3%
Industrial w ood 7.0%
Co-firing 8.8% (2)
Waste combustion 12.1%
Other biofuels 11.2% (3)

Total renew ables used= 3.81 million tonnes of oil equivalent

(1) *Excludes all passive use of solar energy and all non-biodegradable wastes.*
(2) *Biomass co-fired with fossil fuels in power stations*
(3) *'Other biofuels' include farm waste, poultry litter, meat and bone, and short rotation coppice.*

7.8   The European Union's Renewables Directive (RD) (which came into force in October 2001) has a different definition of eligible renewables. The Directive's definition is the same as the international definition used in this chapter (in that it excludes non-biodegradable wastes) but with the addition of imports of renewable sources electricity because the Directive is concerned with consumption of electricity from renewable sources. FES has estimated the percentage of MSW that was non-biodegradable for all the years in the RESTATS database. For 2004 the estimate is that 37½ per cent of MSW was non-biodegradable and all of waste tyres (but see paragraph 7.65) and hospital waste. The lower part of Table 7.5 shows the components of total electricity generation on an RD basis.

7.9   In the past the main instruments for pursuing the development of renewables capacity were the Non Fossil Fuel Obligation (NFFO) Orders for England and Wales and for Northern Ireland, and the Scottish Renewable Orders (SRO). In this chapter the term "NFFO Orders" is used to refer to these instruments collectively. For projects contracted under NFFO Orders in England and Wales, details of capacity and generation were provided by the Non Fossil Purchasing Agency (NFPA). The Scottish Executive and Northern Ireland Electricity provided information on the Scottish and Northern Ireland NFFO Orders, respectively.

Renewables Targets

7.10   Thus since February 2000, the United Kingdom's renewables policy has consisted of four key strands:
  * a new Renewables Obligation on all electricity suppliers in Great Britain to supply a specific proportion of electricity from eligible renewables;

- exemption of electricity from renewables[2] from the Climate Change Levy;
- an expanded support programme for new and renewable energy including capital grants and an expanded research and development programme;
- development of a regional strategic approach to planning and targets for renewables.

The aim of the Renewables Obligation (RO) is to increase the contribution of electricity from renewables in the UK so that by 2010, 10 per cent of licensed UK electricity sales should be from renewable sources eligible for the RO, and by 2015 15 per cent should be eligible.

7.11   The EU Directive proposes that Member States adopt national targets for renewables that are consistent with reaching the overall EU target of 12 per cent of energy (22.1 per cent of electricity) from renewables by 2010. The proposed UK "share" of this target is that renewables sources eligible under the RD should account for 10 per cent of UK electricity **consumption** by 2010. Thus any imported electricity certified as coming from eligible renewable sources would count towards the RD target, but any electricity generated in the UK from eligible renewable sources but exported to another country would not. The Office of Gas and Electricity Markets (OFGEM) have advised that in 2004 3,522 GWh of imported electricity were certified as Climate Change Levy exempt and therefore count as eligible renewables.

7.12   Chart 7.2 shows the growth in all sources of renewables generation since 1990 and Table 7A gives renewables shares on three different bases for the three most recent years. They show progress towards the RO and RD 10 per cent targets. Generation from all renewables in the UK (on the international definition basis) accounted for 3.58 per cent of UK electricity generation in 2004 (see paragraph 7.16, below). In 2004 the RO percentage showed its largest ever growth in a single year rising by 0.87 percentage points to 3.08 per cent of electricity sales by licensed suppliers. On the basis favoured by the Renewables Directive, the percentage of UK electricity consumption accounted for by RD eligible renewable sources rose from 3.37 per cent in 2003 to 4.39 per cent in 2004. The main reason for the larger increase in the RD percentage was the 23 per cent increase in imports of renewable sourced electricity over the interconnector with France (mainly hydro). (Total imports of electricity over the interconnector doubled in 2004 – see Chapter 5.) All three percentages are affected by the rate of growth in the respective denominators as well as the numerators. For the overall percentage electricity generation in 2004 fell by ½ per cent, while for the RO percentage there was no increase in electricity sales by licensed suppliers. For the RD basis electricity consumption grew by less than 1 per cent in 2004.

Table 7A: Percentages of electricity derived from renewable sources

	2002	2003	2004
Overall renewables percentage (revised to the international basis)	2.87	2.67	3.58
Percentage on a Renewables Obligation basis	1.80	2.21	3.08
Percentage on a Renewables Directive basis	3.23	3.37	4.39

Commodity balances for renewables in 2004 (Table 7.1), 2003 (Table 7.2) and 2002 (Table 7.3)

7.13   Nine different categories of renewable fuels are identified in the commodity balances. Some of these categories are themselves groups of renewables because a more detailed disaggregation could disclose data for individual companies. In the commodity balance tables the distinction between biodegradable and non-biodegradable wastes cannot be maintained for this reason. The largest contribution to renewables in **input** terms (over 87 per cent) is from biofuels, with large-scale hydro electricity production contributing the majority of the remainder as Chart 7.1 shows. Only 4½ per cent of renewable energy comes from renewable sources other than biofuels and large-scale hydro. These include solar, wind, small-scale hydro and geothermal aquifers.

7.14   82 per cent of the renewable energy produced in 2004 was transformed into electricity. This is an increase from 79 per cent in 2003 and 78 per cent in 2002. While biofuels appear to dominate the picture when fuel inputs are being measured, hydro electricity is the largest contributor when the

---

[2] *Electricity generated by hydro stations with a declared net capacity of more than 10 MW is not exempt from the Climate Change Levy.*

output of electricity is being measured as Table 7.4 shows. This is because on an energy supplied basis (see Chapter 5, paragraph 5.26) hydro (and also wind and wave) inputs are assumed to be equal to the electricity produced. For landfill gas, sewage sludge, municipal solid waste and other renewables a substantial proportion of the energy content of the input is lost in the process of conversion to electricity.

7.15   Overall, renewable sources, excluding passive uses of solar energy, provided 1.7 per cent of the United Kingdom's total primary energy requirements in 2004. This was 0.2 of a percentage point higher than in 2003, which in turn was 0.1 of a percentage point higher than in 2002.

Capacity of, and electricity generated from renewable sources (Table 7.4)

7.16   Table 7.4 shows the capacity of, and the amounts of electricity generated from, each renewable source. Total electricity generation from renewables in 2004 amounted to 14,171 GWh, an increase of 3,533 GWh (+33.2 per cent) on 2003. The main contributors to this record increase were 1,702 GWh (+52.7 per cent) from hydro schemes, 728 GWh from landfill gas (+22.2 per cent), 650 GWh from wind (+51.6 per cent), and 420 GWh from co-firing of biomass with fossil fuels (+69.8 per cent). The increase in hydro was from the particularly low levels in 2003 caused by low rainfall and snowfall during winter 2002/3 and the summer of 2003. Only 30 per cent of generation from renewables was from hydro in 2003 compared with 35 per cent in 2004. The increase in the co-firing of biomass promotes that renewables technology to being the fourth most important in output terms after hydro, landfill gas and wind.

7.17   As a result all renewable sources provided 3.58 per cent of the electricity generated in the United Kingdom in 2004, 0.91 percentage points higher than in 2003. Chart 7.2 shows the growth in the proportion of electricity produced from renewable sources. It includes the progress towards the renewables targets set under the Renewables Obligation and Renewables Directive (see paragraphs 7.10 to 7.12 above and 7.22 below).

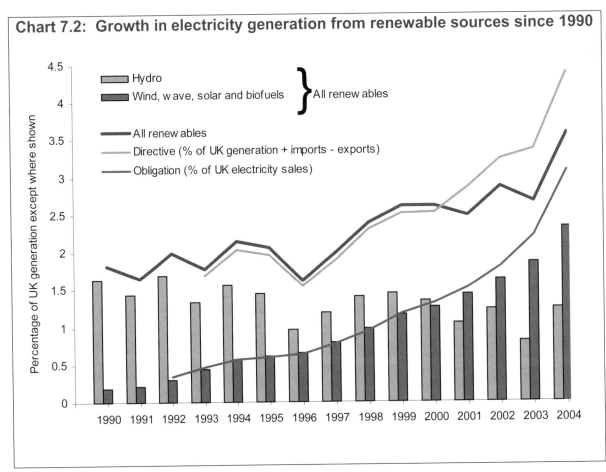

Chart 7.2: Growth in electricity generation from renewable sources since 1990

7.18   There was a 9 per cent increase in the installed generating capacity of renewable sources in 2003, mainly as a result of a 19 per cent increase in onshore wind capacity and a doubling of offshore wind capacity. There was also a 16 per increase in the capacity fuelled by landfill gas and an 18 per cent increase in sewage gas capacity. Large-scale hydro capacity is 2½ per cent lower than it was in 2001 as some stations have been adapted to fall within the capacity limits specified by the renewables obligation. The capacity to generate from solar photovoltaics showed a 37 per cent increase and has thus more than quadrupled in 4 years.

7.19   Chart 7.3 (which covers all renewables capacity except large scale hydro) illustrates the continuing increase in the electricity generation capacity from all significant renewable sources. This upward trend in the capacity of renewable sources will continue as some further projects already contracted under NFFO Orders come on line and recently consented onshore and offshore windfarms and other projects come on stream.

Chart 7.3: Electrical generating capacity of renewable energy plant (excluding large-scale hydro)[1]

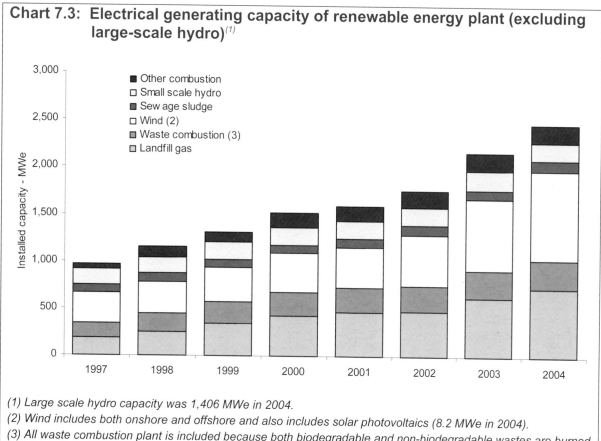

(1) Large scale hydro capacity was 1,406 MWe in 2004.
(2) Wind includes both onshore and offshore and also includes solar photovoltaics (8.2 MWe in 2004).
(3) All waste combustion plant is included because both biodegradable and non-biodegradable wastes are burned together in the same plant.

7.20   In 2004, (excluding large-scale hydro) 54½ per cent of electricity from renewables was generated under NFFO contracts. If ex-NFFO sites (NFFO 1 and 2 in England and Wales – see paragraphs 7.23 to 7.35, below) are included the proportion increases to 73 per cent. Table 7.4, however, includes both electricity generated outside of these contracts and electricity from large-scale hydro schemes and thus reports on total electricity generation from renewables. All electricity generated from renewables is also reported within the tables of Chapter 5 of this Digest (eg Table 5.6).

7.21   Plant load factors in Table 7.4 have been calculated in terms of installed capacity and express the average hourly quantity of electricity generated as a percentage of the average capacity at the beginning and end of the year. The overall figure is heavily influenced by the availability of hydro capacity during the year, which is in turn influenced by the amount of rainfall during the preceding period. Low rainfall in the winter of 2002/2003 led to 2003 having lower hydro load factors than in the previous very dry year of 1996. Two factors contributed to the lower load factor for wind in 2003. Firstly 110 MWe was installed late in the year and had little opportunity to contribute to generation. Secondly the long hot summer of 2003 was not as windy as previous years. For both hydro and wind load factors increased in 2004 and as a result the overall load factor for renewables and wastes was at a record level. Plant load factors for all generating plant in the UK are shown in Chapter 5, Table 5.10.

Electricity generated from renewable sources; Renewables Obligation and Renewables Directive bases (Table 7.5)

7.22   Electricity generated in the UK from renewable sources eligible under the Renewables Obligation in 2004 was 39 per cent greater than in 2003. This compares with growth of 25 per cent in 2003 and 18 per cent in 2002. Electricity generated in the UK from renewable sources eligible under the Renewables Directive in 2004 was 31 per cent greater than in 2003. This compares with growth of 6 per cent in 2003 and 13 per cent in 2002. Chart 7.2 shows the growth in the proportion of electricity produced from renewable sources under these definitions.

Renewable orders and operational capacity (Table 7.6)

7.23   In 1990, the first year of NFFO, projects contracted within NFFO accounted for about 32 per cent of the total capacity (excluding large-scale hydro). This percentage rose to a peak in 2001 of 91 per cent. Following the introduction of the Renewables Obligation it fell back as new capacity eligible for the RO outweighed the growth in NFFO 3, 4 and 5 and SRO and NI-NFFO projects, so that the NFFO capacity proportion (excluding large scale hydro) had decreased to 73 per cent in 2003 and fell further to 69 per cent in 2004. Twenty one new NFFO schemes totalling 53 MW (DNC) came on line during 2004. These trends are shown in Chart 7.4.

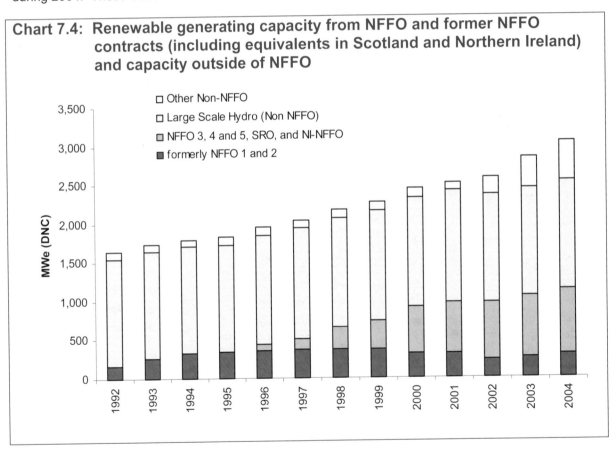

Chart 7.4: Renewable generating capacity from NFFO and former NFFO contracts (including equivalents in Scotland and Northern Ireland) and capacity outside of NFFO

(a)   Non Fossil Fuel Obligation (NFFO)

7.24   The 1989 Electricity Act empowered the Secretary of State to make orders requiring the Regional Electricity Companies in England and Wales (the RECs) to secure specified amounts of electricity from renewable energy sources.

7.25   Five NFFO Orders were made, of which the first in 1990 was set for a total of 102 MW DNC. This first order resulted in contracts for 75 projects for 152 MW DNC and provided a premium price for the electricity produced which was funded from a levy on electricity sales in England and Wales. (The bulk of this levy was used to support electricity from nuclear stations).

7.26   The second Order, made in late 1991, was set for 457 MW DNC. This resulted in 122 separate contracts   (for a total of 472 MW DNC) between the generators and the Non-Fossil Purchasing Agency (NFPA), which acted on behalf of the RECs. For landfill gas, sewage gas and waste-derived generation contracts were awarded at around 6p/kWh, while for wind-based generation a price of 11p/kWh was established. These prices reflected the limited period for the recovery of capital costs.

7.27   The third Order covers the period 1995 to 2014; this was for 627 MW DNC of contracted capacity at an average price of 4.35 p/kWh. The lower bid prices reflect the longer-term contracts, which are now available together with further developments that have led to improvements in the technologies. Taking into account factors such as the failure to gain planning permission it is estimated that about 300-400 MW DNC are likely to go forward for commissioning.

7.28   The fourth Order was announced in February 1997. Contracts have been let to 195 projects with a total DNC of 843 MW, at an average price of 3.46 p/kWh. In the fifth and largest Order, which was announced in September 1998, contracts have been let to 261 projects with a total DNC of 1,177.1 MW, at an average price of 2.71 p/kWh.

7.29   Since the expiry of the NFFO 1 and 2 contracts on 31 December 1998, these projects are no longer included in the monitoring of NFFO Orders and DTI no longer receive any status/output data on them from the NFPA. For some of these projects operational data have been obtained from other sources, while for the others estimates have been made based on output in 1998. From 2002 another source of information became available in the form of the Renewables Obligation data. This enabled Future Energy Solutions to identify which former NFFO 1 and 2 schemes were applying for ROCs and therefore were still running. Of the 113 NFFO 1 and 2 projects identified in this way as still live, 40 were contracted under the first order and 73 under the second order. It is appreciated that there may be some ex NFFO 1 and 2 schemes that are continuing to operate but whose output is too small to qualify for ROCs or which may need to re-furbish in order to qualify for ROCs. To that extent the estimates of NFFO capacity may be an underestimate.

7.30   As at the end of December 2004, 83 projects in the third Order were operational, with total capacities of 319 MW DNC. There were also 83 schemes with a capacity of 202 MW DNC commissioned from the fourth Order projects and 86 schemes totalling 172 MW DNC from the fifth Order. Table 7.5 sets out the technologies and capacities of schemes in all five Orders.

(b)   Scottish Renewable Order (SRO)
7.31   In Scotland, the first Renewables Order was made in 1994 for approximately 76 MW DNC of new capacity and comprising 30 schemes. Four generation technology bands were covered; 12 wind, 15 hydro, two waste-to-energy and one biomass. At the end of December 2004, 19 schemes were commissioned with a capacity of 48 MW DNC.

7.32   A second SRO was launched in 1995 and was made in March 1997 for 114 MW DNC of new capacity comprising 26 schemes, 9 of which were waste to energy projects, 9 were hydro projects, 7 were wind projects and one was a biomass project. Under this Order, at the end of 2004 there were 13 commissioned schemes with a capacity of 50 MW DNC.

7.33   A third SRO was laid before Parliament in February 1999 for 145 MW DNC of new capacity comprising 53 schemes. Sixteen of these were waste to energy projects, 5 were hydro projects, 28 were wind projects, one was a biomass project and 3 were wave energy projects. Under this Order, at the end of 2004 there were 17 commissioned schemes with a capacity of 35 MW DNC. Table 7.6 sets out the technologies and capacities of schemes in all three Scottish Orders.

(c)   Northern Ireland Non Fossil Fuel Obligation (NI NFFO)
7.34   In Northern Ireland, a first Order was made in March 1994 for approximately 16 MW DNC comprising 20 schemes. The contracted schemes were spread throughout Northern Ireland and were divided into three technology bands. There were 6 wind schemes of around 2 MW DNC each, totalling 12.7 MW DNC; 5 sewage gas projects totalling 0.56 MW DNC; and 9 small-scale hydro schemes totalling 2.4 MW DNC. At the end of 2004, 14 schemes were commissioned with a capacity of 15 MW DNC.

7.35   A second NI Order was made in 1996 for 10 schemes, totalling 16 MW DNC. These comprised two wind schemes, two hydro schemes, two biomass, one biogas, two landfill gas and one municipal and industrial waste scheme, as shown in Table 7.5. At the end of 2004, 5 schemes were commissioned with a capacity of 3 MW DNC.

Renewable sources used to generate electricity and heat (Table 7.7)

7.36   Between 2003 and 2004 there was an increase of 23 per cent in the input of renewable sources into electricity generation. Biofuels grew by 17½ per cent, and wind by 51 per cent, while hydro recovered from the low level of 2003 caused by the dry weather, growing by 53 per cent during the year to be 3 per cent higher than in 2002.

7.37   Compared with 5 years earlier total inputs to electricity generation have grown by 82 per cent aided by 114 per cent growth in the use of biofuels and a 128 per cent increase in the use of wind.

7.38   Table 7.7 also shows the contribution from renewables to heat generation. Here only a small share comes from geothermal and active solar heating and from various wastes, while the main contribution is from burning wood. However the use of active solar heating has increased by 160 per cent in the last 5 years and the use of heating from biodegradable wastes has increased by 31 per cent over the same period.

Technical notes and definitions

7.39   Energy derived from renewable sources is included in the aggregate energy tables in Chapter 1 of this Digest. The main energy tables (Tables 7.1 to 7.3) present figures in the common unit of energy, the tonne of oil equivalent, which is defined in Chapter 1 paragraph 1.24. The gross calorific values and conversion factors used to convert the data from original units are given on page 205 of Annex A and inside the back cover flap. The statistical methodologies and conversion factors are in line with those used by the International Energy Agency and the Statistical Office of the European Communities. Primary electricity contributions from hydro and wind are expressed in terms of an electricity supplied model (see Chapter 5, paragraph 5.26). Electrical capacities in this chapter are now quoted as Installed capacities.   However, in Chapter 5 Declared Net Capacity (DNC) of renewables is used when calculating the overall UK generating capacity. DNC takes into account the intermittent nature of the power output from some renewable sources (see paragraph 7.75, below).

7.40   The various renewable energy sources are described in the following paragraphs. This section also provides details of the quality of information provided within each renewables area, and the progress made to improve the quality of this information. While the data in the printed and bound copy of this Digest cover only the most recent 5 years, these notes also cover data for earlier years that are available on the DTI web site.

Use of existing solar energy

7.41   Nearly all buildings make use of some passive solar energy because they have windows or roof lights, which allow in natural light and provide a view of the surroundings. This existing use of passive solar energy is making a substantial contribution to the energy demand in the UK building stock. Passive solar design, in which buildings are designed to enhance solar energy use, results in additional savings in energy. A study in 1990, on behalf of the Department of Trade and Industry, estimated that this existing use saves 12.6 million tonnes of oil equivalent per year in the United Kingdom.   This figure reflects an estimate of the net useful energy flow (heat and lighting) across windows and other glazing in the United Kingdom building stock. The figure is very approximate and, as in previous years, has therefore not been included in the tables in this chapter.

Active solar heating

7.42 Active solar heating employs solar collectors to heat water mainly for domestic hot water systems but also for swimming pools and other applications. Updated figures have been obtained by FES (on behalf of the Department for Productivity, Energy and Industry). For 2004 an estimated 73.9 GWh for domestic hot water generation replaces gas heating; for swimming pools, an estimated 132.7 GWh generation for 2004 replaces gas (45 per cent), oil (45 per cent) or electricity (10 per cent).

Photovoltaics

7.43   Photovoltaics is the direct conversion of solar radiation into direct current electricity by the interaction of light with the electrons in a semiconductor device or cell. There has been a significant increase in capacity and generation of PV over the last year due to increased support from the Government.   There is a Major Photovoltaic Demonstration Programme offering grants for small, medium and large-scale installations, which is encouraging a significant number of new projects. This was preceded by a two-phase Domestic Field Trial, which has supported the installation of approximately 200 kW in the first phase and 500 kW in the second phase, and the Large Scale Field Trial for Public Buildings, which should result in another 700-800 kW capacity. The installed capacity increased from 6.0 kW in 2003 to 8.2 kW in 2004.

Onshore wind power

7.44   A wind turbine extracts energy from the wind by means of a rotor fitted with aerodynamic-section blades using the lifting forces on the blades to turn the rotor primary shaft. This mechanical power is used to drive an electrical generator. The figures included for generation from wind turbines are based on the installed capacities, together with an average capacity factor for the United Kingdom or, where figures are available, on actual generation.

7.45   There have been a total of 302 wind projects awarded contracts under NFFO. Many of these are new projects, so this has resulted in a considerable increase in electricity generation from wind since 1990. At the end of 2004, there were 93 wind generation projects operational under NFFO.

More are anticipated to be commissioned over the next 2-3 years. However Non-NFFO wind projects at the end of 2004 accounted for 44 per cent of wind capacity in DNC terms. The figures for wind in this chapter cover all known schemes in the United Kingdom.

Offshore wind power

7.46   The UK's offshore wind resource is vast, with the potential to provide more than the UK's current demand for electricity. Offshore wind speeds are higher than those onshore (typically up to 0.5m/s higher 10 km offshore) and also less turbulent. However, elevated inland sites can have higher wind speeds.

7.47   Due to the higher costs of installing each turbine offshore it is expected that, in general, the machines will be larger than their onshore counterparts (2 MW and above). This is driven by economics, with larger machine more cost effective per unit of electricity generated. The larger turbines also experience higher wind speeds, because taller towers put the rotors into the stronger winds. In addition, onshore constraints such as planning, noise effects and visual impact are likely to be reduced offshore. There are 18 sites with pre-lease agreements for offshore wind farms from Crown Estates. North Hoyle was the first to come on stream in autumn 2003.

Wave and Tidal Stream Power

7.48   Waves in the oceans are created by the interaction of winds with the surface of the sea. Because of the direction of the prevailing winds and the size of the Atlantic Ocean, the United Kingdom has wave power levels, which are amongst the highest in the world. Under the DTI's shoreline programme a 75kW experimental prototype an oscillating water column device came on line in late 1991 on the Hebridean island of Islay but this has now been decommissioned. Three wave schemes won contracts under the third SRO for a declared net capacity of 2 MW. One of these contract holders, Wavegen, has built a new 500kW scheme called the LIMPET near to the site of the prototype. This plant is now operating. Since 1999 the DTI under its Technology Programme has supported the development of a number of concepts. One of these the 'Pelamis' developed by an Edinburgh based company Ocean Power Delivery has been tested at the European Marine Energy Centre in Orkney since August 2005.

Tidal streams are high velocity sea currents created by the movement of the tides, often magnified by local topographical features such as headlands, inlets to inland lakes, and straits. Tidal stream energy is derived from the kinetic energy of the moving flow, analogous to the way a wind turbine operates in air. A recent study estimated that the available UK resource is up to 22 TWh per year. Since 2000 the DTI's Technology Programme has supported the development of a number of concepts. A full-scale prototype has been developed by a Bristol based company Marine Current Turbines and deployed and tested at Lynmouth off the coast of North Devon since June 2003. A number of other concepts are currently under development with some expected to test at full-scale at the European Marine Energy Centre in 2006.

Although the development of these technologies is reducing predicted energy costs, studies have shown that these costs are still not fully competitive with electricity supplied from the grid at today's costs. Further innovation is needed to overcome the technical challenges that hinder this competitiveness. Although a number of the current developers have plans for large scale pre-commercial demonstrations of their technologies by 2010 it is unlikely that these technologies would be deployed commercially on a large scale until later.

Large scale hydro

7.49   In hydro schemes the turbines that drive the electricity generators are powered by the direct action of water either from a reservoir or from the run of the river. Large-scale hydro covers plants belonging to companies with capacity of 5 MWe and over. Most of the plants are located in Scotland and Wales and mainly draw their water from high-level reservoirs with their own natural catchment areas. Major Power Producers (MPPs) report their output to the Department of Trade and Industry in DTI's regular electricity surveys. In previous years these data were submitted in aggregate form and not split down by size of scheme. This meant that some small-scale schemes were hidden within the generation data for the large-scale schemes. This year, MPPs have provided a more detailed breakdown of their data and some smaller sites previously included under "large scale" are for 2004 under "small scale". There is over 1,400MW of installed capacity for large-scale hydroelectric schemes in the UK. The coverage of these large-scale hydro figures is the same as that used in the tables in the Chapter 5 of this Digest. The data in this Chapter exclude pumped storage stations (see paragraph 5.49).

Small scale hydro

7.50   Electricity generation schemes with a hydro capacity below 5 MWe are classified as small scale. These are schemes being used for either domestic/farm purposes or for local sale to electricity supply companies. A new survey of small-scale hydro sites was carried out in 2004 giving a more detailed picture of the current situation. The survey concentrated on the non-NFFO and non-RO funded small-scale hydroelectric sites. Small-scale hydro capacity has decreased compared with previous years despite some re-allocation to small scale of schemes belonging to major power producers (see paragraph 7.49, above). This is through a combination of some scheme closures coupled with others re-powering and being elevated into the large-scale hydro band. Small scale sites continue to be built. Data given for generation are actual figures where available, but otherwise are estimated using a typical load factor (based on NFFO schemes actual data). The variation in the time-series generation figures primarily reflects the variation in precipitation.

Geothermal aquifers

7.51   Aquifers containing water at elevated temperatures occur in some parts of the United Kingdom at between 1,500 and 3,000 metres below the surface. This water can be pumped to the surface and used, for example, in community heating schemes. There is currently only one scheme operating in the UK at Southampton.

Biofuels

(a)   Landfill gas

7.52   Landfill gas is a methane-rich biogas formed from the decomposition of organic material in landfill. The gas can be used to fuel reciprocating engines or turbines to generate electricity or used directly in kilns and boilers. In other countries, the gas is cleaned to pipeline quality or used as a vehicle fuel. Landfill gas exploitation has benefited considerably from the NFFO and this can be seen from the large rise in the amount of electricity generated since 1992. Further commissioning of landfill gas projects under NFFO will continue to increase the amount of electricity generated from this technology. Ofgem's ROC's Database also provides details of landfill gas sites claiming ROCs. Information on landfill gas was supplemented by a RESTATS survey carried out by FES in 2004 on behalf of the DTI, and covered the period up to the end of 2004. The landfill gas industry had changed in recent years with a number of mergers and takeovers. In 2004, 14 new schemes came on line under NFFO.

(b)   Sewage sludge digestion

7.53   In all sewage sludge digestion projects, some of the gas produced is used to maintain the optimum temperature for digestion. In addition, many use combined heat and power (CHP) systems. The electricity generated is either used on site or sold under the NFFO. Information from these projects was provided from the CHAPSTAT Database, which is compiled and maintained by FES on behalf of the Department of Trade and Industry (See Chapter 6).

(c)   Domestic wood combustion

7.54   Domestic wood use includes the use of logs in open fires, "AGA"-type cooker boilers and other wood burning stoves. The figure given is an approximate estimate based on a survey carried out in 1989. The Forestry Commission carried out a survey of domestic wood fuel use in 1997 but the results from this were inconclusive. As an upper limit, about 600,000 oven-dried tonnes (ODTs) were estimated to be available for domestic heating. In 2001, FES undertook a study of UK domestic wood use on behalf of DTI. A methodology was devised for surveying the three major sectors involved in wood use – the stove or boiler supplier, the wood supplier and the end user. Questionnaires were devised for all these parties and then attempts were made to contact representative samples in the various regions of the UK. From the evidence obtained via the questionnaires and telephone interviews we believe that the domestic wood burning market is growing but not in the area of wood as the primary heat source. This still remains a relatively small market and a small percentage of the wood burnt. Unfortunately, the survey was unable to provide statistically sound evidence as to the amount of wood used in the domestic sector and although it was felt that there has been a small increase in the domestic use of wood as a fuel, on the basis of the results of the approach, we could not justify modifying the current estimate for the UK. In view of the importance attached to finding out about domestic wood use, the Forestry Commission has therefore decided to undertake another study guided by the lessons learnt from the previous work. In particular they would approach the newly emerging wood cooperatives, as they are likely to be a good source if information now that they should be more well established, the National House-Building Council (NHBC) to examine new build and treating equipment suppliers, fuel suppliers and users under separate surveys. This year, a pilot study was undertaken in Scotland by the Forestry Commission to assist in developing the correct methodology prior to a National survey. Preliminary results suggest that current usage may be less than in 1997.

(d) Industrial wood combustion
7.55 In 1997, the industrial wood figure (which includes sawmill residues, furniture manufacturing waste etc.) was included as a separate category for the first time. This was due to the availability of better data as a result of a survey carried out in 1996 on wood fired combustion plants above 400 kW thermal input. A follow-up survey was subsequently carried out for 2000. This survey highlighted that there were fewer sites (174) operating than in 1996 due to the imposition of more stringent emissions control. It is proposed to carry out a further survey of industrial wood use in 2005.

(e) Short rotation coppice
7.56 Short rotation willow coppice plantations have become well established but the rate of uptake of the technology has been fairly slow. Under Northern Ireland's second Non-Fossil Fuel Renewable Energy order for electricity, two projects were live at the end of 2004.

7.57 In England, Project ARBRE in South Yorkshire was contracted under NFFO 3 to generate 10 MW of electricity of which 8 MW were to be exported to the local grid. This project ran into difficulties and was sold to new owners who are still evaluating their options on taking the project forward. However, SembCorp Utilities UK have announced that they are to build at 30 MW wood-burning power station at Wilton to come on line in 2007 and require 55,000 tonnes a year of Short Rotation Willow Coppice.

(f) Straw combustion
7.58 Straw can be burnt in high temperature boilers, designed for the efficient and controlled combustion of solid fuels and biomass to supply heat, hot water and hot air systems. There are large numbers of these small-scale batch-fed whole bale boilers. The figures given are estimates based partly on 1990 information and partly on a survey of straw-fired boilers carried out in 1993-94. A 37 MW straw fired power station near Ely, Cambridgeshire is currently the only electricity generation scheme in operation

(g) Waste combustion
7.59 Domestic, industrial and commercial wastes represent a significant resource for materials and energy recovery. Wastes may be combusted, as received, in purpose built incinerators or processed into a range of refuse derived fuels for both on-site and off-site utilisation. Only the non-biodegradable portion of waste is counted in renewables statistics although non-biodegradable wastes are included in this chapter as "below the line" items. The paragraphs below describe various categories of waste combustion in greater detail.

7.60 Twenty three waste-to-energy plants were in operation in 2004 burning municipal solid waste (MSW), refuse derived fuel (RDF) and general industrial waste (GIW).

7.61 **Municipal solid waste combustion:** Information was provided from the refuse incinerator operators in the United Kingdom that practice energy recovery using the RESTATS questionnaire. This included both direct combustion of unprocessed MSW and the combustion of RDF. In the latter, process waste can be partially processed to produce coarse RDF that can then be burnt in a variety of ways. By further processing the refuse, including separating off the fuel fraction, compacting, drying and densifying, it is possible to produce an RDF pellet. This pellet has around 60 per cent of the gross calorific value of British coal. The generation from MSW has been split between biodegradable sources and non-biodegradable sources using information outlined in paragraph 7.62 below. Approximately 62.5 per cent of generation from MSW was estimated to be from biodegradable sources. Non-biodegradable municipal solid waste is not included in the overall renewables percentage under the international definition of renewables (see paragraph 7.1). However, such wastes are still shown in the tables accompanying this chapter as 'below the line' items.

7.62   There has been an ongoing programme of waste analysis in the UK for many years; such analyses may be carried out to an accuracy of + 1 per cent. Such studies are guided by the use of ACORN (A Classification of Residential Neighbourhoods) socio-economic profiles which are used to select sample areas for the analysis of household collected waste and is based on the premise that households of similar socio-economic characteristics are likely to have similar behavioural, purchasing and lifestyle characteristics; this will be reflected in the quantity and composition of waste that those households produce. The large and recently completed study in Wales showed that the only category in domestic waste to show a statistically significant seasonal variation was garden waste; as garden waste is a small percentage (certainly when compared to food and kitchen waste), the effect on the operation of biomass-to-energy plants should be almost unnoticed. Although this study was carried out for Wales, there is virtually no regional variation to be seen any more so it is likely that these figures will become the UK standard. Recent work has shown that UK domestic waste has a biodegradable content of 67.5 per cent $\pm$ 1 per cent his accounts for about 62.5 per cent of the energy generated from its combustion. Municipal Solid Waste (MSW) comprises of domestic waste plus other feedstocks, such as, general industrial waste, building demolition waste and tree clippings from civil amenities. This has the net effect of reducing the percentage composition of the biodegradable content to 61 per cent $\pm$ 1 per cent. Because the combustion properties of some of the other biodegradable materials added is similar to that of domestic waste, this has virtually no effect on the percentage of the energy generated from the biodegradables component, which remains at about 62.5 per cent.

7.63   **General industrial waste combustion:** Certain wastes produced by industry and commerce can be used as a source of energy for industrial processes or space heating. These wastes include general waste from factories such as paper, cardboard, wood and plastics.

7.64   A survey conducted in 2001 noted that GIW is now burnt in MSW waste-to-energy facilities. As no sites are solely burning GIW for heat or electricity generation, this feedstock is being handled under the MSW category.

7.65   **Specialised waste combustion:** Specialised wastes arise as a result of a particular activity or process. Materials in this category include scrap tyres, hospital wastes, poultry litter, meal and bone and farm waste digestion. The large tyre incineration plant with energy recovery did not generate in 2004. Although part of waste tyre combustion is of biodegradable waste, because there is no agreed method of calculating the small biodegradable content, all of the generation from waste tyres has been included under non-biodegradable wastes in this chapter (see paragraph 7.62, above).

7.66   In 2004 information on hospital waste incineration was supplemented by a RESTATS survey, carried out by FES in 2004 on behalf of DTI, and covered a period up to the end of 2003. The survey confirmed whether the older sites were still operating, and identified any new operating facilities. Information on both their thermal and electrical outputs between 2000 and 2003 were gathered where data were available. There were no major changes, as the sector appeared to have stabilised since the introduction of the new emission legislation. There may, however, be future changes due to the appearance of new technologies, such as microwave treatment, and increased segregation of clinical waste.

7.67   One poultry litter combustion project started generating electricity in 1992; a second began in 1993. Both of these are NFFO projects. In addition, a small-scale CHP scheme began generating towards the end of 1990 however this has now closed due to new emissions regulations. A further NFFO scheme started generating in 1998, and during 2000 an SRO scheme began to generate. Over the most recent 4 years one of the earlier poultry litter projects was fuelled mainly by meat and bone. A new poultry litter scheme became fully operational in 2001.

7.68   Information on farm waste digestion in the United Kingdom is based on a survey carried out during 1991-1992 with a follow-up study in 1996. There was a farm digestion project generating electricity under the NFFO; its output was included in the commodity balances but is has now ceased to operate. In 2003, however, a large centralised anaerobic digestion scheme (Holsworthy) generating electricity under NFFO 5 came on-line. With the exception of this scheme, data collected from the 1996 survey were used to derive estimates for 1997 through to 2003. A new survey was carried out in 2005, which gathered information from previous years, and from industry experts and various government departments. The number of sites using farm waste digestion fell significantly, which was mainly attributed to tightening waste regulations and lack of maintenance. However, this has not prevented new digesters being commissioned and built in recent months.

(h)   Co-firing of biomass with fossil fuels

7.69   Co-firing of biomass fuel in fossil fuel power stations is not a new idea. Technically it has been proven in power stations worldwide, although, until recently, it was not practised in the UK. The biomass fuel is usually fed by means of the existing stoking mechanism as a partial substitute for the fossil fuel. The combustion system may cope with up to a 25 per cent substitution without any major changes to the boiler design and airflows, but fuel preparation and transport systems may be the limiting feature at percentages much lower than this.

7.70   Since 2002, co-firing of biomass with fossil fuels has been eligible under the RO, the first time that any renewable energy initiative has included co-firing. As the purpose of this was to enable markets and supply chains for biomass to develop, and not to support coal fired power stations, the following limits were placed on co-firing:
- only electricity generated before 1 April 2011 would be eligible;
- from 1 April 2006 at least 75 per cent of the biomass must consist of energy crops.

7.71   However, the scheme has now been extended to allow longer for an energy crop market to develop, through establishing biomass operations at co-fired stations. The key changes are as follows:
- fossil fuel stations are allowed to convert to biomass without refurbishment;
- any biomass can be co-fired until 31 March 2009 with no minimum percentage of energy crops;
- 25 per cent of co-fired biomass must be energy crops from 1 April 2009 until 31 March 2010;
- 50 per cent of co-fired biomass must be energy crops from 1 April 2010 until 31 March 2011;
- 75 per cent of co-fired biomass must be energy crops from 1 April 2011 until 31 March 2016. Co-firing ceases to be eligible for ROCs after this date.

To balance the above changes and reduce the risk of flooding the ROC market with co-firing ROCs, thereby affecting ROC prices and investor confidence adversely, it is proposed that the 25 per cent cap from 1 April 2006 on an individual supplier should be changed to:
- 10 per cent from 1 April 2006 until 31 March 2011;
- 5 per cent from 1 April 2011 until 31 March 2016.

(i) Biodiesel and bioblend

7.72   In the UK biodiesel is defined for taxation purposes as diesel quality liquid fuel produced from biomass or waste cooking oil, the ester content of which is not less than 96.5 per cent by weight and the sulphur content of which does not exceed 0.005 per cent by weight or is nil. "Bioblend" is any mixture that is produced by mixing biodiesel and heavy oil. The use of biofuels in the UK has yet to become significant. A plant in Scotland has the capacity to produce 50,000 tonnes of biodiesel a year and in 2005 a 250,000 tonnes per year plant is due to open on Teesside. The most usual way for biodiesel to be sold is for it to be blended with ordinary diesel fuel and thus it would be reported as part of the road transport use of diesel in Chapter 3. The duty payable on biodiesel is just over half the duty payable on road diesel and in blended fuels the duty payable is proportionate to the duty payable on the constituent fuels.

Combined Heat and Power

7.73   A Combined Heat and Power (CHP) plant is an installation where there is a simultaneous generation of usable heat and power (usually electricity) in a single process. Some CHP installations are fuelled either wholly or partially by renewable sources of energy. The main renewable sources that are used for CHP are biofuels particularly sewage gas.

7.74   Chapter 6 of this Digest summarises information on the contribution made by CHP to the United Kingdom's energy requirements in 2000 to 2004 using the results of annual studies undertaken to identify all CHP schemes. Included in Tables 6.1 to 6.9 of that chapter is information on the contribution of renewable sources to CHP generation in each year from 2000 to 2004. Corresponding data for 1996 to 1999 are available on the DTI web site. The information contained in those tables is therefore a subset of the data contained within the tables presented in this chapter.

Capacity and load factor

7.75   The electrical capacities are given in Table 7.4 as installed capacities ie the maximum continuous rating of the generating sets in the stations. In Chapter 5 DNC (Declared Net Capacity) is used, ie the maximum continuous rating of the generating sets in the stations, less the power consumed by the plant itself, and reduced by a specified factor to take into account the intermittent nature of the energy source e.g. 0.43 for wind and 0.33 for shoreline wave. DNC represents the nominal maximum capability of a generating set to supply electricity to consumers. For electrical capacities of generation using renewables in DNC terms see Table 7.1.1 on the DTI web site.

7.76   Plant load factors in this chapter have been calculated in terms of installed capacity (ie the maximum continuous rating of the generating sets in the stations) and express the average hourly quantity of electricity generated as a percentage of the average of the capacities at the beginning and end of the year.

Contact :   *Steve Dagnall, Future Energy Solutions*   *Mike Janes, DTI, Statistician*
                steve.dagnall@aeat.co.uk   *mike.janes@dti.gsi.gov.uk*
                0870 190 6092   *020-7215 5186*

7.1 Commodity balances 2004
Renewables and waste

	Wood waste	Wood	Poultry litter, meat and bone, biomass, straw, farm waste and SRC(3)	Sewage gas	Landfill gas
Supply					
Production	266	204	550	177	1,327
Other sources	-	-		-	-
Imports	-	-	212	-	-
Exports	-	-	-	-	-
Marine bunkers	-	-	-	-	-
Stock change (1)	-	-	-	-	-
Transfers	-	-	-	-	-
Total supply	266	204	762	177	1,327
Statistical difference (2)	-	-	-	-	-
Total demand	266	204	762	177	1,327
Transformation	-	-	688	124	1,313
Electricity generation	-	-	688	124	1,313
Major power producers	-	-	449	-	-
Autogenerators	-	-	239	124	1,313
Heat generation	-	-	-	-	-
Petroleum refineries	-	-	-	-	-
Coke manufacture	-	-	-	-	-
Blast furnaces	-	-	-	-	-
Patent fuel manufacture	-	-	-	-	-
Other	-	-	-	-	-
Energy industry use	-	-	-	-	-
Electricity generation	-	-		-	
Oil and gas extraction	-	-		-	
Petroleum refineries	-	-		-	
Coal extraction	-	-		-	
Coke manufacture	-	-		-	
Blast furnaces	-	-		-	
Patent fuel manufacture	-	-		-	
Pumped storage	-	-		-	
Other	-	-		-	
Losses	-	-	-	-	-
Final consumption	266	204	74	53	14
Industry	266	-	-	-	14
Unclassified	266	-	-	-	14
Iron and steel	-	-	-	-	-
Non-ferrous metals	-	-	-	-	-
Mineral products	-	-	-	-	-
Chemicals	-	-	-	-	-
Mechanical engineering, etc	-	-	-	-	-
Electrical engineering, etc	-	-	-	-	-
Vehicles	-	-	-	-	-
Food, beverages, etc	-	-	-	-	-
Textiles, leather, etc	-	-	-	-	-
Paper, printing, etc	-	-	-	-	-
Other industries	-	-	-	-	-
Construction	-	-	-	-	-
Transport	-	-	-	-	-
Air	-	-	-	-	-
Rail	-	-	-	-	-
Road	-	-	-	-	-
National navigation	-	-	-	-	-
Pipelines	-	-	-	-	-
Other	-	204	74	53	-
Domestic	-	204	-	-	-
Public administration	-	-	-	53	-
Commercial	-	-	-	-	-
Agriculture	-	-	74	-	-
Miscellaneous	-	-	-	-	-
Non energy use	-	-	-	-	-

(1) Stock fall (+), stock rise (-).
(2) Total supply minus total demand.
(3) SRC is short rotation coppice.
(4) Municipal solid waste, general industrial waste and hospital waste.
(5) The amount of shoreline wave included is less than 0.1 ktoe.

7.1 Commodity balances 2004 (continued)
Renewables and waste

Waste(4) and tyres	Geothermal and active solar heat	Hydro	Wind and wave (5)	Total renewables	
					Supply
792	25	424	167	3,932	Production
-	-	-	-	-	Other sources
-	-		-	212	Imports
-	-	-	-	-	Exports
-	-	-	-	-	Marine bunkers
-	-	-	-	-	Stock change (1)
-	-	-	-	-	Transfers
792	25	424	167	4,144	**Total supply**
-	-	-	-	-	**Statistical difference** (2)
792	25	424	167	4,144	**Total demand**
693	-	424	167	3,409	**Transformation**
693	-	424	167	3,409	Electricity generation
90	-	344	-	883	Major power producers
603	-	80	167	2,526	Autogenerators
-	-	-	-	-	Heat generation
-	-	-	-	-	Petroleum refineries
-	-	-	-	-	Coke manufacture
-	-	-	-	-	Blast furnaces
-	-	-	-	-	Patent fuel manufacture
-	-	-	-	-	Other
-	-	-	-	-	**Energy industry use**
-	-	-	-	-	Electricity generation
-	-	-	-	-	Oil and gas extraction
-	-	-	-	-	Petroleum refineries
-	-	-	-	-	Coal extraction
-	-	-	-	-	Coke manufacture
-	-	-	-	-	Blast furnaces
-	-	-	-	-	Patent fuel manufacture
-	-	-	-	-	Pumped storage
-	-	-	-	-	Other
-	-	-	-	-	**Losses**
99	25	-	-	735	**Final consumption**
6	-	-	-	286	**Industry**
6	-	-	-	286	Unclassified
-	-	-	-	-	Iron and steel
-	-	-	-	-	Non-ferrous metals
-	-	-	-	-	Mineral products
-	-	-	-	-	Chemicals
-	-	-	-	-	Mechanical engineering, etc
-	-	-	-	-	Electrical engineering, etc
-	-	-	-	-	Vehicles
-	-	-	-	-	Food, beverages, etc
-	-	-	-	-	Textiles, leather, etc
-	-	-	-	-	Paper, printing, etc
-	-	-	-	-	Other industries
-	-	-	-	-	Construction
-	-	-	-	-	**Transport**
-	-	-	-	-	Air
-	-	-	-	-	Rail
-	-	-	-	-	Road
-	-	-	-	-	National navigation
-	-	-	-	-	Pipelines
93	25	-	-	449	**Other**
23	25	-	-	252	Domestic
51	-	-	-	104	Public administration
10	-	-	-	10	Commercial
-	-	-	-	74	Agriculture
9	-	-	-	9	Miscellaneous
-	-	-	-	-	**Non energy use**

7.2 Commodity balances 2003

Renewables and waste

Thousand tonnes of oil equivalent

	Wood waste	Wood	Poultry litter, meat and bone, biomass, straw, farm waste and SRC(3)	Sewage gas	Landfill gas
Supply					
Production	266	204	504	165	1,088
Other sources	-	-	-	-	-
Imports	-	-	110	-	-
Exports	-	-	-	-	-
Marine bunkers	-	-	-	-	-
Stock change (1)	-	-	-	-	-
Transfers	-	-	-	-	-
Total supply	266	204	614	165	1,088
Statistical difference (2)	-	-	-	-	-
Total demand	266	204	614	165	1,088
Transformation	-r	-	542	113	1,075
Electricity generation	-	-	542	113	1,075
Major power producers	-	-	292	-	-
Autogenerators	-	-	250	113	1,075
Heat generation	-r	-	-	-	-
Petroleum refineries	-	-	-	-	-
Coke manufacture	-	-	-	-	-
Blast furnaces	-	-	-	-	-
Patent fuel manufacture	-	-	-	-	-
Other	-	-	-	-	-
Energy industry use	-	-	-	-	-
Electricity generation	-	-	-	-	-
Oil and gas extraction	-	-	-	-	-
Petroleum refineries	-	-	-	-	-
Coal extraction	-	-	-	-	-
Coke manufacture	-	-	-	-	-
Blast furnaces	-	-	-	-	-
Patent fuel manufacture	-	-	-	-	-
Pumped storage	-	-	-	-	-
Other	-	-	-	-	-
Losses	-	-	-	-	-
Final consumption	265r	204	72	53	14
Industry	265r	-	-	-	14
Unclassified	265r	-	-	-	14
Iron and steel	-	-	-	-	-
Non-ferrous metals	-	-	-	-	-
Mineral products	-	-	-	-	-
Chemicals	-	-	-	-	-
Mechanical engineering, etc	-	-	-	-	-
Electrical engineering, etc	-	-	-	-	-
Vehicles	-	-	-	-	-
Food, beverages, etc	-	-	-	-	-
Textiles, leather, etc	-	-	-	-	-
Paper, printing, etc	-	-	-	-	-
Other industries	-	-	-	-	-
Construction	-	-	-	-	-
Transport	-	-	-	-	-
Air	-	-	-	-	-
Rail	-	-	-	-	-
Road	-	-	-	-	-
National navigation	-	-	-	-	-
Pipelines	-	-	-	-	-
Other	-	204	72	53	-
Domestic	-	204	-	-	-
Public administration	-	-	-	53	-
Commercial	-	-	-	-	-
Agriculture	-	-	72	-	-
Miscellaneous	-	-	-	-	-
Non energy use	-	-	-	-	-

(1) Stock fall (+), stock rise (-).
(2) Total supply minus total demand.
(3) SRC is short rotation coppice.
(4) Municipal solid waste, general industrial waste and hospital waste.
(5) The amount of shoreline wave included is less than 0.1 ktoe.

7.2 Commodity balances 2003 (continued)

Renewables and waste

Waste(4) and tyres	Geothermal and active solar heat	Hydro	Wind and wave (5)	Total renewables	
					Supply
819	21	278	111	3,454	Production
-	-	-	-	-	Other sources
-	-	-	-	110	Imports
-	-	-	-	-	Exports
-	-	-	-	-	Marine bunkers
-	-	-	-	-	Stock change (1)
-	-	-	-	-	Transfers
819	21	278	111	3,565	**Total supply**
-	-	-	-	-	**Statistical difference (2)**
819	21	278	111	3,565	**Total demand**
720	-	278	111	2,837r	**Transformation**
720	-	278	111	2,837	Electricity generation
89	-	221	-	602	Major power producers
630	-	57	111	2,235	Autogenerators
-	-	-	-	-r	Heat generation
-	-	-	-	-	Petroleum refineries
-	-	-	-	-	Coke manufacture
-	-	-	-	-	Blast furnaces
-	-	-	-	-	Patent fuel manufacture
-	-	-	-	-	Other
-	-	-	-	-	**Energy industry use**
-	-	-	-	-	Electricity generation
-	-	-	-	-	Oil and gas extraction
-	-	-	-	-	Petroleum refineries
-	-	-	-	-	Coal extraction
-	-	-	-	-	Coke manufacture
-	-	-	-	-	Blast furnaces
-	-	-	-	-	Patent fuel manufacture
-	-	-	-	-	Pumped storage
-	-	-	-	-	Other
-	-	-	-	-	**Losses**
99	21	-	-	728r	**Final consumption**
6	-	-	-	285r	**Industry**
6	-	-	-	285r	Unclassified
-	-	-	-	-	Iron and steel
-	-	-	-	-	Non-ferrous metals
-	-	-	-	-	Mineral products
-	-	-	-	-	Chemicals
-	-	-	-	-	Mechanical engineering, etc
-	-	-	-	-	Electrical engineering, etc
-	-	-	-	-	Vehicles
-	-	-	-	-	Food, beverages, etc
-	-	-	-	-	Textiles, leather, etc
-	-	-	-	-	Paper, printing, etc
-	-	-	-	-	Other industries
-	-	-	-	-	Construction
-	-	-	-	-	**Transport**
-	-	-	-	-	Air
-	-	-	-	-	Rail
-	-	-	-	-	Road
-	-	-	-	-	National navigation
-	-	-	-	-	Pipelines
93	21	-	-	443	**Other**
23	21	-	-	248	Domestic
51	-	-	-	104	Public administration
10r	-	-	-	10r	Commercial
-	-	-	-	72	Agriculture
9r	-	-	-	9r	Miscellaneous
-	-	-	-	-	**Non energy use**

7.3 Commodity balances 2002

Renewables and waste

Thousand tonnes of oil equivalent

	Wood waste	Wood	Poultry litter, meat and bone, straw, farm waste and SRC(3)	Sewage gas	Landfill gas
Supply					
Production	266	204	440	174	892
Other sources	-	-	-	-	-
Imports	-	-	-	-	-
Exports	-	-	-	-	-
Marine bunkers	-	-	-	-	-
Stock change (1)	-	-	-	-	-
Transfers	-	-	-	-	-
Total supply	266	204	440	174	892
Statistical difference (2)	-	-	-	-	-
Total demand	266	204	440	174	892
Transformation	-r	-	368	121	879
Electricity generation	-	-	368	121	879
Major power producers	-	-	184	-	-
Autogenerators	-	-	184	121	879
Heat generation	-r	-	-	-	-
Petroleum refineries	-	-	-	-	-
Coke manufacture	-	-	-	-	-
Blast furnaces	-	-	-	-	-
Patent fuel manufacture	-	-	-	-	-
Other	-	-	-	-	-
Energy industry use	-	-	-	-	-
Electricity generation	-	-	-	-	-
Oil and gas extraction	-	-	-	-	-
Petroleum refineries	-	-	-	-	-
Coal extraction	-	-	-	-	-
Coke manufacture	-	-	-	-	-
Blast furnaces	-	-	-	-	-
Patent fuel manufacture	-	-	-	-	-
Pumped storage	-	-	-	-	-
Other	-	-	-	-	-
Losses	-	-	-	-	-
Final consumption	266r	204	72	53	14
Industry	266r	-	-	-	14
Unclassified	266r	-	-	-	14
Iron and steel	-	-	-	-	-
Non-ferrous metals	-	-	-	-	-
Mineral products	-	-	-	-	-
Chemicals	-	-	-	-	-
Mechanical engineering, etc	-	-	-	-	-
Electrical engineering, etc	-	-	-	-	-
Vehicles	-	-	-	-	-
Food, beverages, etc	-	-	-	-	-
Textiles, leather, etc	-	-	-	-	-
Paper, printing, etc	-	-	-	-	-
Other industries	-	-	-	-	-
Construction	-	-	-	-	-
Transport	-	-	-	-	-
Air	-	-	-	-	-
Rail	-	-	-	-	-
Road	-	-	-	-	-
National navigation	-	-	-	-	-
Pipelines	-	-	-	-	-
Other	-	204	72	53	-
Domestic	-	204	-	-	-
Public administration	-	-	-	53	-
Commercial	-	-	-	-	-
Agriculture	-	-	72	-	-
Miscellaneous	-	-	-	-	-
Non energy use	-	-	-	-	-

(1) Stock fall (+), stock rise (-).
(2) Total supply minus total demand.
(3) SRC is short rotation coppice.

(4) Municipal solid waste, general industrial waste and hospital waste.
(5) The amount of shoreline wave included is less than 0.1 ktoe.

7.3 Commodity balances 2002 (continued)

Renewables and waste

Thousand tonnes of oil equivalent

Waste(4) and tyres	Geothermal and active solar heat	Hydro	Wind and wave (5)	Total renewables	
					Supply
797	17	412	108	3,310	Production
-	-	-	-	-	Other sources
-	-	-	-	-	Imports
-	-	-	-	-	Exports
-	-	-	-	-	Marine bunkers
-	-	-	-	-	Stock change (1)
-	-	-	-	-	Transfers
797	17	412	108	3,310	**Total supply**
-	-	-	-	-	**Statistical difference** (2)
797	17	412	108	3,310	**Total demand**
706	-	412	108	2,593r	**Transformation**
706	-	412	108	2,593	Electricity generation
90	-	338	-	612	Major power producers
616	-	74	108	1,981	Autogenerators
-	-	-	-	-r	Heat generation
-	-	-	-	-	Petroleum refineries
-	-	-	-	-	Coke manufacture
-	-	-	-	-	Blast furnaces
-	-	-	-	-	Patent fuel manufacture
-	-	-	-	-	Other
-	-	-	-	-	**Energy industry use**
-	-	-	-	-	Electricity generation
-	-	-	-	-	Oil and gas extraction
-	-	-	-	-	Petroleum refineries
-	-	-	-	-	Coal extraction
-	-	-	-	-	Coke manufacture
-	-	-	-	-	Blast furnaces
-	-	-	-	-	Patent fuel manufacture
-	-	-	-	-	Pumped storage
-	-	-	-	-	Other
-	-	-	-	-	**Losses**
91	17	-	-	717r	**Final consumption**
6	-	-	-	286r	**Industry**
6	-	-	-	286r	Unclassified
-	-	-	-	-	Iron and steel
-	-	-	-	-	Non-ferrous metals
-	-	-	-	-	Mineral products
-	-	-	-	-	Chemicals
-	-	-	-	-	Mechanical engineering, etc
-	-	-	-	-	Electrical engineering, etc
-	-	-	-	-	Vehicles
-	-	-	-	-	Food, beverages, etc
-	-	-	-	-	Textiles, leather, etc
-	-	-	-	-	Paper, printing, etc
-	-	-	-	-	Other industries
-	-	-	-	-	Construction
-	-	-	-	-	**Transport**
-	-	-	-	-	Air
-	-	-	-	-	Rail
-	-	-	-	-	Road
-	-	-	-	-	National navigation
-	-	-	-	-	Pipelines
85	17	-	-	431	**Other**
23	17	-	-	244	Domestic
43	-	-	-	96	Public administration
10r	-	-	-	10r	Commercial
-	-	-	-	72	Agriculture
9r	-	-	-	9r	Miscellaneous
-	-	-	-	-	**Non energy use**

7.4 Capacity of, and electricity generated from, renewable sources

	2000	2001	2002	2003	2004
Installed Capacity (MWe) *(1)*					
Wind:					
Onshore	408.0	423.4r	530.6	678.4	809.4
Offshore	3.8	3.8	3.8	63.8	123.8
Shoreline wave	0.5	0.5	0.5	0.5	0.5
Solar photovoltaics	1.9r	2.7r	4.1	6.0	8.2
Hydro:					
Small scale	183.6	188.7	194.2	202.9	184.0
Large scale *(2)*	1,419.0	1,440.0	1,396.0	1,394.0	1,406.3
Biofuels and wastes:					
Landfill gas	425.1	464.7r	472.9	619.1	722.2
Sewage sludge digestion	85.3	85.0	96.0	100.6	119.0
Municipal solid waste combustion	253.2	260.0	278.9	298.8	307.4
Other *(3)*	157.0	157.0	176.5	183.9	184.3
Total biofuels and wastes	920.6	966.8	1,024.3	1,202.4	1,332.8
Total	**2,937.4**	**3,025.9r**	**3,153.6**	**3,548.0**	**3,864.9**
Co-firing *(4)*	-	-	..	92.4	146.2
Generation (GWh)					
Wind:					
Onshore *(5)*	945	960	1,251	1,276	1,736
Offshore *(6)*	1	5	5	10	199
Solar photovoltaics	1	2	3	3	4
Hydro:					
Small scale *(5)*	214	210	204	115	282
Large scale *(2)*	4,871	3,845	4,584	3,113	4,648
Biofuels:					
Landfill gas	2,188	2,507	2,679	3,276	4,004
Sewage sludge digestion	367	363	368	343	379
Municipal solid waste combustion *(7)*	840	880	907	965	971
Co-firing with fossil fuels	-	-	286	602	1,022
Other *(8)*	487r	776r	840r	937r	927
Total biofuels	3,882r	4,526r	5,080r	6,122r	7,302
Total generation	**9,914r**	**9,549r**	**11,127r**	**10,638r**	**14,171**
Non-biodegradable wastes *(9)*	519r	528r	545r	579r	583
Load factors (per cent) (10)					
Onshore wind	28.2	26.4	29.9	24.1	26.6
Offshore wind (from 2004 only)	..	..	..	..	24.2
Hydro	36.4	28.7	34.0	23.1	35.3
Biofuels	52.4r	54.7r	58.3r	62.8r	65.8r
Total (including wastes)	42.1r	38.6r	43.1r	38.2r	45.4r

(1) Capacity on a DNC basis is shown in Long Term Trends Table 7.1.1 available on the DTI web site - see paragraph 7.74.
(2) Excluding pumped storage stations. Capacities are as at the end of December.
(3) Includes the use of farm waste digestion, waste tyres, poultry litter, meat and bone, straw combustion, and short rotation coppice.
(4) This is the proportion of fossil fuelled capacity used for co-firing of renewables based on the proportion of generation accounted for by the renewable source.
(5) Actual generation figures are given where available, but otherwise are estimated using a typical load factor or the design load factor, where known.
(6) In 2000 and subsequent years includes less than 0.05 GWh of electricity from shoreline wave.
(7) Biodegradable part only.
(8) Includes the use of farm waste digestion, poultry litter combustion, meat and bone combustion, straw and short rotation coppice.
(9) Non-biodegradable part of municipal solid waste plus waste tyres, hosptal waste and general industrial waste.
(10) Load factors are calculated based on installed capacity at the beginning and the end of the year - see paragraph 7.75.

7.5 Electricity generated from renewable sources - Renewables Obligation basis and Renewables Directive basis

GWh

	2000	2001	2002	2003	2004
Generation : Renewables Obligation basis					
Wind:					
Onshore *(1)*	945	960	1,251	1,276	1,736
Offshore *(2)*	1	5	5	10	199
Solar photovoltaics	1	2	3	3	4
Hydro:					
Small scale *(1)*	214	210	204	115	282
Refurbished large scale hydro	-	61	120	616	1,434
Biofuels:					
Landfill gas	2,188	2,507	2,679	3,276	4,004
Sewage sludge digestion	367	363	368	343	379
Co-firing with fossil fuels	-	-	286	602	1,022
Other *(3)*	487	776	840	937	927
Total biofuels	3,042	3,646	4,173	5,158	6,331
Total renewables generation on an obligation basis *(4)*	**4,203r**	**4,884r**	**5,755r**	**7,177r**	**9,986**
Generation : Renewables Directive basis					
Wind:					
Onshore *(1)*	945	960	1,251	1,276	1,736
Offshore *(2)*	1	5	5	10	199
Solar photovoltaics	1	2	3	3	4
Hydro:					
Small scale *(1)*	214	210	204	115	282
Large scale *(5)*	4,871	3,845	4,584	3,113	4,648
Imports of electricity certified as CCL exempt *(6)*	-	1,740	1,668	2,865r	3,522
Biofuels:					
Landfill gas	2,188	2,507	2,679	3,276	4,004
Sewage sludge digestion	367	363	368	343	379
Municipal solid waste combustion *(7)*	840	880	907	965	971
Co-firing with fossil fuels	-	-	286	602	1,022
Other *(3)*	487	776	840	937	927
Total biofuels	3,882	4,526	5,080	6,122	7,302
Total renewables generation on a directive basis *(4)*	**9,914r**	**11,289r**	**12,795r**	**13,503r**	**17,693**

(1) Actual generation figures are given where available, but otherwise are estimated using a typical load factor or the design load factor, where known.
(2) In 2000 and subsequent years includes less than 0.05 GWh of electricity from shoreline wave.
(3) Includes the use of farm waste digestion, poultry litter combustion, meat and bone combustion, straw and short rotation coppice.
(4) See paragraphs 7.7 and 7.8 for definitions.
(5) Excluding pumped storage stations.
(6) Mainly hydro electricity exported to England from France
(7) Biodegradable part only.

7.6 Renewable orders and operational capacity

Technology band	Contracted projects		Live projects operational at 31 December 2004 (1)	
	Number	Capacity MW	Number	Capacity MW
England and Wales				
NFFO - 1 (1990)				
Hydro	26	11.85	13	8.19
Landfill gas	25	35.50	13	25.09
Municipal and industrial waste	4	40.63	4	40.63
Other	4	45.48	3	45.38
Sewage gas	7	6.45	4	1.55
Wind	9	12.21	3	7.53
Total *(2)*	**75**	**152.11**	**40**	**128.37**
NFFO - 2 (late 1991)				
Hydro	12	10.86	8	10.16
Landfill gas	28	48.45	22	35.67
Municipal and industrial waste	10	271.48	2	31.50
Other	4	30.15	1	12.50
Sewage gas	19	26.86	17	25.69
Wind	49	84.43	23	52.45
Total *(2)*	**122**	**472.23**	**73**	**167.97**
NFFO - 3 (1995)				
Energy crops and agricultural and forestry waste - gasification	3	19.06		
Energy crops and agricultural and forestry waste - other	6	103.81	2	69.50
Hydro	15	14.48	8	11.74
Landfill gas	42	82.07	42	82.07
Municipal and industrial waste	20	241.87	8	102.92
Wind - large	31	145.92	10	41.02
Wind - small	24	19.71	13	11.86
Total	**141**	**626.90**	**83**	**319.11**
NFFO - 4 (1997)				
Hydro	31	13.22	9	2.49
Landfill gas	70	173.68	60	148.36
Municipal and industrial waste - CHP	10	115.29	4	33.48
Municipal and industrial waste - fluidised bed combustion	6	125.93		
Wind - large	48	330.36	4	12.97
Wind - small	17	10.33	5	3.27
Anaerobic digestion of agricultural waste	6	6.58	1	1.43
Energy crops and forestry waste gasification	7	67.34		
Total	**195**	**842.72**	**83**	**202.00**
NFFO - 5 (1998)				
Hydro	22	8.87		
Landfill gas	141	313.73	77	164.32
Municipal and industrial waste	22	415.75		
Municipal and industrial waste - CHP	7	69.97		
Wind - large	33	340.16		
Wind - small	36	28.67	9	7.45
Total	**261**	**1,177.15**	**86**	**171.77**
NFFO Total	**794**	**3,271.11**	**365**	**989.21**

(1) Sites that have closed and sites that are not currently using renewables as fuel have been excluded.

(2) See footnote 2, overleaf.

This table continues on the next page.

7.6 Renewable orders and operational capacity (continued)

	Technology band	Contracted projects		Live projects operational at 31 December 2004 (1)	
		Number	Capacity MW	Number	Capacity MW
Scotland					
SRO - 1 (1994)	Biomass	1	9.80	1	9.80
	Hydro	15	17.25	9	8.81
	Waste to Energy	2	3.78	2	3.78
	Wind	12	45.60	7	25.13
	Total	**30**	**76.43**	**19**	**47.52**
SRO - 2 (1997)	Biomass	1	2.00		
	Hydro	9	12.36	2	1.46
	Waste to Energy	9	56.05	6	17.65
	Wind	7	43.63	5	31.29
	Total	**26**	**114.04**	**13**	**50.40**
SRO - 3 (1999)	Biomass	1	12.90		
	Hydro	5	3.90		
	Waste to Energy	16	49.11	10	22.36
	Wave	3	2.00	1	0.20
	Wind - large	11	63.43	1	8.29
	Wind - small	17	14.06	5	4.28
	Total	**53**	**145.40**	**17**	**35.13**
SRO Total		**109**	**335.87**	**49**	**133.05**
Northern Ireland					
NI NFFO - 1 (1994)	Hydro	9	2.37	8	2.33
	Sewage gas	5	0.56		
	Wind	6	12.66	6	12.66
	Total	**20**	**15.60**	**14**	**14.99**
NI NFFO - 2 (1996)	Biogas	1	0.25		
	Biomass	2	0.30	2	0.30
	Hydro	2	0.25	1	0.08
	Landfill gas	2	6.25		
	Municipal and industrial waste	1	6.65		
	Wind	2	2.57	2	2.57
	Total	**10**	**16.27**	**5**	**2.95**
NI NFFO Total		**30**	**31.87**	**19**	**17.94**
All NFFO and equivalents		**933**	**3,638.85**	**433**	**1,140.20**

(1) Sites that have closed and sites that are not currently using renewables as fuel have been excluded.

(2) The NFPA NFFO database has reported that at the end of December 2003 442 sites totalling 1,146.29 MW had gone live under NFFO, but this includes all NFFO-1 and NFFO-2 sites for England and Wales, some of which have closed or are not currently using renewables as fuels. The following table compares the totals for live projects, above, with the overall NFFO total:

	Number	MW
All live NFFO and equivalents	433	1,140.20
NFFO-1 no longer classed as live and operational	19	12.63
NFFO-2 no longer classed as live and operational	7	4.39
All NFFO and equivalents	459	1,157.22

7.7 Renewable sources used to generate electricity and heat[1][2]

Thousand tonnes of oil equivalent

	2000	2001	2002	2003	2004
Used to generate electricity (3)					
Wind:					
Onshore	81.3	82.5	107.6	109.7	149.3
Offshore	0.1	0.4	0.4	0.8r	17.1
Solar photovoltaics	0.1	0.2	0.2	0.3	0.3
Hydro:					
Small scale	18.4	18.1	17.5	9.9	24.2
Large scale (4)	418.8	330.7	394.2	267.7	399.6
Biofuels:					
Landfill gas	717.6	822.2	878.5	1,074.5	1,313.1
Sewage sludge digestion	120.4	119.0	120.6	112.5	124.1
Municipal solid waste combustion (5)	350.1	387.1	420.2	445.8	429.5
Co-firing with fossil fuels	-	-	94.0	197.3	335.1
Other (6)	192.8r	282.2r	273.6	344.6	353.1
Total biofuels	1,380.8r	1,610.5r	1,786.8	2,174.8	2,554.9
Total	**1,899.6**	**2,042.4**	**2,306.7**	**2,563.1**	**3,145.5**
Non-biodegradable wastes (7)	253.3	266.2	286.1	273.8r	263.9
Used to generate heat					
Active solar heating	11.1	13.2	16.1	19.8	24.6
Biofuels :					
Landfill gas	13.6	13.6	13.6	13.6	13.6
Sewage sludge digestion	48.3	49.4	53.4	52.5	52.5
Wood combustion - domestic	204.2	204.2	204.2	204.2	204.2
Wood combustion - industrial	298.6	264.6	265.6	265.6	265.6
Straw combustion, farm waste digestion and short rotation coppice	72.2	72.2	72.2	72.2	73.9
Municipal solid waste combustion (5)	25.6	29.0	33.6	33.6	33.6
Total biofuels	662.3	632.9	642.6	641.7	643.4
Geothermal aquifers	0.8	0.8	0.8	0.8	0.8
Total	**674.2**	**647.0**	**659.5**	**662.3**	**668.8**
Non-biodegradable wastes (7)	52.3	54.5	57.2	65.5	65.5
Total use of renewable sources and wastes					
Solar heating and photovoltaics	11.2	13.4	16.3	20.0	24.9
Onshore and offshore wind (9)	81.3	83.0	108.0	110.5	166.4
Hydro	437.3	348.7	411.7	277.5	423.9
Biofuels	2,043.2	2,243.4	2,429.4	2,816.5	3,198.3
Geothermal aquifers	0.8	0.8	0.8	0.8	0.8
Total	**2,573.8**	**2,689.4**	**2,966.3**	**3,225.4**	**3,814.3**
Non-biodegradable wastes (7)	305.6	320.7	343.4	339.2	329.4
All renewables and wastes (8)	**2,879.4**	**3,010.1**	**3,309.6**	**3,564.7**	**4,143.7**

(1) Includes some waste of fossil fuel origin.

(2) See paragraphs 7.39 to 7.76 for technical notes and definitions of the categories used in this table.

(3) For wind, solar PV and hydro, the figures represent the energy content of the electricity supplied but for biofuels the figures represent the energy content of the fuel used.

(4) Excluding pumped storage stations.

(5) Biodegradable part only.

(6) Includes electricity from farm waste digestion, poultry litter combustion, meat and bone combustion, straw and short rotation coppice.

(7) Non-biodegradable part of municipal solid waste plus waste tyres, hospital waste, and general industrial waste.

(8) The figures in this row correspond to the total demand and total supply figures in Tables 7.1, 7.2 and 7.3.

(9) In 2000 and subsequent years includes energy from shoreline wave

Digest of United Kingdom Energy Statistics 2005

Annexes

Annex A: Energy and commodity balances, conversion factors and calorific values

Annex B: Glossary and Acronyms

Annex C: Further sources

Annex D: Major events in the Energy Industry, 2003-2005

Department of Trade and Industry

Annex A
Energy and commodity balances, conversion factors and calorific values

Balance principles

A.1   This Annex outlines the principles behind the balance presentation of energy statistics. It covers these in general terms. Fuel specific details are given in the appropriate chapters of this publication.

A.2   Balances are divided into two types, each of which performs a different function.

a) *commodity balance* – a balance for each energy commodity that uses the units usually associated with that commodity. By using a single column of figures, it shows the flow of the commodity from its sources of supply through to its final use. Commodity balances are presented in the individual fuel chapters of this publication.

b) *energy balance* - presents the commodity balances in a common unit and places them alongside one another in a manner that shows the dependence of the supply of one commodity on another. This is useful as some commodities are manufactured from others. The layout of the energy balance also differs slightly from the commodity balance. The energy balance format is used in Chapter 1.

A.3   Energy commodities can be either primary or secondary. Primary energy commodities are drawn (extracted or captured) from natural reserves or flows, whereas secondary commodities are produced from primary energy commodities. Crude oil and coal are examples of primary commodities, whilst petrol and coke are secondary commodities manufactured from them. For balance purposes, electricity may be considered to be both primary electricity (for example, hydro, wind) or secondary (produced from steam turbines using steam from the combustion of fuels).

A.4   Both commodity and energy balances show the flow of the commodity from its production, extraction or import through to its final use.

A.5   A simplified model of the commodity flow underlying the balance structure is given in Chart A.1. It illustrates how primary commodities may be used directly and/or be transformed into secondary commodities. The secondary fuels then enter final consumption or may also be transformed into another energy commodity (for example, electricity produced from fuel oil). To keep the diagram simple these "second generation" flows have not been shown.

A.6   The arrows at the top of the chart represent flows to and from the "pools" of primary and secondary commodities, from imports and exports and, in the case of the primary pool, extraction from reserves (eg the production of coal, gas and crude oil).

Commodity balances (Tables 2.1 to 2.6, 3.1 to 3.6, 4.1, 5.1, and 7.1 to 7.3)
A.7   A commodity balance comprises a supply section and a demand section. The supply section gives available sources of supply (ie exports are subtracted). The demand section is divided into a transformation section, a section showing uses in the energy industries (other than for transformation) and a section covering uses by final consumers for energy or non-energy purposes. Final consumption for energy purposes is divided into use by sector of economic activity. The section breakdowns are described below.

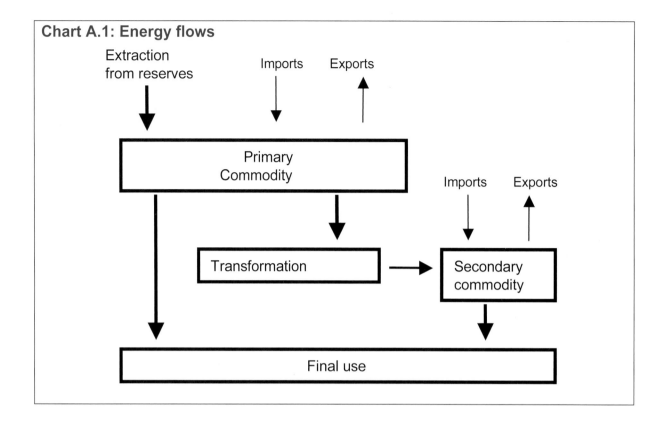

Chart A.1: Energy flows

Extraction from reserves → Primary Commodity

Imports → Primary Commodity

Exports ← (from above Primary Commodity)

Primary Commodity → Transformation

Transformation → Secondary commodity

Imports → Secondary commodity

Exports ← Secondary commodity

Primary Commodity → Final use

Secondary commodity → Final use

Supply

Production

A.8   Production, within the commodity balance, covers indigenous production (extraction or capture of primary commodities) and generation or manufacture of secondary commodities. Production is always gross, that is, it includes the quantities used during the extraction or manufacturing process.

Other sources

A.9   Production from other sources covers sources of supply that do not represent "new" supply. These may be recycled products, recovered fuels (slurry or waste coal), or electricity from pumped storage plants. The production of these quantities will have been reported in an earlier accounting period or have already been reported in the current period of account. Exceptionally, the *Other sources* row in the commodity balances for ethane, propane and butane is used to receive transfers of these hydrocarbons from gas stabilisation plants at North Sea terminals. In this manner, the supplies of primary ethane, propane and butane from the North Sea are combined with the production of these gases in refineries, so that the disposals may be presented together in the balances.

Imports and exports

A.10   The figures for imports and exports relate to energy commodities moving into or out of the United Kingdom as part of transactions involving United Kingdom companies. Exported commodities are produced in the United Kingdom and imported commodities are for use within the United Kingdom (although some may be re-exported before or after transformation).   The figures thus exclude commodities either exported from or imported into HM Customs bonded areas or warehouses. These areas, although part of the United Kingdom, are regarded as being outside of the normal United Kingdom's customs boundary, and so goods entering into or leaving them are not counted as part of the statistics on trade used in the balances.

A.11   Similarly, commodities that only pass through the United Kingdom on their way to a final destination in another country are also excluded. However, for gas these transit flows are included because it is difficult to identify this quantity separately, without detailed knowledge of the contract information covering the trade. This means that for gas, there is some over statement of the level of imports and exports, but the net flows are correct.

A.12   The convention in these balances is that exports are shown with a negative sign.

Marine bunkers

A.13   These are deliveries of fuels (usually fuel oil or gas oil) to ships of any flag (including the United Kingdom) for consumption during the voyage to other countries. Marine bunkers are treated rather like exports and shown with a negative sign.

Stock changes

A.14   Additions to (- sign) and withdrawals from stocks (+ sign) held by producers and transformation industries correspond to withdrawals from and additions to supply, respectively.

Transfers

A.15   There are several reasons why quantities may be transferred from one commodity balance to another:

- a commodity may no longer meet the original specification and be reclassified;
- the name of the commodity may change through a change in use;
- to show quantities returned to supply from consumers. These may be by-products of the use of commodities as raw materials rather than fuels.

A.16   A quantity transferred from a balance is shown with a negative sign to represent a withdrawal from supply and with a positive sign in the receiving commodity balance representing an addition to its supply.

Total supply

A.17   The total supply available for national use is obtained by summing the flows above this entry in the balance.

Total demand

A.18   The various figures for the disposals and/or consumption of the commodities are summed to provide a measure of the demand for them. The main categories or sectors of demand are described in paragraphs A.32 to A.42.

Statistical difference

A.19   Any excess of supply over demand is shown as a statistical difference. A negative figure indicates that demand exceeds supply. Statistical differences arise when figures are gathered from a variety of independent sources and reflect differences in timing, in definition of coverage of the activity, or in commodity definition. Differences also arise for methodological reasons in the measurement of the flow of the commodity eg if there are differences between the volumes recorded by the gas producing companies and the gas transporting companies. A non-zero statistical difference is normal and, provided that it is not too large, is preferable to a statistical difference of zero as this suggests that a data provider has adjusted a figure to balance the account.

Transformation

A.20   The transformation sector of the balance covers those processes and activities that transform the original primary (and sometimes secondary) commodity into a form which is better suited for specific uses than the original form. Most of the transformation activities correspond to particular energy industries whose main business is to manufacture the product associated with them. Certain activities involving transformation take place to make products that are only partly used for energy needs (coke oven coke) or are by-products of other manufacturing processes (coke oven and blast furnace gases). However, as these products and by-products are then used, at least in part, for their energy content they are included in the balance system.

A.21   The figures given under the activity headings of this sector represent the quantities used for transformation. The production of the secondary commodities will be shown in the *Production* row of the corresponding commodity balances.

Electricity generation
A.22 The quantities of fuels burned for the generation of electricity are shown in their commodity balances under this heading. The activity is divided into two parts, covering the major power producers (for whom the main business is the generation of electricity for sale) and autogenerators (whose main business is not electricity generation but who produce electricity for their own needs and may also sell surplus quantities). The amounts of fuels shown in the balance represent the quantities consumed for the gross generation of electricity. Where a generator uses combined heat and power plant, the figures include only the part of the fuel use corresponding to the electricity generated.

A.23 In relation to autogenerators' data, the figures for quantities of fuel used for electricity generation appear under the appropriate fuel headings in the *Transformation* sector heading for *Autogenerators,* whilst the electricity generated appears in the *Electricity* column under *Production*. A breakdown of the information according to the branch of industry in which the generation occurs is not shown in the balance but is given in Chapter 1, Table 1.9. The figures for energy commodities consumed by the industry branches shown under final consumption include all use of electricity, but exclude the fuels combusted by the industry branches to generate the electricity.

Heat generation
A.24 The quantities of fuel burned to generate heat that is sold under the provision of a contract to a third party are shown in their commodity balances under this heading. It includes heat that is generated and sold by combined heat and power plants and by community heating schemes (also called district heating).

Petroleum refineries
A.25 Crude oil, natural gas liquids and other oils needed by refineries for the manufacture of finished petroleum products are shown under this heading.

Coke manufacture and blast furnaces
A.26 Quantities of coal for coke ovens and all fuels used within blast furnaces are shown under this heading. The consumption of fuels for heating coke ovens and the blast air for blast furnaces are shown under "Energy industry use".

Patent fuel manufacture
A.27 The coals and other solid fuels used for the manufacture of solid patent fuels are reported under this heading.

Other
A.28 Any minor transformation activities not specified elsewhere are captured under this heading.

Energy industry use
A.29 Consumption by both extraction and transformation industries to support the transformation process (but not for transformation itself) are included here according to the energy industry concerned. Typical examples are the consumption of electricity in power plants (eg for lighting, compressors and cooling systems) and the use of extracted gases on oil and gas platforms for compressors, pumps and other uses. The headings in this sector are identical to those used in the transformation sector with the exception of *Pumped storage*. In this case, the electricity used to pump the water to the reservoir is reported.

Losses
A.30 This heading covers the intrinsic losses that occur during the transmission and distribution of electricity and gas (including manufactured gases). Other metering and accounting differences for gas and electricity are within the statistical difference, as are undeclared losses in other commodities.

Final consumption
A.31 *Final consumption* covers both final energy consumption (by different consuming sectors) and the use of energy commodities for non-energy purposes, that is *Non energy use*. Final consumption occurs when the commodities used are not for transformation into secondary commodities. The energy concerned disappears from the account after use. Any fuel used for electricity generation by

final consumers is identified and reported separately within the transformation sector. When an enterprise generates electricity, the figure for final consumption of the industrial sector to which the enterprise belongs includes its use of the electricity it generates itself (as well as supplies of electricity it purchases from others) but does not include the fuel used to generate that electricity.

A.32   The classification of consumers according to their main business follows, as far as practicable, the *Standard Industrial Classification (SIC2003)*. The qualifications to, and constraints on, the classification are described in the technical notes to Chapter 1, paragraphs 1.24 to 1.57. Table 1E in Chapter 1 shows the breakdown of final consumers used, and how this corresponds to the SIC2003.

Industry
A.33   Two sectors of industry (iron and steel and chemicals) require special mention because the activities they undertake fall across the transformation, final consumption and non-energy classifications used for the balances. Also, the data permitting an accurate allocation of fuel use within each of these major divisions are not readily available.

Iron and steel
A.34   The iron and steel industry is a heavy energy user for transformation and final consumption activities. Figures shown under final consumption for this industry branch reflect the amounts that remain after quantities used for transformation and energy sector own use have been subtracted from the industry's total energy requirements. Use of fuels for transformation by the industry may be identified within the transformation sector of the commodity balances.

A.35   The amounts of coal used for coke manufacture by the iron and steel industry are in the transformation sector of the coal balance. Included in this figure is the amount of coal used for coke manufacture by the companies outside of the iron and steel industry, ie solid fuel manufacturers. The corresponding production of coke and coke oven gas may be found in the commodity balances for these products. The use of coke in blast furnaces is shown in the commodity balance for coke, and the gases produced from blast furnaces and the associated basic oxygen steel furnaces are shown in the production row of the commodity balance for blast furnace gas.

A.36   Fuels used for electricity generation by the industry are included in the figures for electricity generation by autogenerators and are not distinguishable as being used by the iron and steel sector in the balances. Electricity generation and fuel used for this by broad industry group are given in Table 1.9.

A.37   Fuels used to support coke manufacture and blast furnace gas production are included in the quantities shown under *Energy industry use*. These gases and other fuels do not enter coke ovens or blast furnaces, but are used to heat the ovens and the blast air supplied to furnaces.

Chemicals
A.38   The petro-chemical industry uses hydrocarbon fuels (mostly oil products and gases) as feedstock for the manufacture of its products. Distinguishing the energy use of delivered fuels from their non-energy use is complicated by the absence of detailed information. The procedures adopted to estimate the use are described in paragraphs A.41 and A.42 under *Non energy use*.

Transport
A.39   Figures under this heading are almost entirely quantities used strictly for transport purposes. However, the figures recorded against road transport usually include some fuel that is actually consumed in some "off-road" activities. Similarly, figures for railway fuels include some amounts of burning oil not used directly for transport purposes. Transport sector use of electricity includes all electricity used in industries classified to SIC2003 Groups 60 to 63. Fuels supplied to cargo and passenger ships undertaking international voyages are reported as *Marine bunkers* (see paragraph A.13). Supplies to fishing vessels are included under "agriculture".

Other sectors
A.40   The classification of all consumers groups under this heading, except *domestic*, follows *SIC2003* and is described in Table 1E in Chapter 1. The consistency of the classification across

different commodities cannot be guaranteed because the figures reported are dependent on what the data suppliers can provide.

Non energy use

A.41   The non energy use of fuels may be divided into two types. They may be used directly for their physical properties eg lubricants or bitumen used for road surfaces, or by the petro-chemical industry as raw materials for the manufacture of goods such as plastics. In their use by the petro-chemical industry, relatively little combustion of the fuels takes place and the carbon and/or hydrogen they contain are largely transferred into the finished product. However, in some cases heat from the manufacturing process or from combustion of by-products may be used. Data for this energy use are rarely available. Depending on the feedstock, non energy consumption is either estimated or taken to be the deliveries to the chemicals sector.

A.42   Both types of non energy use are shown under the *Non energy use* heading at the foot of the balances.

The energy balance (Tables 1.1 to 1.3)

Principles

A.43   The energy balance conveniently presents:

- an overall view of the United Kingdom's energy supplies;
- the relative importance of each energy commodity;
- dependence on imports;
- the contribution of our own fossil and renewable resources;
- the interdependence of commodities on one another.

A.44   The energy balance is constructed directly from the commodity balances by expressing the data in a common unit, placing them beside one another and adding appropriate totals. Heat sold is also included as a fuel. However, some rearrangement of the commodity balance format is required to show transformation of primary into secondary commodities in an easily understood manner.

A.45   Energy units are widely used as the common unit, and the current practice for the United Kingdom and the international organisations which prepare balances is to use the tonne of oil equivalent or a larger multiple of this unit, commonly thousands. One tonne of oil equivalent is defined as 10^7 kilocalories (41.868 gigajoules). The tonne of oil equivalent is another unit of energy like the gigajoule, kilocalorie or kilowatt hour, rather than a physical quantity. It has been chosen as it is easier to visualise than the other units. Due to the natural variations in heating value of primary fuels such as crude oil, it is rare that one tonne of oil has an energy content equivalent to one tonne of oil equivalent, however it is generally within a few per cent of the heating value of a tonne of oil equivalent. The energy figures are calculated from the natural units of the commodity balances by multiplying by factors representing the calorific (heating) value of the fuel. The gross calorific values of fuels are used for this purpose. When the natural unit of the commodity is already an energy unit (electricity in kilowatt hours, for example) the factors are just constants, converting one energy unit to another.

A.46   Most of the underlying definitions and ideas of commodity balances can be taken directly over into the energy balance. However, production of secondary commodities and, in particular, electricity are treated differently and need some explanation.   The components of the energy balance are described below, drawing out the differences of treatment compared with the commodity balances.

Primary supply

A.47   Within the energy balance, the production row covers only extraction of primary fuels and the generation of primary energy (hydro, nuclear, wind). Note the change of row heading from *Production* in the commodity balances to *Indigenous production* in the energy balance. Production of secondary fuels and secondary electricity are shown in the transformation sector and not in the indigenous production row at the top of the balance.

A.48   For fossil fuels, indigenous production represents the marketable quantity extracted from the reserves. Indigenous production of *Primary electricity* comprises hydro-electricity, wind and nuclear energy. The energy value for hydro-electricity is taken to be the energy content of the electricity produced from the hydro power plant and not the energy available in the water driving the turbines. A similar approach is adopted for electricity from wind generators. The electricity is regarded as the primary energy form because there are currently no other uses of the energy resource "upstream" of the generation. The energy value attached to nuclear electricity is discussed in paragraph A.52.

A.49   The other elements of the supply part of the balance are identical to those in the commodity balances. In particular, the sign convention is identical, so that figures for exports and international marine bunkers carry negative signs. A stock build carries a negative sign to denote it as a withdrawal from supply whilst a stock draw carries a positive sign to show it as an addition to supply.

A.50   The *Primary supply* is the sum of the figures above it in the table, taking account of the signs, and expresses the national requirement for primary energy commodities from all sources and foreign supplies of secondary commodities. It is an indicator of the use of indigenous resources and external energy supplies. Both the amount and mixture of fuels in final consumption of energy commodities in the United Kingdom will differ from the primary supply. The "mix" of commodities in final consumption will be much more dependent on the manufacture of secondary commodities, in particular electricity.

Transformation

A.51   Within an energy balance the presentation of the inputs to and outputs from transformation activities requires special mention, as it is carried out using a compact format. The transformation sector also plays a key role in moving primary electricity from its own column in the balance into the electricity column, so that it can be combined with electricity from fossil fuelled power stations and the total disposals shown.

A.52   Indigenous production of primary electricity comprises nuclear electricity, hydro electricity and electricity from wind generation. Nuclear electricity is obtained by passing steam from nuclear reactors through conventional steam turbine sets. The heat in the steam is considered to be the primary energy available and its value is calculated from the electricity generated using the average thermal efficiency of nuclear stations, currently 37.9 in the United Kingdom. The electrical energy from hydro and wind is transferred from the *Primary electricity* column to the *Electricity* column using the *transfers* row because electricity is the form of primary energy and no transformation takes place. However, because the form of the nuclear energy is the steam from the nuclear reactors, the energy it contains is shown entering electricity generation and the corresponding electricity produced is included with all electricity generation in the figure, in the same row, under the *Electricity* column.

A.53   Quantities of fuels entering transformation activities (fuels into electricity generation and heat generation, crude oil into petroleum product manufacture (refineries), or coal into coke ovens) are shown with a negative sign to represent the input and the resulting production is shown as a positive number.

A.54   For electricity generated by Major power producers, the inputs are shown in the *Major power producers* row of the *coal, manufactured fuel, primary oils, petroleum products, gas, renewables* and *primary electricity* columns. The total energy input to electricity generation is the sum of the values in these first seven columns. The *Electricity* column shows total electricity generated from these inputs and the transformation loss is the sum of these two figures, given in the *Total* column.

A.55   Within the transformation sector, the negative figures in the *Total* column represent the losses in the various transformation activities. This is a convenient consequence of the sign convention chosen for the inputs and outputs from transformation. Any positive figures represent a transformation gain and, as such, are an indication of incorrect data.

A.56   In the energy balance, the columns containing the input commodities for electricity generation, heat generation and oil refining are separate from the columns for the outputs. However, for the transformation activities involving solid fuels this is only partly the case. Coal used for the manufacture of coke is shown in the coke manufacture row of the transformation section in the coal column, but the related coke and coke oven gas production are shown combined in the *Manufactured fuels* column. Similarly, the input of coke to blast furnaces and the resulting production of blast furnace gas are not identifiable and have been combined in the *Manufactured fuels* column in the *Blast furnace* row. As a result, only the net loss from blast furnace transformation activity appears in the column.

A.57 The share of each commodity or commodity group in primary supply can be calculated from the table. This table also shows the demand for primary as well as foreign supplies. Shares of primary supplies may be taken from the *Primary supply* row of the balance. Shares of fuels in final consumption may be calculated from the final consumption row.

Energy industry use and final consumption
A.58 The figures for final consumption and energy industry use follow, in general, the principles and definitions described under commodity balances in paragraphs A.29 to A.42.

Standard conversion factors

1 tonne of oil equivalent (toe)	$= 10^7$ kilocalories	
	$= 396.83$ therms	
	$= 41.868$ GJ	
	$= 11,630$ kWh	
100,000 British thermal units (Btu)	$= 1$ therm	

The following prefixes are used for multiples of joules, watts and watt hours:

kilo (k)	$= 1,000$	or 10^3
mega (M)	$= 1,000,000$	or 10^6
giga (G)	$= 1,000,000,000$	or 10^9
tera (T)	$= 1,000,000,000,000$	or 10^{12}
peta (P)	$= 1,000,000,000,000,000$	or 10^{15}

WEIGHT

1 kilogramme (kg)	$= 2.2046$ pounds (lb)
1 pound (lb)	$= 0.4536$ kg
1 tonne (t)	$= 1,000$kg
	$= 0.9842$ long ton
	$= 1.102$ short ton (sh tn)
1 Statute or long ton	$= 2,240$ lb
	$= 1.016$ t
	$= 1.102$ sh tn

VOLUME

1 cubic metre (cu m)	$= 35.31$ cu ft
1 cubic foot (cu ft)	$= 0.02832$ cu m
1 litre	$= 0.22$ Imperial gallons (UK gall)
1 UK gallon	$= 8$ UK pints
	$= 1.201$ US gallons
	$= 4.54609$ litres
1 barrel	$= 159.0$ litres
	$= 34.97$ UK gal
	$= 42$ US gal

LENGTH

1 mile	$= 1.6093$ kilometres
1 kilometre (km)	$= 0.62137$ miles

TEMPERATURE

1 scale degree Celsius (C) $= 1.8$ scale degrees Fahrenheit (F)

For conversion of temperatures: $^{\circ}C = 5/9\ (^{\circ}F -32)$; $^{\circ}F = 9/5\ ^{\circ}C +32$

Average conversion factors for petroleum

	Imperial gallons per tonne	Litres per tonne		Imperial gallons per tonne	Litres per tonne
Crude oil:			Gas/diesel oil:		
Indigenous	264	1,199	Gas oil	261	1,187
Imported	260	1,181	Marine diesel oil	255	1,157
Average of refining throughput	262	1,192			
			Fuel oil:		
Ethane	601	2,730	All grades	227	1,031
Propane	435	1,975	Light fuel oil:		
Butane	377	1,715	1% or less sulphur	231	1,048
Naphtha (l.d.f.)	304	1,382	>1% sulphur	231	1,048
			Medium fuel oil:		
Aviation gasoline	307	1,397	1% or less sulphur	238	1,083
			>1% sulphur	225	1,025
Motor spirit:			Heavy fuel oil:		
All grades	300	1,362	1% or less sulphur	220	1,002
Unleaded Super	299	1,361	>1% sulphur	222	1,009
Premium	299	1,357			
Ultra low sulphur petrol	300	1,362			
Lead replacement petrol	299	1,361	Lubricating oils:		
			White	251	1,142
Middle distillate feedstock	205	930	Greases	252	1,147
Kerosene:			Other	248	1,127
Aviation turbine fuel	275	1,251	Bitumen	214	974
Burning oil	275	1,248	Petroleum coke	185	843
			Petroleum waxes	271	1,231
DERV fuel: all	265	1,203	Industrial spirit	274	1,247
0.005% or less sulphur	265	1,203	White spirit	282	1,282
>0.005% sulphur	261	1,187			

Note: The above conversion factors, which for refined products have been compiled by the UK Petroleum Industry Association, apply to the year 2004, and are only approximate for other years.

A.1 Estimated average calorific values of fuels - 2004

Coal:	GJ per tonne net	gross
All consumers (weighted average) (1)	25.4	26.7
Power stations (1)	24.9	26.2
Coke ovens (1)	29.0	30.5
Low temperature carbonisation plants and manufactured fuel plants	29.0	30.5
Collieries	28.4	29.9
Agriculture	26.6	28.0
Iron and steel	28.9	30.4
Other industries (weighted average)	24.6	25.9
Non-ferrous metals	23.6	24.8
Food, beverages and tobacco	27.9	29.4
Chemicals	25.3	26.6
Textiles, clothing, leather etc.	28.0	29.5
Pulp, paper, printing etc.	27.3	28.7
Mineral products	26.5	27.9
Engineering (mechanical and electrical engineering and vehicles)	29.1	30.6
Other industries	24.6	25.9
Domestic		
House coal	29.4	30.9
Anthracite and dry steam coal	32.1	33.8
Other consumers	28.3	29.8
Imported coal (weighted average)	25.8	27.2
Exports (weighted average)	30.7	32.3
Coke (including low temperature carbonisation cokes)	30.4	30.4
Coke breeze	31.1	31.1
Other manufactured solid fuel	30.2	31.8

Renewable sources:	GJ per tonne net	gross
Domestic wood (2)	5.0	10.0
Industrial wood (3)	10.0	11.9
Straw	12.8	15.0
Poultry litter	7.4	8.8
Meat and bone	15.6	18.6
General industrial waste	15.2	16.0
Hospital waste	13.3	14.0
Municipal solid waste (4)	6.7	9.5
Refuse derived waste (4)	13.0	18.5
Short rotation coppice (5)	9.0	10.6
Tyres	..	32.0

Petroleum:	GJ per tonne net	gross
Crude oil (weighted average)	43.4	45.7
Petroleum products (weighted average)	43.6	45.9
Ethane	48.1	50.7
Butane and propane (LPG)	46.9	49.4
Light distillate feedstock for gasworks	45.1	47.5
Aviation spirit and wide cut gasoline	45.1	47.5
Aviation turbine fuel	43.9	46.2
Motor spirit	44.8	47.1
Burning oil	43.9	46.2
Gas/diesel oil (DERV)	43.3	45.6
Fuel oil	41.3	43.5
Power station oil	41.3	43.5
Non-fuel products (notional value)	41.2	43.4

	MJ per cubic metre net	gross
Natural gas (6)	35.6	39.6
Coke oven gas	16.2	18.0
Blast furnace gas	3.0	3.0
Landfill gas	34.7	38.6
Sewage gas	34.7	38.6

(1) Applicable to UK consumption - based on calorific value for home produced coal plus imports and, for "All consumers" net of exports.

(2) Based on a 50 per cent moisture content.

(3) Average figure covering a range of possible feedstock.

(4) Average figure based on survey returns.

(5) On an "as received" basis. On a "dry" basis 18.6 GJ per tonne.

(6) The gross calorific value of natural gas can also be expressed as 10.992 kWh per cubic metre. This value represents the average calorific value seen for gas when extracted. At this point it contains not just methane, but also some other hydrocarbon gases (ethane, butane, propane). These gases are removed before the gas enters the National Transmission System for sale to final consumers. As such, this calorific value will differ from that readers will see quoted on their gas bills.

Note: The above estimated average calorific values apply only to the year 2004. For calorific values of fuels in earlier years see Tables A.2 and A.3 and previous issues of this Digest. See the notes in Chapter 1, paragraph 1.52 regarding net calorific values. The calorific values for coal other than imported coal are based on estimates provided by the main coal producers, but with some exceptions as noted on Table A.2. The calorific values for petroleum products have been calculated using the method described in Chapter 1, paragraph 1.27. The calorific values for coke oven gas and blast furnace gas are provided by the Iron and Steel Statistics Bureau (ISSB).

Data reported in this Digest in 'thousand tonnes of oil equivalent' have been prepared on the basis of 1 tonne of oil equivalent having an energy content of 41.868 gigajoules (GJ), (1 GJ = 9.478 therms) - see notes in Chapter 1, paragraphs 1.24 to 1.26.

A.2 Estimated average gross calorific values of fuels, 1980, 1990 and 2000 to 2004

GJ per tonne (gross)

	1980	1990	2000	2001	2002	2003	2004
Coal							
All consumers (1)(2)	25.6	25.5	26.2	26.1	26.2	26.1	26.0
All consumers - home produced plus imports minus exports (1)	..	..	27.0	26.9	26.9	26.7r	26.7
Power stations (2)	23.8	24.8	25.6	25.4	25.6	25.5	25.4
Power stations - home produced plus imports (1)	..	..	26.0	26.1	26.1	26.0r	26.2
Coke ovens (2)	30.5	30.2	31.2	31.5	31.3	31.4	31.6
Coke ovens - home produced plus imports (1)	..	..	30.4	30.5	30.5	30.5	30.5
Low temperature carbonisation plants and manufactured fuel plants	19.1	29.2	30.3	30.3	30.5	31.0	30.5
Collieries	27.0	28.6	29.6	29.8	29.7	30.1	29.9
Agriculture	30.1	28.9	29.2	29.0	28.5	28.0	28.0
Iron and steel industry (3)	29.1	28.9	30.7	29.4r	30.4	30.4	30.4
Other industries (1)	27.1	27.8	26.7	26.6	26.5	26.8	25.9
Non-ferrous metals	..	23.1	25.1	24.9	25.0	25.3	24.8
Food, beverages and tobacco	28.6	28.1	29.5	29.3	30.0	30.5	29.4
Chemicals	25.8	27.3	28.7	27.1	27.4	27.8	26.6
Textiles, clothing, leather and footwear	27.5	27.7	30.4	30.0	29.9	29.9	29.5
Pulp, paper, printing, etc.	26.5	27.9	28.7	28.8	28.9	28.8	28.7
Mineral products (4)	..	28.2	27.0	27.0	27.0	27.9	27.9
Engineering (5)	27.7	28.3	29.3	29.3	30.7	30.6	30.6
Other industry (6)	28.4	28.5	30.2	30.5	28.4	28.3	25.7
Unclassified	..	27.1	..	..	..	..	..
Domestic							
House coal	30.1	30.2	30.9	30.9	31.1	31.0	30.9
Anthracite and dry steam coal	33.3	33.6	33.6	33.9	33.9	33.8	33.8
Other consumers	27.5	27.5	29.2	29.2	30.1	29.6	29.8
Imported coal (1)	..	28.3	28.0	27.6	27.6	27.6	27.3
of which Steam coal	..	..	26.6	26.7	26.5	26.7	26.7
Coking coal	..	..	30.4	30.4	30.4	30.4	30.4
Anthracite	..	..	31.2	31.1	30.4	30.1	30.6
Exports (1)	..	29.0	32.0	32.1	31.7	31.6	32.3
of which Steam coal	..	..	31.0	30.7	30.0	29.9	29.9
Anthracite	..	..	32.6	32.7	32.6	32.3	32.5
Coke (7)	28.1	28.1	29.8	29.8	29.8	29.8	29.8
Coke breeze	24.4	24.8	24.8	24.8	24.8	24.8	24.8
Other manufactured solid fuels (1)	27.6	27.6	30.8	30.6	30.9	31.1	31.8
Petroleum							
Crude oil (1)	45.2	45.6	45.7	45.7	45.7	45.7	45.7
Liquified petroleum gas	49.6	49.4	49.4	49.4	49.4	49.4	49.4
Ethane	52.3	50.6	50.7	50.7	50.7	50.7	50.7
LDF for gasworks/Naphtha	47.8	47.9	47.7	47.6	47.6	47.2	47.5
Aviation spirit and wide-cut gasoline (AVGAS and AVTAG)	47.2	47.3	47.3	47.3	47.3	47.3	47.5
Aviation turbine fuel (AVTUR)	46.4	46.2	46.2	46.2	46.2	46.2	46.2
Motor spirit	47.0	47.0	47.0	47.1	47.1	47.1	47.1
Burning oil	46.5	46.2	46.2	46.2	46.2	46.2	46.2
Vaporising oil	45.9	45.9	..	..	..	..	..
Gas/diesel oil (including DERV)	45.5	45.4	45.6	45.6	45.6	45.6	45.6
Fuel oil	42.8	43.2	43.1	43.5	43.4	43.6	43.5
Power station oil	42.8	43.2	43.1	43.5	43.4	43.6	43.5
Non-fuel products (notional value)	42.2	43.2	43.8	42.8	42.7	43.2	43.4
Petroleum coke	..	39.5	35.8	35.8	35.8	35.8	35.8
Orimulsion (8)	..	29.7	..	..	..	..	..

(1) Weighted averages.
(2) Home produced coal only.
(3) From 2001 onwards almost entirely sourced from imports.
(4) Based on information provided by the British Cement Industry Association; almost all coal used by this sector in the latest 4 years was imported.
(5) Mechanical engineering and metal products, electrical and instrument engineering and vehicle manufacture.
(6) Includes construction.
(7) Since 1995 the source of these figures has been the ISSB.
(8) Orimulsion use ceased in 1997.

A.3 Estimated average net calorific values of fuels, 1980, 1990 and 2000 to 2004

GJ per tonne (net)

	1980	1990	2000	2001	2002	2003	2004
Coal							
All consumers (1)(2)	24.3	24.2	24.9	24.8	24.9	24.8	24.7
All consumers - home produced plus imports minus exports (1)	..	..	25.7	25.6	25.6	25.4	25.4
Power stations (2)	22.6	23.6	24.3	24.1	24.3	24.2	24.1
Power stations - home produced plus imports (1)	..	..	24.7	24.8	24.8	24.7	24.9
Coke ovens (2)	29.0	28.7	29.6	29.9	29.7	29.8	30.0
Coke ovens - home produced plus imports (1)	..	..	28.9	29.0	29.0	29.0	29.0
Low temperature carbonisation plants and manufactured fuel plants	18.1	27.7	28.8	28.8	29.0	29.5	29.0
Collieries	25.7	27.2	28.1	28.3	28.2	28.6	28.4
Agriculture	28.6	27.5	27.7	27.6	27.1	26.6	26.6
Iron and steel industry (3)	27.6	27.5	29.2	27.9	28.9	28.9	28.9
Other industries (1)	25.7	26.4	25.4	25.3	25.2	25.5	24.6
Non-ferrous metals	..	21.9	23.8	23.7	23.8	24.0	23.6
Food, beverages and tobacco	27.2	26.7	28.0	27.8	28.5	29.0	27.9
Chemicals	24.5	25.9	27.3	25.7	26.0	26.4	25.3
Textiles, clothing, leather and footwear	26.1	26.3	28.9	28.5	28.4	28.4	28.0
Pulp, paper, printing, etc.	25.2	26.5	27.3	27.4	27.5	27.4	27.3
Mineral products (4)	..	26.8	25.7	25.7	25.7	26.5	26.5
Engineering (5)	26.3	26.9	27.8	27.8	29.2	29.1	29.1
Other industry (6)	27.0	27.1	28.7	29.0	27.0	26.9	24.4
Unclassified	..	25.7	..	..	..	..	..
Domestic							
House coal	28.6	28.7	29.4	29.4	29.5	29.5	29.4
Anthracite and dry steam coal	31.6	31.9	31.9	32.2	32.2	32.1	32.1
Other consumers	26.1	26.1	27.7	27.7	28.6	28.1	28.3
Imported coal (1)	..	26.9	26.6	26.2	26.2	26.2	25.9
of which Steam coal	..	..	25.3	25.4	25.2	25.4	25.4
Coking coal	..	..	28.9	28.9	28.9	28.9	28.9
Anthracite	..	..	29.6	29.5	28.9	28.6	29.1
Exports (1)	..	27.6	30.4	30.5	30.1	30.0	30.7
of which Steam coal	..	..	29.5	29.2	28.5	28.4	28.4
Anthracite	..	..	31.0	31.1	31.0	30.7	30.9
Coke (7)	28.1	28.1	29.8	29.8	29.8	29.8	29.8
Coke breeze	24.4	24.8	24.8	24.8	24.8	24.8	24.8
Other manufactured solid fuels (1)	26.2	26.2	29.3	29.1	29.4	29.5	30.2
Petroleum							
Crude oil (1)	42.9	43.3	43.4	43.4	43.4	43.4	43.4
Liquified petroleum gas	47.1	46.9	46.9	46.9	46.9	46.9	46.9
Ethane	49.7	48.1	48.2	48.2	48.2	48.2	48.2
LDF for gasworks/Naphtha	45.4	45.5	45.3	45.2	45.2	44.8	45.1
Aviation spirit and wide-cut gasoline (AVGAS and AVTAG)	44.8	44.9	44.9	44.9	44.9	44.9	45.1
Aviation turbine fuel (AVTUR)	44.1	43.9	43.9	43.9	43.9	43.9	43.9
Motor spirit	44.7	44.7	44.7	44.7	44.7	44.7	44.7
Burning oil	44.2	43.9	43.9	43.9	43.9	43.9	43.9
Vaporising oil	43.6	43.6	..	..	..	..	..
Gas/diesel oil (including DERV)	43.2	43.1	43.3	43.3	43.3	43.3	43.3
Fuel oil	40.7	41.0	40.9	41.3	41.2	41.4	41.3
Power station oil	40.7	41.0	40.9	41.3	41.2	41.4	41.3
Non-fuel products (notional value)	40.1	41.0	41.6	40.7	40.6	41.0	41.2
Petroleum coke	..	37.5	34.0	34.0	34.0	34.0	34.0
Orimulsion (8)	..	28.2	..	..	..	..	..

For footnotes see table A.2

The net calorific values of natural gas and coke oven gas are the gross calorific values x 0.9.

Annex B
Glossary and Acronyms

Advanced gas-cooled reactor (AGR)   A type of nuclear reactor cooled by carbon dioxide gas.

AES   Association of Electricity Supplies

Anthracite   Within this publication, anthracite is coal classified as such by UK coal producers and importers of coal. Typically it has a high heat content making it particularly suitable for certain industrial processes and for use as a domestic fuel.

Anthropogenic   Produced by human activities.

Associated Gas   Natural gas found in association with crude oil in a reservoir, either dissolved in the oil or as a cap above the oil.

Autogeneration   Generation of electricity by companies whose main business is not electricity generation, the electricity being produced mainly for that company's own use.

Aviation spirit   A light hydrocarbon oil product used to power piston-engined aircraft power units.

Aviation turbine fuel   The main aviation fuel used for powering aviation gas-turbine power units (jet aircraft engine).

BE   British Energy

Benzole   A colourless liquid, flammable, aromatic hydrocarbon by-product of the iron and steel making process. It is used as a solvent in the manufacture of styrenes and phenols but is also used as a motor fuel.

BETTA   British Electricity Trading and Transmission Arrangements (BETTA) refers to changes to electricity generation, distribution and supply licences. On 1 April 2005, the England and Wales trading arrangements were extended to Scotland by the British Electricity Trading and Transmission Arrangements creating a single GB market for trading of wholesale electricity, with common arrangements for access to and use of GB transmission system. From 1 April 2005, NGC has become the System Operator for the whole of GB. BETTA is the replaced NETA (see page 213) on 4 April 2005.

Biogas   Energy produced from the anaerobic digestion of sewage and industrial waste.

Bitumen   The residue left after the production of lubricating oil distillates and vacuum gas oil for upgrading plant feedstock. Used mainly for road making and construction purposes.

Blast furnace gas   Mainly produced and consumed within the iron and steel industry. Obtained as a by-product of iron making in a blast furnace, it is recovered on leaving the furnace and used partly within the plant and partly in other steel industry processes or in power plants equipped to burn it. A similar gas is obtained when steel is made in basic oxygen steel converters; this gas is recovered and used in the same way.

Breeze	Breeze can generally be described as coke screened below 19 mm (¾ inch) with no fines removed, but the screen size may vary in different areas and to meet the requirements of particular markets.
BG	British Gas
BOS	Basic Oxygen Steel furnace gas
BNFL	British Nuclear Fuels plc.
BRE	Building Research Establishment
Burning oil	A refined petroleum product, with a volatility in between that of motor spirit and gas diesel oil primarily used for heating and lighting.
Butane	Hydrocarbon (C_4H_{10}), gaseous at normal temperature, but generally stored and transported as a liquid. Used as a component in Motor Spirit to improve combustion, and for cooking and heating (see LPG).
Calorific values (CVs)	The energy content of a fuel can be measured as the heat released on complete combustion. The SI (Système International - see note below) derived unit of energy and heat is the Joule. This is the energy per unit volume of the fuel and is often measured in GJ per tonne. The energy content can be expressed as an upper (or gross) value and a lower (or net) value. The difference between the two values is due to the release of energy from the condensation of water in the products of combustion. Gross calorific values are used throughout this publication.
CCL	Climate Change Levy
CO_2	Carbon dioxide. Carbon dioxide contributes about 60 per cent of the potential global warming effect of man-made emissions of greenhouse gases. Although this gas is naturally emitted by living organisms, these emissions are offset by the uptake of carbon dioxide by plants during photosynthesis; they therefore tend to have no net effect on atmospheric concentrations. The burning of fossil fuels, however, releases carbon dioxide fixed by plants many millions of years ago, and thus increases its concentration in the atmosphere.
Co-firing	The burning of biomass products in fossil fuel power stations
Coke oven coke	The solid product obtained from carbonisation of coal, principally coking coal, at high temperature, it is low in moisture and volatile matter. Used mainly in iron and steel industry.
Coke oven gas	Gas produced as a by-product of solid fuel carbonisation and gasification at coke ovens, but not from low temperature carbonisation plants. Synthetic coke oven gas is mainly natural gas which is mixed with smaller amounts of blast furnace and basic oxygen steel furnace gas to produce a gas with almost the same quantities as coke oven gas.
Coking coal	Within this publication, coking coal is coal sold by producers for use in coke ovens and similar carbonising processes. The definition is not therefore determined by the calorific value or caking qualities of each batch of coal sold, although calorific values tend to be higher than for steam coal. Not all coals form cokes. For a coal to coke it must exhibit softening and agglomeration properties, ie the end product must be a coherent solid.

Colliery methane	Methane released from coal seams in deep mines which is piped to the surface and consumed at the colliery or transmitted by pipeline to consumers.
Combined cycle gas Turbine (CCGT)	Combined cycle gas turbine power stations combine gas turbines and steam turbines which are connected to one or more electrical generators in the same plant. The gas turbine (usually fuelled by natural gas or oil) produces mechanical power (to drive the generator) and heat in the form of hot exhaust gases. These gases are fed to a boiler, where steam is raised at pressure to drive a conventional steam turbine, which is also connected, to an electrical generator.
Combined Heat and Power (CHP)	CHP is the simultaneous generation of usable heat and power (usually electricity) in a single process. The term CHP is synonymous with cogeneration and total energy, which are terms often used in the United States or other Member States of the European Community. The basic elements of a CHP plant comprise one or more prime movers driving electrical generators, where the steam or hot water generated in the process is utilised via suitable heat recovery equipment for use either in industrial processes, or in community heating and space heating. For further information see Chapter 6 paragraph 6.32.
CHPQA	Combined Heat and Power Quality Assurance Scheme
Conventional thermal power stations	These are stations which generate electricity by burning fossil fuels to produce heat to convert water into steam, which then powers steam turbines.
Cracking/conversion	A refining process using combinations of temperature, pressure and in some cases a catalyst to produce petroleum products by changing the composition of a fraction of petroleum, either by splitting existing longer carbon chain or combining shorter carbon chain components of crude oil or other refinery feedstock's. Cracking allows refiners to selectively increase the yield of specific fractions from any given input petroleum mix depending on their requirements in terms of output products.
Crude oil	A mineral oil consisting of a mixture of hydrocarbons of natural origins, yellow to black in colour, of variable density and viscosity.
DEFRA	Department for Environment, Food and Rural Affairs
DERV	Diesel engined road vehicle fuel used in internal combustion engines that are compression-ignited (see gas diesel oil).
DFT	Department for Transport
Distillation	A process of separation of the various components of crude oil and refinery feedstocks using the different temperatures of evaporation and condensation of the different components of the mix received at the refineries.
DNC	Declared net capacity and capability are used to measure the maximum power available from generating stations at a point in time. See Chapter 5 paragraphs 5.54 and 5.55 and Chapter 7 paragraph 7.75 for a fuller definition.
DNO	Distribution Network Operator

Downstream	Used in oil and gas processes to cover the part of the industry after the production of the oil and gas. For example, it covers refining, supply and trading, marketing and exporting.
DUKES	Digest of United Kingdom Energy Statistics, the Digest provides essential information for everyone, from economists to environmentalists and from energy suppliers to energy users.
ECA	Enhanced Capital Allowances
EHCS	English House Condition Survey
Embedded Generation	Embedded generation is electricity generation by plant which has been connected to the distribution networks of the public electricity distributors rather than directly to the National Grid Company's transmission systems. Typically they are either smaller stations located on industrial sites, or combined heat and power plant, or renewable energy plant such as wind farms, or refuse burner generators. The category also includes some domestic generators such as those with electric solar panels. For a description of the current structure of the electricity industry in the UK see Chapter 5 paragraphs 5.3 to 5.8.
Energy use	Energy use of fuel mainly comprises use for lighting, heating or cooling, motive power and power for appliances. See also non-energy use.
ESA	European System of National and Regional Accounts. An integrated system of economic accounts which is the European version of the System of National Accounts (SNA).
EESs	The Energy Efficiency Commitment (formerly known as Energy Efficiency Standards of Performance) is an obligation placed on all energy suppliers to offer help and advice to their customers to improve the energy efficiency of their homes.
Ethane	A light hydrocarbon gas (C_2H_6) in natural gas and refinery gas streams (see LPG).
EU-ETS	European Union Emissions Trading Scheme. This is due to commence on 1st January 2005 and involves the trading of emissions allowances as means of reducing emissions by a fixed amount.
EUROSTAT	Statistical Office of the European Communities (SOEC).
Exports	For some parts of the energy industry, statistics on trade in energy related products can be derived from two separate sources. Firstly, figures can be reported by companies as part of systems for collecting data on specific parts of the energy industry (eg as part of the system for recording the production and disposals of oil from the UK continental shelf). Secondly, figures are also available from the general systems that exist for monitoring trade in all types of products operated by HM Revenue and Customs.
FES	Future Energy Solutions, part of the company AEA Technology Environment (AEAT)
Feedstock	In the refining industry, a product or a combination of products derived from crude oil, destined for further processing other than blending. It is distinguished from use as a chemical feedstock etc. See non-energy use.

Final energy Consumption	Energy consumption by final user – ie which is not being used for transformation into other forms of energy.
Fossil fuels	Coal, natural gas and fuels derived from crude oil (for example petrol and diesel) are called fossil fuels because they have been formed over long periods of time from ancient organic matter.
Fuel oils	The heavy oils from the refining process; used as fuel in furnaces and boilers of power stations, industry, in domestic and industrial heating, ships, locomotives, metallurgic operations, and industrial power plants etc.
Fuel oil - Light	Fuel oil made up of heavier straight-run or cracked distillates and used in commercial or industrial burner installations not equipped with pre-heating facilities.
Fuel oil - Medium	Other fuel oils, sometimes referred to as bunker fuels, which generally require pre-heating before being burned, but in certain climatic conditions do not require pre-heating.
Fuel oil - Heavy	Other heavier grade fuel oils which in all situations require some form of pre-heating before being burned.
Fuel poverty	The common definition of a fuel poor household is one needing to spend in excess of 10 per cent of household income to achieve a satisfactory heating regime (21°C in the living room and 18°C in the other occupied rooms).
Gas Diesel Oil	The medium oil from the refinery process; used as a fuel in diesel engines (ie internal combustion engines that are compression-ignited), burned in central heating systems and used as a feedstock for the chemical industry.
GDP	Gross Domestic Product.
GDP deflator	An index of the ratio of GDP at current prices to GDP at constant prices. It provides a measure of general price inflation within the whole economy.
Gigajoule (GJ)	A unit of energy equal to 10^9 joules (see note on joules below).
Gigawatt (GW)	A unit of electrical power, equal to 10^9 watts.
Heat sold	Heat (or steam) that is produced and sold under the provision of a contract. Heat sold is derived from heat generated by Combined Heat and Power (CHP) plants and from community heating schemes without CHP plants.
HMRC	HM Revenue and Customs.
Imports	See the first paragraph of the entry for exports above. Before the 1997 edition of the Digest, the term "arrivals" was used to distinguish figures derived from the former source from those import figures derived from the systems operated by HM Revenue and Customs. To make it clearer for users, a single term is now being used for both these sources of figures (the term imports) as this more clearly states what the figures relate to, which is goods entering the UK.

International Energy Agency (IEA)	The IEA is an autonomous body located in Paris which was established in November 1974 within the framework of the Organisation for Economic Co-operation and Development (OECD) to implement an international energy programme.
Indigenous production	For oil this includes production from the UK Continental Shelf both onshore and offshore.
Industrial spirit	Refined petroleum fractions with boiling ranges up to 200°C dependent on the use to which they are put – eg seed extraction, rubber solvents, perfume etc.
ISSB	Iron and Steel Statistics Bureau
ITF	Industry Technology Facilitator
Joules	A joule is a generic unit of energy in the conventional SI system (see note on SI below). It is equal to the energy dissipated by an electrical current of 1 ampere driven by 1 volt for 1 second; it is also equal to twice the energy of motion in a mass of 1 kilogram moving at 1 metre per second.
Kilowatt (kW)	1,000 watts
Landfill gas	The methane-rich biogas formed from the decomposition of organic material in landfill.
LDF	Light distillate feedstock.
LDZ	Local distribution zone
Liquefied petroleum Gas (LPG)	Gas usually propane or butane, derived from oil and put under pressure so that it is in liquid form. Often used to power portable cooking stoves or heaters and to fuel some types of vehicle, eg some specially adapted road vehicles, forklift trucks.
Lead Replacement Petrol (LRP)	An alternative to Leaded Petrol containing a different additive to lead (in the UK usually potassium based) to perform the lubrication functions of lead additives in reducing engine wear.
Lubricating oils	Refined heavy distillates obtained from the vacuum distillation of petroleum residues. Includes liquid and solid hydrocarbons sold by the lubricating oil trade, either alone or blended with fixed oils, metallic soaps and other organic and/or inorganic bodies.
Magnox	A type of gas-cooled nuclear fission reactor developed in the UK, so called because of the magnesium alloy used to clad the uranium fuel.
Major power producers	Companies whose prime purpose is the generation of electricity (paragraph 5.50 of Chapter 5 gives a full list of major power producers).
Megawatt (MW)	1,000 kilowatts. MWe is used to emphasise when electricity is being measured. MWt is used when heat ("thermal") is being measured.
Micro CHP	Micro CHP is a new technology that is expected to make a significant contribution to domestic energy efficiency in the future.
MMC	Monopolies and Mergers Commission

Motor spirit	Blended light petroleum product used as a fuel in spark-ignition internal combustion engines (other than aircraft engines).
NAEI	National Atmospheric Emmissions Inventory
Natural gas	Natural gas is a mixture of naturally occurring gases found either in isolation, or associated with crude oil, in underground reservoirs. The main component is methane; ethane, propane, butane, hydrogen sulphide and carbon dioxide may also be present, but these are mostly removed at or near the well head in gas processing plants.
Naphtha	(Light distillate feedstock) – Petroleum distillate boiling predominantly below 200ºC.
Natural gas - compressed	Natural gas that has been compressed to reduce the volume it occupies to make it easier to transport other than in pipelines. Whilst other petroleum gases can be compressed such that they move into liquid form, the volatility of natural gas is such that liquefaction cannot be achieved without very high pressures and low temperatures being used. As such, the compressed form is usually used as a "half-way house".
Natural gas liquids (NGLs)	A mixture of liquids derived from natural gas and crude oil during the production process, including propane, butane, ethane and gasoline components (pentanes plus).
NDA	Nuclear Decommissioning Authority
NETA	New Electricity Trading Arrangements - In England and Wales these arrangements replaced "the pool" from 27 March 2001. The arrangements are based on bi-lateral trading between generators, suppliers, traders and customers and are designed to be more efficient, and provide more market choice.
NETCEN	National EnvironmentTechnology Centre
NIE	Northern Ireland Electricity
NI NFFO	Northern Ireland Non Fossil Fuel Obligation
Non-energy use	Includes fuel used for chemical feedstock, solvents, lubricants, and road making material.
NFFO	Non Fossil Fuel Obligation. The 1989 Electricity Act empowers the Secretary of State to make orders requiring the Regional Electricity Companies in England and Wales to secure specified amounts of electricity from renewable sources.
NFPA	Non Fossil Purchasing Agency
NO$_x$	Nitrogen oxides. A number of nitrogen compounds including nitrogen dioxide are formed in combustion processes when nitrogen in the air or the fuel combines with oxygen. These compounds can add to the natural acidity of rainfall.
NSCP	National Statistics Code of Practice
NUTS	Nonmenclature of Units for Territorial Statistics
OFGEM	The regulatory office for gas and electricity markets.

OFT	Office of Fair Trading
Orimulsion	An emulsion of bitumen in water that can be used as a fuel in some power stations.
ONS	Office for National Statistics.
OTS	Overseas Trade Statistics of the United Kingdom.
OXERA	Oxford Economic Research Association Ltd.
Patent fuel	A composition fuel manufactured from coal fines by shaping with the addition of a binding agent (typically pitch). The term manufactured solid fuel is also used.
Petrochemical feedstock	All petroleum products intended for use in the manufacture of petroleum chemicals. This includes middle distillate feedstock of which there are several grades depending on viscosity. The boiling point ranges between 200°C and 400°C.
Petroleum cokes	Carbonaceous material derived from hydrocarbon oils, uses for which include metallurgical electrode manufacture and in the manufacture of cement.
PILOT	Phase 2 (PILOT) is the successor body to the Oil & Gas Industry Task Force (OGTIF) and was established on 1 Janauary 2000, to secure the long-term future of the oil and gas industry in the UK. A forum that brings together Government and industry to address the challenges facing the oil and gas industry. One outcome of PILOT's work is the published Code of Practice on Supply Chain Relationships.
Photovoltaics	The direct conversion of solar radiation into electricity by the interaction of light with the electrons in a semiconductor device or cell.
Plant capacity	The maximum power available from a power station at a point in time (see also Chapter 5 paragraph 5.54).
Plant loads, demands and efficiency	Measures of how intensively and efficiently power stations are being used. These terms are defined in Chapter 5 paragraphs 5.56 and 5.57
PPRS	Petroleum production reporting system. Licensees operating in the UK Continental Shelf are required to make monthly returns on their production of hydrocarbons (oil and gas) to the DTI. This information is recorded in the PPRS, which is used to report flows, stocks and uses of hydrocarbon from the well-head through to final disposal from a pipeline or terminal (see paragraphs F.29 to F.31 of Annex F on DTI's energy statistics website).
Process oils	Partially processed feedstocks which require further processing before being classified as a finished product suitable for sale. They can also be used as a reaction medium in the production process.
Primary fuels	Fuels obtained directly from natural sources, eg coal, oil and natural gas.
Primary electricity	Electricity obtained other than from fossil fuel sources, eg nuclear, hydro and other non-thermal renewables. Imports of electricity are also included.

Propane	Hydrocarbon containing three carbon atoms (C_3H_8), gaseous at normal temperature, but generally stored and transported under pressure as a liquid.
PWR	Pressurised water reactor. A nuclear fission reactor cooled by ordinary water kept from boiling by containment under high pressure.
Reforming	Processes by which the molecular structure of different fractions of petroleum can be modified. It usually involves some form of catalyst, most often platinum, and allows the conversion of lower grades of petroleum product into higher grades, improving their octane rating. It is a generic term for processes such as cracking, cyclization, dehydrogenation and isomerisation. These processes generally led to the production of hydrogen as a by-product, which can be used in the refineries in some desulphurization procedures.
Refinery fuel	Petroleum products produced by the refining process that are used as fuel at refineries.
Renewable energy sources	Renewable energy includes solar power, wind, wave and tide, and hydroelectricity. Solid renewable energy sources consist of wood, straw, short rotation coppice, other biomass and the biodegradable fraction of wastes. Gaseous renewables consist of landfill gas and sewage gas. Non-biodegradable wastes are not counted as a renewables source but appear in the Renewable sources of energy chapter of this Digest for completeness.
Reserves	With oil and gas these relate to the quantities identified as being present in underground cavities. The actual amounts that can be recovered depend on the level of technology available and existing economic situations. These continually change; hence the level of the UK's reserves can change quite independently of whether or not new reserves have been identified.
RESTATS	The Renewable Energy Statistics System
RO	Renewables Obligation
ROC	Renewables Obligation Certificates
SEPN	Sustainable Energy Policy Network represents the body of people responsible for delivering the white paper directly or indirectly through having links to business and other organidsations nationally and regionally.
SI (Système International)	Refers to the agreed conventions for the measurement of physical quantities.
SIC	Standard Industrial Classification in the UK. Last revised in 2003 and known as SIC(2003), replaced previous classifications SIC(92), SIC(80) and SIC(68). SIC(92) was compatible with European Union classification NACE Rev1 (Nomenclature générale des activités économiques dans les Communautés européennes as revised in October 1990) and similarly SIC(2003) is consistent with NACE Rev1.1 which came into effect in January 2003. Classification systems need to be periodically revised because over time new products, processes and industries emerge.
Secondary fuels	Fuels derived from natural primary sources of energy. For example electricity generated from burning coal, gas or oil is a secondary fuel, as are coke and coke oven gas.

Steam coal	Within this publication, steam coal is coal classified as such by UK coal producers and by importers of coal. It tends to be coal having lower calorific values; the type of coal that is typically used for steam raising.
SO₂	Sulphur Dioxide. Sulphur dioxide is a gas produced by the combustion of sulphur-containing fuels such as coal and oil.
SOEC	Statistical Office of the European Communities
SRO	Scottish Renewable Orders
Synthetic coke oven gas	Mainly a natural gas, which is mixed with smaller amounts of blast furnace, and BOS (basic oxygen steel furnace) gas to produce a gas with almost the same quantities as coke oven gas.
Temperature correction	The temperature corrected series of total inland fuel consumption indicates what annual consumption might have been if the average temperature during the year had been the same as the average for the years 1961 to 1990.
Terawatt (TW)	1,000 gigawatts
TWh	Terawatt Hour
Thermal Sources of Electricity	These include coal, oil, natural gas, nuclear, landfill gas, sewage gas, municipal solid waste, farm waste, tyres, poultry litter, short rotation coppice, straw, coke oven gas, blast furnace gas, and waste products from chemical processes.
Tonne of oil equivalent (toe)	A common unit of measurement which enables different fuels to be compared and aggregated. (See Chapter 1 paragraphs 1.24 to 1.25 for further information and Annex A page 203 for conversion factors).
Tars	Viscous materials usually derived from the destructive distillation of coal which are by-products of the coke and iron making processes.
Therm	A common unit of measurement similar to a tonne of oil equivalent which enables different fuels to be compared and aggregated. (see Annex A).
Thermal efficiency	The thermal efficiency of a power station is the efficiency with which heat energy contained in fuel is converted into electrical energy. It is calculated for fossil fuel burning stations by expressing electricity supplied as a percentage of the total energy content of the fuel consumed (based on average gross calorific values). For nuclear stations it is calculated using the quantity of heat released as a result of fission of the nuclear fuel inside the reactor.
UKCS	United Kingdom Continental Shelf.
UKOOA	United Kingdom Ofshore Operators Association
UKPIA	UK Petroleum Industry Association. The trade association for the UK petroleum industry.
Ultra low sulphur Diesel (ULSD)	A grade of diesel fuel which has a much lower sulphur content (less than 0.005 per cent or 50 parts per million) and of a slightly higher volatility than ordinary diesel fuels. As a result it produces fewer emissions when burned. As such it enjoys a lower rate of excise duty in the UK than ordinary diesel (by 3 pence per litre) to promote its use. Virtually 100 per cent of sales of DERV fuel in the UK are ULSD.

Ultra low sulphur Petrol (ULSP)	A grade of motor spirit with a similar level of sulphur to ULSD (less than 0.005 per cent or 50 parts per million). In the March 2000 Budget it was announced that a lower rate of excise duty than ordinary petrol for this fuel would be introduced during 2000, which was increased to 3 pence per litre in the March 2001 Budget. It has quickly replaced ordinary premium grade unleaded petrol in the UK market place.
Upstream	A term to cover the activities related to the exploration, production and delivery to a terminal or other facility of oil or gas for export or onward shipment within the UK.
USBS	United States Bureau of Standards refers to legislation that sets minimum safety standards in the coal market and mining industry.
VAT	Value added tax.
Watt (W)	The conventional unit to measure a rate of flow of energy. One watt amounts to 1 joule per second.
White spirit	A highly refined distillate with a boiling range of about 150ºC to 200ºC used as a paint solvent and for dry cleaning purposes etc.

Annex C
Further sources of United Kingdom energy publications

Some of the publications listed below give shorter term statistics, some provide further information about energy production and consumption in the United Kingdom and in other countries, and others provide more detail on a country or fuel industry basis. The list also covers recent publications on energy issues and policy, including statistical information, produced or commissioned by the DTI. The list is not exhaustive and the titles of publications and publishers may alter. Unless otherwise stated, all titles are available from

DTI Publications Orderline
Web: www.dti.gov.uk/publications
Phone: 0845 015 0010
Address: ADMAIL, 528, London, SW1W 0YT
Email: publications@dti.gsi.gov.uk

and can also be found on the DTI Web site at www.dti.gov.uk/energy/inform/ .

Department of Trade and Industry publications on energy

Energy Statistics
Monthly, quarterly and annual statistics on production and consumption of overall energy and individual fuels in the United Kingdom together with energy prices is available in MS Excel format on the Internet at www.dti.gov.uk/energy/inform/energy_stats/ .

Energy Trends
Quarterly publication. Covers all major aspects of energy. Provides a comprehensive picture of energy production and use. Contains analysis of data and articles covering energy issues. Available on subscription, with Quarterly Energy Prices publication, from EMU3-SID2, Department of Trade and Industry, Bay 209, 1 Victoria Street, London, SW1H 0ET, tel. 020-7215 2697/2698. Single copies are available from the DTI Publications Orderline at the address given at the start of this Annex, price £5.

Quarterly Energy Prices
Quarterly publication. From June 2001 replaced energy prices information formerly available in the monthly publication Energy Trends and the annual Digest of UK Energy Statistics. Contains tables, charts and commentary covering energy prices to domestic and industrial consumers for all the major fuels as well as presenting comparisons of fuel prices in the European Union and G7 countries. Available on subscription, with Energy Trends publication, from EMU3-SID2, Department of Trade and Industry, Bay 209, 1 Victoria Street, London, SW1H 0ET, tel. 020-7215 2697/2698. Single copies are available from the DTI Publications Orderline at the address given at the start of this Annex, price £7.

Energy Sector Indicators 2005
Energy Sector Indicators for 2005 will be published in July 2005 as a supplement to the Second Annual Report on the Energy White Paper (see below). The content is designed to show the extent to which secure, diverse and sustainable supplies of energy to UK Businesses and consumers at competitive prices are ensured. As well as the four key indicators used in the Report, and 27 supporting indicators there is the full range of background indicators that have been published in the corresponding booklet for earlier years. Energy Sector Indicators 2005 is available on the DTI web site at:
www.dti.gov.uk/energy/inform/energy_indicators/index.shtml
and in hard copy (free of charge) from DTI Publications Orderline.

UK Energy in Brief

This booklet summarises the latest statistics on energy production, consumption and prices in the United Kingdom. The figures are taken from "Digest of UK Energy Statistics". Available free from EMU3-SID2, Department of Trade and Industry, Bay 209, 1 Victoria Street, London, SW1H 0ET, tel. 020-7215 2697/2698 and from the DTI Publications Orderline

Development of the Oil and Gas Resources of the United Kingdom

Publication of Development of UK Oil and Gas Resources, commonly known as the "Brown Book", ended with the 2001 edition. That edition, as well as more up-to-date information on the UK offshore industry, is available via DTI's Oil and Gas website: www.og.dti.gov.uk .

Industrial Energy Markets: Energy markets in UK manufacturing industry 1973 to 1993 - Energy Paper 64

Using tables of data drawn from the 1989 Purchases Inquiry conducted by the Office for National Statistics, the report, which updates one produced in 1989, sets out the implications for the trends in industrial energy consumption over the period from 1973 to 1993. Available from The Stationery Office, tel 0870 600 5522 and can be ordered through Government Bookshops. Not available on the Internet.

Energy Consumption in the UK

Energy Consumption in the United Kingdom brings together statistics from a variety of sources to produce a comprehensive review of energy consumption in the UK since the 1970s. This booklet describes the key trends in energy consumption in the UK since 1970 with a particular focus on trends since 1990. The information is presented in five sections covering firstly overall energy consumption, then energy consumption in the transport, domestic, industrial and service sectors. It includes an analysis of the factors driving the changes in energy consumption, the impact of increasing activity, increased efficiency, and structural change in the economy, while detailed tables can be found on the Internet at www.dti.gov.uk/energy/inform/energy_consumption/ecuk.pdf .

Energy Projections for the UK:- Energy Paper 68

Energy Paper 68 presents the results of an exercise to update the Government's projections of future UK energy demand and related emissions of carbon and sulphur dioxides to 2020. It builds on work issued as a working paper in March 2000 and its projections underpin the Climate Change Programme launched by the DETR (now Defra) in November 2000. The paper contributes to policy development and assessment of the UK's efforts to meet its national and international greenhouse gases targets. Available from The Stationery Office, tel 0870 600 5522.

Updated emissions projections

The results of further revisions to the emissions projects that have taken place since May 2004 were published on the DTI web site on 11 November 2004. These results have helped to inform the final decision on the level of the overall UK emissions cap in October 2004 and the revisions to the April NAP. The results are presented as a paper in four parts. Part one provides a summary of the headline projection and main changes since the April NAP projection. Part two provides the sectoral projections. Part three provides energy demand results and part four provides detail on energy supply. The projections document is available at: http://www.dti.gov.uk/energy/sepn/uep2004.pdf.

Social Effects of Energy Liberalisation: The UK Experience

This paper reviews the impact of liberalisation of the energy markets, and the effects on the fuel industries, the consumer and the environment. Available free from EMU3-SID2, Department of Trade and Industry, Bay 209, 1 Victoria Street, London, SW1H 0ET, tel. 020 7215 2697/2698.

Energy Liberalisation Indicators in Europe: A preliminary report of a study carried out by OXERA for the Governments of the UK and the Netherlands.

This paper presents preliminary results from a study carried out by OXERA on behalf of the Governments of the UK and the Netherlands. The study develops a set of indicators, within a hierarchical structure, for monitoring the development of competition in gas and electricity markets across Europe. The study mainly concentrates on the electricity market and presents some preliminary results for a subset of European countries including the UK and Netherlands. Available free from

EMU3-SID2, Department of Trade and Industry, Bay 209, 1 Victoria Street, London, SW1H 0ET, tel. 020 7215 2697/2698.

Energy Liberalisation Indicators in Europe: A consultation paper based on a study carried out by OXERA for the Governments of the UK and the Netherlands.

This consultation paper sets out the methodology used and presents results for a subset of European countries including the UK and the Netherlands. Available free from EMU3-SID2, Department of Trade and Industry, Bay 209, 1 Victoria Street, London SW1H 0ET, tel. 020 7215 2697/2698.

Social, Environmental and Security of Supply Policies in a Competitive Energy Market: A Review of Delivery Mechanisms in the United Kingdom, Summary Paper

This paper outlines the UK experience so far in using competitive energy markets to deliver social, environmental and security of supply policies. It highlights the benefits that have emerged from this approach and sets out the instruments the Government has used to enhance policy delivery. Available free from EMU3-SID2, Department of Trade and Industry, Bay 209, 1 Victoria Street, London, SW1H 0ET, tel. 020 7215 2697/2698.

The UK Fuel Poverty Strategy: November 2001

Produced by the Department of Trade and Industry and the Department for Environment, Food and Rural Affairs (Defra). The strategy sets out the Government's objectives, policies and targets for alleviating fuel poverty in the UK over the next 10 years. Available free from Department of Trade and Industry Publications Orderline.

The UK Fuel Poverty Strategy, 1st, 2nd and 3rd Annual Progress Reports

Produced by the Department of Trade and Industry and Defra in association with the Devolved Administrations. These reports set out what progress has been made on tackling fuel poverty following the publication of the UK Fuel Poverty Strategy in November 2001. The third report is accompanied by a series of annexes published on the DTI web site. These annexes include a detailed analysis of the profile of the fuel poor and an update of the 19 Fuel Poverty Indicators as developed by the Fuel Poverty Monitoring and Technical Group. Also published with the third report is an independent peer review into the fuel poverty methodology and a Government response to the recommendations at this time. The web reference for these documents is:
www.dti.gov.uk/energy/consumers/fuel_poverty/fuel_strategy.shtml.
The reports are also available free from Department of Trade and Industry the DTI Publications Orderline.

Energy– Its impact on the environment and society

This 2005 booklet outlines the environmental and social impacts of energy production and use and covers similar ground to the previous version published in 2002. It sets out the key social and environmental consequences of the production and use of energy and shows through figures and charts, where we have come from, where we are now, what the policy challenges are, and what the current responses are. Available free from EMU3-SID2, Department of Trade and Industry, Bay 209, 1 Victoria Street, London SW1H 0ET, tel. 020-7215 2697/2698 and from the DTI Publications Orderline.

Energy White Paper and 2nd Annual Report

The Government's Energy White Paper, "Our energy future - creating a low carbon economy", was published by the Secretary of State for Trade and Industry on 24 February 2003. The report addresses the challenges facing energy, by setting out a long-term strategic vision for energy policy. It is the product of extensive consultative and analytical work and has over 6,500 contributions. The White Paper is available on the DTI web site at www.dti.gov.uk/energy/whitepaper/index.shtml and in hard copy from The Stationery Office or through Government Bookshops.

The second annual report, to be published in July 2005, reviews progress over the last 12 months and the way ahead. It is available on the DTI web site at:
www.dti.gov.uk/energy/sepn/

Other publications including energy information

General

Basic Statistics of the Community (annual); *Statistical Office of the European Communities*

Digest of Welsh Statistics (annual); *Welsh Office* (available from ESS Division, Welsh Office, Cathays Park, Cardiff)

Eurostatistics - Data for Short Term Analysis; *Statistical Office of the European Communities*

Monthly Digest of Statistics; *Office for National Statistics*

Northern Ireland Annual Abstract of Statistics (annual); *Department of Finance and Personnel,* (available from the Policy & Planning Unit, Department of Finance & Personnel, Stormont, Belfast BT4 3SW)

Overseas Trade Statistics of the United Kingdom; *H.M. Revenue and Customs*
- Business Monitor MM20 (monthly) (extra-EU trade only)
- Business Monitor MM20A (monthly) (intra and extraEU
- trade data, relatively limited level of production detail)
- Business Monitor MQ20 (quarterly) (intra-EU trade only)
- Business Monitor MA20 (annual) (intra- and extra-EU trade);

Purchases Inquiry 1989, 1994-1998; Office *for National Statistics*

Rapid Reports - energy and industry (ad hoc); *Statistical Office of the European Communities*

Regional Trends (annual); *Office for National Statistics*

Scottish Abstract of Statistics (annual); *Scottish Office*

United Kingdom Minerals Yearbook (annual); *British Geological Survey* (available from the British Geological Survey, Keyworth, Nottingham, NG12 5GG)

Yearbook of Regional Statistics (annual); *Statistical Office of the European Communities*

Energy

Annual Bulletin of General Energy Statistics for Europe; *United Nations Economic Commission for Europe*

BP Statistical Review of World Energy (annual); (available from The Editor, BP Statistical Review, The British Petroleum Company plc, Corporate Communications Services, Britannic House, 1 Finsbury Circus, London EC2M 7BA)

Energy - Monthly Statistics; *Statistical Office of the European Communities*

Energy Balances of OECD Countries (annual); *OECD International Energy Agency*

Energy Statistics and Balances of OECD Countries (annual); *OECD International Energy Agency*

Energy Statistics and Balances of Non-OECD Countries (annual); *OECD International Energy Agency*

Energy - Yearly Statistics; *Statistical Office of the European Communities*

UN Energy Statistics Yearbook (annual); *United Nations Statistical Office*

Coal

Annual Bulletin of Coal Statistics for Europe; *United Nations Economic Commission for Europe*

Annual Reports and Accounts of The Coal Authority and the private coal companies; (*apply to the Headquarters of the company concerned)*

Coal Information (annual); *OECD International Energy Agency*

Oil and gas

Annual Bulletin of Gas Statistics for Europe; *United Nations Economic Commission for Europe*

BP Review of World Gas (annual); (*available from British Petroleum Company plc, Corporate Communications Services, Britannic House, 1 Finsbury Circus, London EC2M 7BA)*

Annual Reports and Accounts of National Grid Transco, Centrica and other independent gas supply companies; (contact *the Headquarters of the company concerned directly)*

Oil and Gas Information (annual); *OECD International Energy Agency*

Quarterly Oil Statistics and Energy Balances; *OECD International Energy Agency*

UK Petroleum Industry Statistics Consumption and Refinery Production (annual and quarterly); *Institute of Petroleum (available from IP, 61 New Cavendish Street, London W1M 8AR)*

Electricity

Annual Bulletin of Electric Energy Statistics for Europe; *United Nations Economic Commission for Europe*

Annual Reports and Accounts of the Electricity Supply Companies, Distributed Companies and Generators; (*apply to the Headquarters of the company concerned*)
Annual Report of the Office of Electricity Regulation; OFGEM
Electricity Supply in OECD Countries; *OECD International Energy Agency*
National Grid Company - Seven Year Statement - (annual) *National Grid Transco - For further details telephone 01203 423065*
Operation of Nuclear Power Stations (annual); *Statistical Office of the European Communities*
Electricity Information (annual); *OECD International Energy Agency*

Prices

Energy Prices (annual); *Statistical Office of the European Communities* (summarises price information published in the European Commissions Weekly Oil Price, and half-yearly Statistics in Focus on Gas Prices and Electricity Prices)
Energy Prices and Taxes (quarterly); *OECD International Energy Agency*
Electricity prices (annual); *Eurostat*
Gas prices (annual); *Eurostat*

Environment

Digest of Environmental Statistics (Annual); *Department for Environment, Food and Rural Affairs (Defra)*.
Indicators of Sustainable Development for the United Kingdom; *Department for Environment, Food and Rural Affairs (Defra)*
Quality of life counts, Indicators for a strategy for sustainable development for the United Kingdom: a baseline assessment; *Department for Environment, Food and Rural Affairs (Defra)*
Environment Statistics (annual); *Eurostat*
UK Environment (adhoc/one-off release); *Department for Environment, Food and Rural Affairs (Defra)*

Renewables

New and Renewable Energy, Prospects for the 21st Century. A series of consultation papers reports on the outcome of the review conducted by the Government and the possible ways forward in implementing the Government's new drive for renewables. Available on the DTI website and via the DTI Publications Orderline, publications@dti.gsi.gov.uk

Fuel Poverty

English House Condition Survey – 1996 Energy Report:- Produced by the Department for Environment, Food and Rural Affairs. This report presents the detailed findings of the 1996 English House Condition Survey (EHCS) on the energy efficiency and thermal performance of the stock, energy action by occupants and landlords and the potential for future energy and carbon savings.

Useful energy related websites

The DTI website can be found at www.dti.gov.uk, the energy information and statistics website is at www.dti.gov.uk/energy/inform/index.shtml

Other Government websites

Central Office of Information	www.coi.gov.uk
HM Revenue and Customs	www.hmrc.gov.uk
Department for Environment, Food and Rural Affairs	www.defra.gov.uk
HM Government Online	www.direct.gov.uk/
Department for Transport	www.dft.gov.uk
National Statistics	www.statistics.gov.uk
Northern Ireland Departments	www.northernireland.gov.uk
Office of the Deputy Prime Minister	www.odpm.gov.uk
Ofgem (The Office of Gas and Electricity Markets)	www.ofgem.gov.uk
Scottish Executive	www.scotland.gov.uk
The Scottish Parliament	www.scottish.parliament.uk
National Assembly for Wales	www.wales.gov.uk
UK Parliament	www.parliament.uk

Other useful energy related websites

Air Quality Archive	www.airquality.co.uk
Association of Electricity Producers	www.aepuk.com
BP	www.bp.com/home.do
British Wind Energy Association	www.bwea.com
Building Research Establishment	www.bre.co.uk
Changes to Joint Environmental Markets Unit (JEMU)	www.dti.gov.uk/JEMU
Coal Authority	www.coal.gov.uk/
Energywatch	www.energywatch.org.uk/
Energy Institute	www.energyinst.org.uk
Energy Networks Association	www.energynetworks.org
Europa (European Union Online)	www.europa.eu.int/
Eurostat	epp.eurostat.cec.eu.int/
Future Energy Solutions	www.future-energy-solutions.com
Interconnector (UK) Ltd	www.interconnector.com
International Energy Agency	www.iea.org
Iron and Steel Statistics Bureau	www.issb.co.uk
National Grid Transco	www.ngtgroup.com
NETCEN (National Environmental Technology Centre)	www.netcen.co.uk
The Stationery Office	www.tso.co.uk/
UKOOA (UK Offshore Operators Association)	www.ukooa.co.uk
UK Petroleum Industry Association	www.ukpia.com
United Nations Statistics Division	unstats.un.org/unsd/default.htm
US Department of Energy	www.energy.gov
US Energy Information Administration	www.eia.doe.gov

Annex D
Major events in the Energy Industry

2005
Sustainable Energy Policy

The Energy White Paper published in February 2003 set out the strategy for energy policy until 2050. A second annual report reviewing progress over the last 12 months and the way ahead is to be published in July 2005. Energy Sector Indicators for 2005 is also to be published in July 2005 as a supplement to the Second Annual Report on the Energy White Paper.

Fuel Poverty

The Fuel Poverty Advisory Group has published its Third Annual Report. Whilst welcoming progress made, as well as the enhancements to the Warm Front. Energy Ministers held a follow up event with the energy supply companies with a proposal to set up a new helpline; a central point of contact for fuel poverty referrals, developed by the energy companies. The Helpline, is due to be launched in October.

Emissions Trading

The EU Emissions trading scheme (ETS) commenced on 1 January. It is one of the policies being introduced across Europe to tackle emissions of carbon dioxide and other greenhouse gases and combat the serious threat of climate change. The first phase runs from 2005-2007 and the second phase will run from 2008-2012 to coincide with the first Kyoto Commitment Period. Further 5-year periods are expected subsequently.

The scheme works on a "Cap and Trade" basis. EU Member State governments are required to set an emission cap for all installations covered by the scheme. Each installation is then be allocated allowances for the particular commitment period in question. The number of allowances allocated to each installation for any given period, (the number of tradable allowances each installation will receive), will be set down in a document called the National Allocation Plan.

On 14 February the UK published revised provisional list of installation level allocations under the EU Emissions Trading Scheme, but on 12 April the European Commission formally rejected the British Government's request to increase the number of allowances for use in the first phase by 20 million tonnes, but the UK has lodged an appeal. Distribution of the 736 million tonnes of CO_2 allowances by Defra to eligible installations in the UK will begin at the end of April 2005.

Coal

Ellington colliery ceased production in January 2005.

The Live Fast Track Offer Scheme for respiratory disease claimants, which will see around 80,000 miners offered optional risk payments where initial medical tests show very low levels of lung disease, went live on 28 February.

The cut-off date for the majority of live Vibration White Finger Services claimants passed on 31 March 2005. However, there are some agreed exceptions to this date – live claimants have until 6 months from the General Damages medical to claim and beneficiaries have up to 31 January 2006 to make claims on behalf of claimants who died before 31 March 2005.

Oil and gas

BP's Clair field inaugurated in February 2005. Clair was largest undeveloped UKCS resource. BP and partners invested around £650 million in the project, which is expected to recover reserves of up to 300 million barrels of oil, with potential for a further 400 million.

Formal signature of the new gas interconnector treaty with the Dutch took place in March 2005. The treaty will be laid before UK Parliament (to enable UK to bring it into force) in early autumn 2005.

On 21 March 2005 the UK and Netherlands Governments signed an interconnector treaty to allow the construction and operation of the BBL gas pipeline between Balzand in the Netherlands to Bacton in the UK. This will provide a second direct link between the UK's gas transmission system and that of continental Europe. It is due to be operational from December 2006.

On 4 April 2005 the UK and Norwegian Governments signed a new oil and gas co-operation treaty designed to remove the need for a separate treaty each time there is a new project involving cross- boundary development. In particular it will underpin the construction of the Norwegian Langeled gas pipeline (supplying up to 20 per cent of UK gas demand from Winter 2006/07) and will also cover the development of new trans-boundary fields and the use of host infrastructures for developments across the median line.

Electricity

On 1 April 2005, the British Electricity Trading and Transmission Arrangements (BETTA) took effect. BETTA has introduced a single wholesale electricity market across Britain by extending the England and Wales market arrangements to Scotland. This will push prices down for Scottish consumers, and will open up the market and increase competition. The legislation underpinning BETTA was delivered in the Energy Act 2004. Under BETTA, National Grid, who previously operated the transmission network in England and Wales, is now the System Operator for the whole GB network.

Coolkeeragh's new gas-fired power station replaced the Londonderry coal fired power station in March 2005.

On 6 May 2005, E.On UK announced that it had purchased the 392 MW Enfield Energy CCGT power station.

Nuclear

British Energy announced on 14 January that it had successfully completed the restructuring plan it announced in November 2002.

The Nuclear Decommissioning Authority was established on 1 April, following the transfer of assets and other property rights from BNFL and the signature of initial site Management and Operation contracts between NDA and BNFL/UKAEA.

Renewables

On 8 March 2005, the Energy Minister announced that the Government intended to exercise the power in section 185 of the Energy Act to adjust the level of transmission charges paid by renewable generators on the Scottish islands, and possibly the North of mainland Scotland, subject to consultation. A consultation will be launched in the summer of 2005.

The DTI has developed and will implement this year a "Wave and Tidal Stream Energy Demonstration Scheme" worth up to £42 million that will support the first larger-scale wave and tidal farms. This is funded under the £50 million 'Marine Renewables Deployment Fund' announced by the Secretary of State for Trade and Industry in August 2004.

The final conclusions and recommendations of the Eskdalemuir Working Group have been accepted by the Ministry of Defence in full. Defence Estates are removing all associated holding objections in place against the 1.6 GW of wind developments in the vicinity of the seismic array at Eskdalemuir.

2004

Sustainable Energy Policy
DTI published the first annual report on implementation of the Energy White Paper on 26 April as part of a series of documents, all of which contribute to creating a low-carbon economy. These included the Government's Energy Efficiency Implementation Plan (Defra), the Combined Heat and Power strategy (Defra), a consultation paper about biofuels (DFT), and a range of statistical indicators to monitor progress towards the goals of the White Paper (DTI).

Energy Act
The Energy Act 2004 received Royal Assent on 22 July 2004. It will promote "cleaner, greener power" and competitive and reliable energy supplies for now and generations to come. It implements a range of commitments made in the Energy White Paper.

For the first time, one public body (the new Nuclear Decommissioning Authority), which published its draft Annual Plan for public consultation on 10 December 2004 will have complete responsibility for the decommissioning and clean-up of the UK's civil nuclear sites, and for the safe and effective management of our nuclear waste.

The Act also creates a single wholesale electricity market for Britain, the British Electricity Trading and Transmission Arrangements ("BETTA"). Provisions within the Act covering electricity and gas interconnectors implement a number of requirements in the EU's 2003 Gas and Electricity Directives and its Electricity Regulation.

Fuel Poverty
The Fuel Poverty Action Plan, which is a Government publication, was issued on 30 November 2004 and sets out how the Government intends to meet its first fuel poverty target for England – that of eradicating fuel poverty in vulnerable households.

Emissions Trading
On 27 October 2004, an announcement was made of the UK's intention to amend the National Allocation Plan for Phase 1 of the EU Emissions Trading Scheme (2005-07) to a higher number of allowances. This reflects finalisation of emission projections showing higher forecast emissions. The new proposed allocation represented a greater reduction against projections than previously indicated.

On 11 November 2004, the final Updated Energy Projections (UEP) informing the National Allocation Plan (NAP) for EU Emissions Trading Scheme (EUETS) were published on the DTI website. This paper presented the results of further revisions to the carbon emission projections that have taken place since May 2004.

Renewables
On 2 August 2004, the Secretary of State announced the new £50m Marine Research Development Fund. This is another step towards promoting renewable energy and complements support already given for other emerging technologies including wind, solar and biomass.

On 4 November 2004, the final terms of reference for the 2005/06 review of the Renewables Obligation (RO) were published. In a separate exercise, a statutory consultation excise for proposed amendments to secure the Renewables Obligation was published on 8 September 2004.

Climate Change
On 8 December 2004 the consultation on the review of the UK Climate Change Programme was launched. The consultation highlights areas where the Government has identified opportunities further to reduce carbon emissions.

Coal
Hatfield colliery closed in January 2004. As part of the closure of the Selby complex Wistow mine closed in May 2004, Stillingfleet in September 2004 and Riccall in December 2004.

Period 2 of the Coal Investment Aid scheme closed on 1 June 2004. 13 applications were received requesting £94.7 million of aid.

The Department reached the key milestone of £1 billion in British Coal Vibration White Finger compensation being paid in week commencing 19 July 2004.

Oil and gas
US oil firm Apache announced plans to spend around £137 million in 2004 on various projects in the Forties field in the North Sea. This included drilling more than 20 wells to gain a "substantial" increase in production.

The 22nd Offshore and 12th Onshore Oil and Gas Licensing Rounds were announced on 4 March 2004. The 22nd Round made available the largest number of offshore blocks since the 2nd Round in 1965. As well as continuing to include options for "promote" licences and traditional licences, the Round offered a further new form of licence, the "frontier" licence, for blocks in the Atlantic Margin, West of the Shetland Islands.

On 6 July 2004, DTI approved the 300th North Sea field development, Total's Glenelg field, with expected peak production of 30,000 barrels of oil equivalent a day.

On 28 July 2004, DTI approved the Saturn gas field development. Operator, ConocoPhillips, expected first gas in Q4 2005 at an initial rate of 74 million cubic feet a day, with a maximum daily rate of 169 million cubic feet in the following year. Produced gas will be transported via the Lincolnshire Offshore Gas Gathering System to the Theddlethorpe Terminal.

On 3 August 2004, production started from the Lundin-operated Broom field. Oil reserves were estimated to be 36 million barrels for the first phase, with further development opportunities in area currently being evaluated. Broom will also assist substantially in extending the Heather field life.

On 8 October 2004, the UK and Norwegian Governments agreed arrangements to allow the development of two new North Sea fields - Boa and Playfair.

The official launch of the 'Goldeneye' development took place on 11 November 2004. The £300m project, supported by co-venturers Shell, ExxonMobil, Paladin Resources and Centrica Energy, will provide around 3 per cent of the UK's gas.

Electricity
On 1 September 2004, the British Electricity and Trading Arrangements (BETTA) went "Active". This involved the Secretary of State using her powers in the Energy Act 2004 to change licence conditions so that trailing and testing of the new arrangements could begin, in preparation for BETTA going "Live" on 1 April 2005.

The findings of the investigation by DTI's Engineering Inspectorate into the major power failures in London on 28 August 2003 and in Birmingham on 5 September 2003 were communicated to the respective electricity companies in January 2004. Inspectors worked closely with the companies to ensure their recommendations were taken forward.

Scottish Power purchased Damhead Creek power station in June 2004 and became the sole owner of the Shoreham Power station in September 2004. Centrica purchased Killingholme power station in June 2004. In July 2004 Scottish and Southern Energy acquired the Ferrybridge C and Fiddlers Ferry power stations formerly owned by American Electric Power. Carron Energy re-opened the Fifoots Point power station in August 2004 and changed the name of the power station back to Uskmouth.

Nuclear

The Secretary of State announced on 5 January 2004 that British Energy (BE) had completed the sale of its interest in its US joint venture, Amergen, in December 2003. All amounts outstanding under the Government's loan facility to BE have been paid off, but facility remained available to BE up to a maximum of £200 million.

At the end of February 2004 BNFL's Chapelcross nuclear power station closed.

2003

Sustainable Energy Policy

The Sustainable Energy Policy Network (SEPN) website was launched in June 2003. SEPN represented a new way of working for government, ensuring the right communications and links are made across and beyond government to deliver the Energy White Paper.

Royal Assent for the Brian White Sustainable Energy Act was announced on Thursday 30 October 2003. The Act implements the DTI Energy White Paper commitment to provide statutory backing to regulatory impact assessments, including environmental impact assessments, undertaken by Ofgem for all significant new policies. It also provides the legal basis for accessing surplus funds from the Non-Fossil Fuels Obligation held by Ofgem.

Energy White Paper

On 24 February 2003 the Government published its Energy White Paper "Our energy future – creating a low carbon economy". The White Paper set out a new energy policy, designed to deal with the three major challenges that confront the UK's energy system: the challenge of climate change, the challenge of declining indigenous energy supplies, and the need to keep the UK's energy infrastructure up to date with changing technologies and needs.

To address these challenges, the White Paper set four new goals for energy policy: to put the United Kingdom on a path to cut carbon dioxide emissions by some 60 per cent by about 2050, with real progress by 2020; to maintain the reliability of energy supplies; to promote competitive energy markets in the UK and beyond, helping to raise the rate of sustainable economic growth and improve UK productivity; and to ensure that every home is adequately and affordably heated.

For the first time, the environment was put at the heart of Government's energy policy, causing energy efficiency and renewables to feature prominently in the White Paper, as the main ways of delivering carbon cuts.

Energy Markets

Proposals to complete the liberalisation of the electricity and gas markets across the EU were adopted on 15 June 2003. The DTI played a leading role in the Energy Council in ensuring the measures will produce a competitive and open market by 2007.

Fuel Poverty

On 4 March 2003, the Government published its first annual progress report on the UK Fuel poverty strategy. The Fuel Poverty Advisory Group also reported on this date for the first time.

Energy Efficiency
In the April 2003 Budget the Government noted that economic growth and social progress must be balanced with action to protect and improve the environment. One of the main areas in which the Government confirmed that it would be undertaking further consultation was on specific measures to encourage household energy efficiency, following on from an earlier consultation on the use of economic instruments to promote energy efficiency in the domestic sector.

Coal
Clipstone colliery closed in April 2003 and in June2003 Betwys colliery announced closure. Output from the Selby complex began to decline prior to its proposed closure by June 2004.

Coal Investment Aid, with a budget of £60m was launched in June 2003. It is intended to create or safeguard jobs in socially and economically disadvantaged areas by encouraging coal producers to enter into commercially realistic projects that maintain access to coal reserves.

Oil and Gas
In February 2003, to encourage a wider range of bids for offshore oil and gas exploration licences, the DTI enhanced the licensing system to include a new "promote" licence in the 21st Offshore Licensing Round. This new type of licence, offered at a tenth of the price of a traditional licence for the first 2 years of its term, was aimed at attracting smaller newcomers wishing to find oil and gas.

On 31 July 2003 the Energy Minister announced the results of the 21st Offshore Round, offering 88 new North Sea licences. The licences went to 62 companies, 27 being new entrants to the area. The awards underlined the success of the new "promote" licences, mentioned above.

In October 2003, the Energy Minister met with his Norwegian counterpart to sign an agreement on key principles that will be incorporated in a new Framework Treaty covering future cross-border oil and gas co-operation between the two countries. The Agreement opened the way for the construction of a large gas pipeline (Langeled) from Norwegian offshore infrastructure capable of delivering up to 20 per cent of the UK's current gas requirements from Winter 2006/7 and clarified the regulatory regime that would apply to a range to future cross-border projects.

In November, the Energy Minister gave approval to the giant Buzzard oil field. With an estimated 500 million barrels of oil to be recovered, and overall investment of £1.35 billion – the largest in the UK North Sea in the last decade, and equivalent to around a third of the industry total annual expenditure - Buzzard will make a significant contribution to the UK's oil production and to the economy.

Power cuts
On 14 August, a large area of the North East USA, including New York, and of Eastern Canada suffered cascading power cuts. Some 60 million people were affected within a matter of minutes as the system operators lost control of the networks, causing an uncontrolled series of power cuts.

On 28 August a power failure occurred affecting large parts of South London and parts of Kent. National Grid Transco redirected supplies via another circuit but at this time a separate fault occurred causing loss of supply to 410,000 customers. Power was restored to all customers in the space of 40 minutes.

Following power failures in London and the West Midlands, The Energy Minister asked the Engineering Inspectorate (EI) to carry out a detailed investigation of these faults, including a review of power supply arrangements for London Underground and Network Rail. In parallel with this, the EI worked on a joint investigation with Ofgem into these incidents.

Electricity

In January 2003, Powergen announced the closure at the end of March of two already partly mothballed coal-fired power stations that it had acquired from TXU in October 2002, namely Drakelow and High Marnham.   International power also re-instated 250 MW at Deeside for winter 2003/04, and RWE Innogy leased Fifoots Point power station from its administrators to operate over the winter.

In May 2003, Centrica completed the acquisition of Lakeland Power's Roosecote Power Station (229 MW), which had suspended operations in November 2002. Centrica also purchased Barry Power station (250 MW) from AES in July. Scottish and Southern Energy bought the distribution network operator, Midland Electricity from Aquila Networks in July and also acquired 100 per cent of Medway power station (688 MW) in October

Nuclear

At the end of March 2003 BNFL's Calder Hall nuclear power station closed.

An agreement was signed in June 2003 allowing UK companies to start nuclear clean-up work to start in North West Russia.

During 2003 the Government and BNFL conducted a joint strategy review of the company. The review conclusions were announced in a written statement to the House of Commons on 11 December 2003. One of the key conclusions of the review was that a new BNFL parent company would be established in April 2005, the principal focus of which would be clean-up activities at UK sites. At the same time, a new group of subsidiary companies would be established which would have initial responsibility for managing clean-up and operations at BNFL's UK sites under transitional arrangements to be agreed with the Nuclear Decommissioning Authority (NDA).

On 24 June 2003, the DTI published the draft Nuclear Sites and Radioactive Substances Bill.   The draft Bill set out provisions to establish the Nuclear Decommissioning Authority (NDA), as foreshadowed in the July 2002 White Paper, *Managing the Nuclear Legacy: A strategy for action.*

Renewables

Two rounds of Offshore Licensing took place in 2003, which brought forwards a large number of proposals. Capital grants of £59 million were given to six of the first round offshore wind projects, with a total capacity of around 530 MW. The awards made in the second round, which covered 15 wind farm projects, will provide enough electricity for more than one in six households (4 million homes). The projects are in three strategic areas (Thames Estuary, Greater Wash and North West) with generation due to begin 2007-08.   North Hoyle – the UK's first major offshore windfarm – began generating electricity.

For major events in earlier years see the DTI web site version of this annex at:
www.dti.gov.uk/energy/inform/dukes2005/04annexdpdf

NOTES

232

NOTES

233

NOTES

234